D1329903

RELATION OF
PSYCHOLOGICAL TESTS
TO PSYCHIATRY

Officers of the
AMERICAN PSYCHOPATHOLOGICAL ASSOCIATION
for 1951

WILLIAM BARCLAY TERHUNE, M.D., *President*

HARRY MERRILL MURDOCK, M.D., *Vice-President*

WILLIAM S. TAYLOR, Ph.D., *Vice-President*

LAURETTA BENDER, M.D., *Councillor*

SAMUEL W. HAMILTON, M.D., *Secretary*

Committee on Program

PAUL H. HOCH, M.D., *Councillor, Chairman*

JOSEPH ZUBIN, Ph.D., *Treasurer*

OSKAR DIETHELM, M.D.

LAWSON G. LOWREY, M.D.

Relation of Psychological Tests to Psychiatry

Edited by PAUL H. HOCH, M.D.

New York State Psychiatric Institute; College of Physicians and Surgeons, Columbia University, New York City.

and JOSEPH ZUBIN, PH.D.

New York State Psychiatric Institute; Department of Psychology, Columbia University, New York City.

THE PROCEEDINGS OF THE FORTIETH ANNUAL MEETING OF THE AMERICAN PSYCHOPATHOLOGICAL ASSOCIATION, HELD IN NEW YORK CITY, JUNE, 1950

GRUNE & STRATTON

NEW YORK

PRINTED IN THE UNITED STATES OF AMERICA

FOREWORD

THE use of psychological tests in psychiatry is so widespread to-day that evaluation of their actual and potential contribution to diagnosis, prognosis and treatment is long overdue. With this in mind, the American Psychopathological Association invited a select number of experts in this field to discuss critically the role of tests in psychiatry. This volume summarizes the results of these discussions.

A review of these contributions indicates that there is a great diversity of opinion regarding not only the clinical usefulness of the tests, but their nature, purpose and scientific value. Nearly all the contributors would like to see these tests improved. Some are hopeful that the quantification of these technics would lead to better understanding of the mind of the normal as well as that of the abnormal. Others do not hold out so much hope for them, and regard them at best as ancillary tools. That the intelligence tests have provided a scientific basis for the measurement of mental function in school children and in the feeble-minded is generally accepted. That they have served well as screening technics and guides in selection of men for military, vocational and scholastic purposes is also generally accepted. That they can prove to be as useful in the field of mental disease and epilepsy has not yet been fully demonstrated.

Personality tests of both the inventory as well as of the projective type arouse the greatest diversity of opinion. According to some investigators they are on a much lower level of scientific development than the intelligence tests. While their clinical usefulness is undeniable, their scientific accuracy and precision leaves much to be desired. Others regard them as far superior to any of the other psychological technics and, although they are aware of their present shortcomings, hold out a bright future for their development.

Heretofore, the chief use of these tests has been for diagnostic purposes. Their use in the evaluation of therapy has only now begun and their use for prognostic purposes is in its early stages.

The encouraging progress made in the treatment of mental disorders by the somatotherapies as well as the psychotherapies, and the rather rapid alteration in patient behavior observed under and after these therapies has provided proving grounds for a crucial investigation of the reliability, validity and prognostic values of these tests. Some of these tests have proved their worth; others have been found wanting. Since the changes which these therapies bring about are chiefly in the sphere of affect, it is highly desirable for test makers to turn their attention to the development of this neglected area in psychological test construction. While waiting for such tests to be developed, it might be well to sharpen the interview technic, provide it with more scientific checks and counterchecks and standardize its procedures and the evaluation of its contents. Armed with the probe of the interview, the new tests that are being further developed will have a ready touchstone for their evaluation.

No apology need be made for the limited number of tests discussed in these papers. To have included all would have strained to the limit the publisher as well as the reader. It is hoped, however, that a sufficient sampling has been presented to give a fair cross-section of present day practice.

THE EDITORS

CONTENTS

PAGE

FOREWORD... v

PART I: HISTORICAL BASES FOR PSYCHOLOGICAL TESTS

1. WHAT IS TESTED BY PSYCHOLOGICAL TESTS? *Robert W. White*   3
2. DEVELOPMENT OF CLINICAL TESTS IN PSYCHOPATHOLOGY.
   Lowell S. Selling...................................   15
3. THEORETICAL BASES OF PSYCHOMETRIC TESTS. *Laurance F.
   Shaffer*...   26
   Discussion I. *David Wechsler*.........................   39
   Discussion II. *Jerome D. Frank*.......................   45

PART II: DIAGNOSTIC USE OF PSYCHOLOGICAL TESTS

4. AN EXPERIMENTAL CRITERION FOR THE PROGNOSTICATION
   OF THE STATUS OF SCHIZOPHRENICS AFTER A THREE-
   YEAR-INTERVAL BASED ON RORSCHACH DATA. *Zygmunt
   A. Piotrowski and Nolan D. C. Lewis*................   51
5. THE DIAGNOSTIC USE OF PSYCHOLOGICAL TESTS FROM THE
   PSYCHIATRIST'S STANDPOINT. *Oskar Diethelm and Charles
   A. Knehr*...   73
6. PERSONALITY AND INTELLIGENCE: INTEGRATION OF PROJEC-
   TIVE AND PSYCHOMETRIC TECHNICS. *Silvan S. Tomkins*.   87
   Discussion I. *Joseph Zubin*..........................   96
   Discussion II. *Joseph F. Kubis*...................... 105

PART III: PRESIDENTIAL ADDRESS

7. THE PHILOSOPHY OF SCIENTIFIC COOPERATION. *William B.
   Terhune*.. 113

PART IV: INFLUENCE OF EXOGENOUS FACTORS ON
PSYCHOLOGICAL TEST PROCEDURES

8. THE RELATIONSHIP OF ABSTRACT THINKING TO THE AUTO-
   NOMIC NERVOUS SYSTEM IN SCHIZOPHRENIA. *Arnold
   Meadow and Daniel H. Funkenstein*................. 131

PAGE

9. THE PREDICTION OF SUCCESS IN CLINICAL PSYCHOLOGY.
   E. Lowell Kelly...................................... 150
10. THE CONDITIONAL REFLEX FUNCTION AS AN AID IN THE
    STUDY OF THE PSYCHIATRIC PATIENT. *W. Horsley Gantt* 165
11. SOME THEORETICAL AND PRACTICAL ASPECTS OF THE DIAG-
    NOSIS OF EARLY AND LATENT SCHIZOPHRENIA BY MEANS
    OF PSYCHOLOGICAL TESTING. *Milton S. Gurvitz and
    Joseph S. A. Miller*............................... 189
    Discussion I. *Lewis R. Wolberg*...................... 208
    Discussion II. *Paul H. Hoch*......................... 212

PART V: INFLUENCE OF THE PSYCHE ON
PSYCHOLOGICAL TEST PERFORMANCE

12. RORSCHACH STUDIES IN COMBAT FLYING PERSONNEL. *Leo
    Alexander and Albert F. Ax* 219
13. THE USE OF SERIAL TESTING IN REGRESSIVE ELECTROSHOCK
    TREATMENT. *Bernard C. Glueck, Jr., Jack D. Krasner
    and Ramon Parres*.................................. 244
14. ILLNESS: THE REALIZATION OF AN INFANT'S FANTASY WITH
    SPECIAL REFERENCE TO TESTING METHODS. *Flanders
    Dunbar*... 258
15. THE INFLUENCE OF PSYCHOPATHOLOGICAL EMOTIONS ON
    PSYCHOLOGICAL TEST PERFORMANCE. *Livingston Welch
    and Thomas A. C. Rennie*........................... 271
    Discussion. *Lothar B. Kalinowsky*.................... 290

INDEX 295

Part One

HISTORICAL BASES FOR PSYCHOLOGICAL TESTS

1

WHAT IS TESTED BY PSYCHOLOGICAL TESTS?

By ROBERT W. WHITE, Ph.D.*

ALL OF US HERE are students of human nature, and as such we suffer from a common professional problem. We suffer from the problem of keeping our subject-matter in hand, of bounding and restricting it so that we can feel ourselves to be studying something less than the whole universe. Human nature is part of biochemistry and biology, it is part of psychology, it is inseparable from society and culture, it is shaped by history and economic circumstances, by philosophy and religion; it is, in short, something complex, related, fluid, changing, the very opposite of the kind of thing a scientist likes to get under his microscope for precise and repeated observation. Obviously we cannot cope with all of human nature at once. In order to continue our professional activities we have to pick out manageable portions of our colossal subject-matter and try our best to deal with a few things at a time. We have to constrict our focus so that our own minds can grasp what is presented for observation. We have to pretend that things are simpler than they are.

There is a danger in this as in other kinds of pretending. We are likely to forget that we are pretending, whereupon we readily fall victim to a ridiculously simple notion of our operations and of the conclusions to be drawn from them. We name one test an intelligence test and then claim to have tested the patient's intelligence. We make up a personality inventory and announce that we have taken an inventory of the patient's personality. We give a projective test and believe that we have disclosed the patient's unconscious strivings or his basic psychological structure. Then we must hurry on to the next patient, for we are all very busy. Thus it happens that our pretendings, our short-cuts, our necessary oversimplifications, may never really go back into perspective. We do not have time to reconsider what our psychological tests really test. This is unfortunate because

* Harvard University.

3

it may blind us to our limitations; equally, it may blind us to unsuspected strengths and new potentialities in our work.

I have often found that a brief immersion in history helped me to escape the deadening effects of daily routine and restore perspective on my own activities. Such was the case when the attic of an old house yielded two volumes of a musty magazine called "The Phrenological Journal and Life Illustrated." These volumes were published in 1871 and 1872, being the fifty-third and fifty-fourth volumes of the journal in question. I wish there were time to share with you in detail the delights of the advertising section, with its Astral Oil that never explodes even though the lamp be overturned, its recently invented spring bed, its golden fountain pen that could write sixty lines without being dipped, its parlor organ in which the usual disagreeable reedy tone had been entirely overcome, its illustrated manual for carriage painters, and its Hygeian Homes where one could take the best and most complete water-cures in America. Oddly modern in sound is the advertisement of an electro-magnetic machine for medical purposes, "having a strong direct current as well as a to and fro current (10)." Closer to our present purpose, however, and to the specialty to which the journal was devoted, is the announcement of a new Phrenological Bust, "showing the latest classification, the exact location of the Organs of the Brain, fully developed, designed for Learners (10)." On one side, the bust was divided so as to show each individual organ or capacity; on the other side, the major groupings, namely, Social, Executive, Intellectual, and Moral. The large size bust, in a box, sold for two dollars, but the hard-pressed young phrenologist not yet established in life could secure a smaller size for one dollar.

The journal itself, though including many topics of general interest, was mainly devoted to the promotion, explanation, and defense of phrenology. Every month there would be two or three biographies of famous men, accompanied by careful steel engravings making it possible to discern the different organs of the mind from the shape of the head. From the modeling of the skull one could detect the relative strengths of Cautiousness and Combativeness, for example, or the endowment with respect to Acquisitiveness, Benevolence, Firmness, Conscientiousness, or Approbativeness. Students of phrenology were satisfied that each of these powers was distinct and separate, having its own little piece of the brain to itself. This belief is nowhere clearer than in the question-and-answer section of the magazine. A correspondent asks about the cause of nepotism and is told that it comes from the organ of Friendship or Adhesiveness. Another wants to know what organs aid in giving decision. He is informed that "Individuality, Comparison, Firmness, Self-Esteem, and Combativeness are the principal faculties involved (10)." Of particular interest was a case in which a phrenologist had been asked to testify in court for the defense of a man accused of murder. There was no doubt about the murder, which had been witnessed by a large number of people, but the phrenologist was able to testify that the defendant possessed such feebly developed intellectual powers and such marked combativeness as to fall into a state of frenzy upon even slight provocation. The jury found the defendant guilty of murder in the first degree, but when the case was carried to the Court of Appeals in Albany the decision was reversed and the prisoner removed to a Lunatic Asylum. This was reckoned a great victory for phrenology.

I find two things particularly instructive in these old journals. In the first place, they testify to the remarkable endurance of phrenology, which was by no means young in 1871. Phrenology was founded by Gall as early as 1800 and had been thoroughly propagandized in America by 1830. Why did a doctrine founded on a complete fallacy concerning the relations among brain tissue, skull tissue, and behavior flourish so actively as late as the seventies? The answer, suggested by Boring, is as follows:

"The most important and greatest puzzle which every man faces is himself, and, secondarily, other persons. Here seemed to be a key to the mystery, a key fashioned in the scientific laboratory and easy to use. It actually constituted a new intellectual gospel (2)."

Phrenology continued, perhaps partly because it was difficult to disprove, but more particularly because it answered the eternal need for a psychology of personality. It pinned down human nature for observation and study. The needed simplification was obtained by classifying man's nature into some forty powers or faculties. The needed definiteness and sharpness was secured by correlating these with specific areas of the brain and protruberances of the skull. A theory which simplified and clarified personality in such a radical fashion was bound to have a long life, no matter how wrong its presuppositions. It was a mighty effort to make personality understandable, measurable, and predictable. Phrenology was a way of making things simpler than they are.

The other thing that intrigues me about these old journals is the evidence they contain that the radical simplification was beginning to break down. Phrenology was old enough to begin to be sophisticated. In 1872 the editor ran a series of four articles under the title: "How the Different Faculties Combine." In these articles he conscientiously grappled with what we would now call the problem of the personality as a whole. He tried as far as possible to stick to a fixed cerebral geography, showing that one faculty most readily arouses others in its immediate neighborhood. But he did not hesitate to introduce other more integrative notions; for instance, the joint action of many faculties in the carrying out of some great purpose, where the purpose, not the structure of the brain, provides the integrative pattern. He also made an opening for learning, pointing out that complex action occurs more often in people who have refined and cultivated their higher faculties. Thus our phrenologist did not altogether shrink from the problems of gestalt, pattern, hierarchy, integration, which the earlier statements of the doctrine seemed to have cast to the winds.

I maintain that this little excursion into history shows us a cycle or trend in thought which is almost inevitable, hence almost universal, in attempts to understand the psychology of personality. First comes the stage in which someone has the courage and ingenuity to propose a manageably small number of distinct but inclusive variables. Success in this stage can be more dramatic if the variables are anchored to bodily processes or are in some other way made objectively measurable. Then follows a period of misgivings in which sensitive observers increasingly realize the violence that has been done the facts, especially those facts that have to do with interrelationships and integrative patterns. The complexities of personality again obtrude themselves upon notice, and the original doctrine is forced to yield to a more adequate scientific model. Notice how this cycle was followed in the field of endocrinology. For a short while in the early twenties we had a new psychology of personality. Each trait was anchored to one of the endocrine glands and was strong in proportion to the activity of that gland The strength of the glands and of the traits could be inferred from certain bodily features, from chemical assays, or, at autopsy, from the weight of the glands. Then came the misgivings. The glands themselves were found to constitute a complex interacting chemical system, regulating each other, and some of them proved to secrete not one but several substances, up to the twenty-eight steroids now attributed to the adrenal cortex. The scientific model adequate to entertain these facts has yet to be developed, and the supposedly correlated traits of personality have long since vanished into other conceptual schemes.

With these two examples of the cycle before us, let us turn directly to the main thesis of this paper. I can state it as follows: that a fairly rapid evolution is going on in our theories of personality, that this change is somewhat reflected in current testing practices, but that the full implications of the change have not yet been realized in our work with psychological tests. When we report on our testing or when we design an investigation, we are still quite likely to conceive of our results in the too simple, too rigid categories that we have long since discarded from personality theory. In both of our previous examples we saw that the cycle moved from a false simplicity to a more nearly true complexity and that this made measurement infinitely harder. Theories of personality are moving in the same cycle, with the same effect on measurement. No wonder we psychologists have difficulty keeping up with our own theoretical advances. It is much easier to change a theory than to change the measuring instruments, all the more so if the theoretical advance is away from the kind of simple variables that facilitate measurement.

I shall first try to characterize, in a very few words, the trend in theories of personality. Then I shall undertake to say what this means, in my opinion, for the science and art of psychological testing.

Theories of personality seem to me to be now in a fairly late stage of the cycle. The happy simple days are pretty much behind us. In the field of mental disorder, for example, the categories of disease boldly sketched by Kraepelin, and assumed by him to depend on specific bodily disorders, have caused no end of diagnostic difficulty. Kraepelin's textbook cases, intended to represent an abstraction of the most common features of each disorder, have come to be regarded as events which simply never happen in nature. It is routine practice nowadays to put each patient in several categories, with features of still others thrown in to complete the description, and if one is irritated at a psychiatrist, the handiest epithet is to call him a Kraepelinian. Brain injury is no longer conceived as knocking out specific capacities but as having quite generalized effects such as the loss of the abstract attitude or the release of psychotic or neurotic patterns already latently present. For the neuroses, the earlier attempts at classification, such as Janet's hysteria and psychasthenia, or Freud's conversion hysteria, anxiety hysteria, and compulsion neurosis, have been washed away by the clinical flood of character disorders and psychosomatic disorders. The better we understand patients, the less can we classify them under the headings of a more primitive psychopathology. Psychiatry is passing through its misgivings concerning the old variables and is searching for more adequate ways to represent the individuality of each case.

The same trend can be discerned in the psychologist's domain. The concept of intelligence is a good case in point. Intellect was one of the variables used in phrenology. General intelligence, represented by the I.Q., was at first conceived just as simply; what it lost through no longer being localized in the brain it gained through being measurable by the Stanford-Binet. Today the concept of intelligence has lost all of its youthful simplicity. If you are irritated at a psychologist you have only to throw the I.Q. in his face. Today we regularly analyze the pattern of scores on each subtest of an intelligence scale, hoping for a qualitative picture, an individualized account of how each person uses his mind, and we are happier if we have additional hints from the Rorschach performance, the Vigotsky test, and several other procedures. Intelligence is probably a complex resultant of several primary abilities, as is suggested by the work of Thurstone (15) and Halstead (4). Moreover, intelligence as a general category has refused to stay isolated from psychodynamics. Ruth Munroe's study of the conscientious, rigid student and the temperamental, scattered student, showing the impress on intellectual functions produced by anxiety and defense, is a modern sophisticated counterpart of those phrenological essays on how the different faculties combine (6). Abilities and personality are no longer distinct categories.

Theories having to do more explicitly with personality are similarly moving through their cycle. There was once a time when we sup-posed we could measure extroversion and introversion by means of self-rating scales. What psychologist today would care whether a person was extroverted or introverted, and what psychologist would suppose that self-ratings could inform him on such matters? These gross variables and their simple measures now outrage our sensitivities as observers. Like McDougall's list of instincts, like Freud's crude anatomy of id, ego, and superego, they strike us as doing such violence to the infinitely complex facts of personality that they help us scarcely at all either in our professional work or in our attempts at building a theory. The search for variables of personality has moved, in Mur-ray's hands, toward increasing fractionation and flexibility (8). With Goldstein (3) and with Allport (1), the problems of organization and integration have assumed a central position. Finally, in Lewin's theories (5) and in Murphy's magnificent synthesis (7), one finds the walls of the individual personality breaking down so as to accom-modate the now fully realized fact of his constant interaction with others, with his culture, and with his world.

In brief, then, our conception of personality seems well advanced toward a mature complexity. We are drastically changing the models for our thinking from the fixed hard outlines of instinct, trait, and anatomy, a model very similar to the original phrenology, to a more fluid model that in some respects resembles current images of the endocrine system. We are trying now to conceive of personality as an interacting system in which all regions tend to influence all other regions, in which abilities and motives and pathologies are only faintly separated, in which hierarchical ordering and integration are the most crucial problems. We are trying to conceive of each in-dividual as only partly separated from his environment, as a system which lies constantly open for exchange in either direction. It is hard to frame such a model and to use it with any rigor, but the facts have forced us inexorably in this direction. Few things are harder to think about than personality.

What does all this mean, then, for measurement? What does it imply for the science and art of psychological testing and for the use of this science and art in the problems of psychopathology? I shall try to present my opinions on this subject in the form of three propositions.

1. Psychological tests can no longer be regarded as tests of specific, restricted functions. They should rather be conceived as inducing sample performances, or specimens of behavior, in which some aspect of the person, say his problem-solving capacity, has designedly been given prominence, but to which many other forces in his personality probably contribute. We should recognize that we can never arrange a situation in which just one important variable is tested. Our problem-solving test will perhaps be also a test of frustration tolerance, a test of control over anxiety, a test of level of aspiration, or a situation that happens to mobilize an infantile trauma, and our report on its results must include as much of this information as can be observed. What we say about our subject's problem-solving thus becomes a statement about his observed problem-solving under a specific set of circumstances, external and internal. We have not measured his capacity; we have merely taken a specimen of his use of his capacity under particular conditions. Our conclusions must be drawn with respect to what we really did and our prognosis must reflect this limitation.

Current testing practice already shows a strong trend in this direction. Our psychological tests simply refuse to "stay put." In the hands of Wechsler (16) and of Rapaport (11), intelligence testing has become diagnostic, not simply of intelligence, complicated as that may be, but also of personality and of psychopathology. A schizophrenic patient may appear schizophrenic not only in his Rorschach responses but also in the scatter of his subtest scores on a test of intelligence. Even an occasional psychodynamic inference may be drawn from his way of giving a definition or doing an object assembly. The Rorschach test, aimed chiefly at basic personality structure, has always had its say about intelligence, and is moving increasingly into the realm of psychodynamics, as for instance in Schachtel's analysis of the movement responses (13) or Phillips' scheme for the symbolic meaning of each card (9). The Thematic Apperception Test, originally beamed at covert strivings, has also been analyzed, for example by Wyatt, with respect to the more formal or structural aspects of the stories, and I have known cases where one's estimate of a subject's intellectual potentialities had to be revised upward in view of his performance on an imaginative task.

Some of the newer tests, such as those that involve drawing, quite frankly aim to gather information concerning all aspects of personality. Our tests, in other words, contribute overlapping information, a thing that we would certainly expect from our theory of the personality as a system in which all parts tend to influence all other parts.

2. My second proposition follows directly from my first. It is to the effect that confidence can no longer be placed in single tests, but only in test batteries. Perhaps you expected me to state a different proposition at this point: that since any one test samples so much of the personality we can be more than ever satisfied with the giving of a single test. This, however, would be a fallacy. A test of problem-solving samples more aspects of the person than we used to suppose; that is true; but it also samples much less of problem-solving than we used to suppose. If we are to find out what we need to know about a patient's problem-solving potentialities we must observe him solving different kinds of problems under different kinds of conditions. The same is true, for example, with his imaginative processes. We cannot be satisfied with the single approach to his fantasies that is offered by the Thematic Apperception Test. We want to observe also his responses to ink blots, his behavior with sentence completions, his performance on a drawing task, and the clues he provides us even in tests predominantly intellectual in character.

It is here, in the use of test batteries, that I foresee the most important advances in the practice of diagnostic testing. It is here also that I see one of those unanticipated strengths that comes to view when we survey the trend of our theorizing. If we believed that each test measured one thing, the effects of a battery would be merely additive, like bricks building up a wall. If, in contrast, we take the view that each test samples many aspects of the person, the test battery increases our knowledge in a sort of geometric progression. We obtain several points of observation on each aspect of the personality and we can check and recheck the findings from one sample to another. I wish I had time to illustrate this procedure, but I need only refer to its elegant use by Rosenzweig in this recent book on psychodiagnosis (12) and to the procedures worked out by Shakow and his former associates at the Worcester State Hospital (14). The use of a test battery, seen in the light of current theories of personality, makes the diagnosis of each case a miniature scientific experiment. Conclusions can be drawn only when independent lines of evidence have been carefully weighed and compared.

It will perhaps be objected that this advocacy of test batteries is a counsel of perfection that cannot often be attained in practice. There is the case load, there is the shortage of trained personnel, there is the limit to the amount we can impose on patients. Our whole metaphor of a battery is a little unfortunate, suggesting that the patient might in the end resemble a target after artillery practice. There are indeed many practical obstacles to the use of extensive testing schedules in the ordinary practice of clinical psychology. As regards research, however, I would be altogether uncompromising in the matter of the testing schedule. If any research is set up in which substantial knowledge of the subjects' personalities forms part of the project, then an attempt to cut the testing schedule below ten to fifteen hours with each subject is merely a proposal to sabotage the research. When such a schedule is impracticable we might as well admit, before wasting the money of some foundation or government service, that a research situation does not exist. We might as well admit that a study of personality cannot be started simply because the patients happen to have a free hour to take the Rorschach test or half an hour to utter some sentence completions. This is a hard lesson, but one which all of us who are interested in psychopathology will have to learn in the years to come, unless we are to regress to a theoretical outlook as simple as phrenology. The progress of our theories of personality has by no means simplified the task of the investigator.

3. My third and last proposition takes cognizance of the idea that personalities are open systems constantly interacting with their environments. It may be stated this way: that the patient being tested interacts with the psychologist as a person and reacts also to the total character of the situation over and above the testing procedure. The word "situation" has become a much overworked part of our professional jargon but I think it is meaningful to say that the patient responds not only to the test materials and tasks, but also to the situation of being tested. The importance of the interaction between patient and investigator must never be overlooked. Its distorting effect is best minimized by having several investigators who differ

as to age, sex, and their own personalities. In the fortunate situation of the Harvard Psychological Clinic, where there is abundant semi-professional help in the form of graduate students, we have often been able to use not only a battery of tests but a battery of investigators, giving our subjects a chance to interact with a considerable range of personalities. It is amazing to see how subjects, when given this opportunity, find their favorite examiners, not always the ones we would have thought most apt, and feel out the relationships in which they can perform with most power, most imaginative freedom, most willingness to confide. The principle of multiple examiners has also the virtue of bringing multiple judgments to bear on the test results. Psychological tests are by no means so objective as to dispense with this safeguard.

The total character of the situation is not easy to describe, but I think the recognition that there is such a thing, and that it influences the patient, will save us from some rather bad errors. This is particularly true when it comes to predicting how patients will behave when not in a similar situation. Predictions of this kind are increasingly demanded: how, for instance, patients will behave after prefrontal lobotomy under the stresses of real life outside the hospital. Here is where we must regretfully realize the limitations of psychological testing. There is a gap between the testing situation and real life that we cannot really bridge. The Thematic Apperception Test involves story-telling, and we might suppose that it would predict a person's gift for imaginative writing. Such is not wholly the case: writers of considerable professional attainment proved not especially outstanding, the test situation evidently not corresponding to the situations in real life that prompted them to write. We can test people under a variety of circumstances but not under all circumstances. We can predict certain things about a person but certainly not all things. The situation of being tested, though sometimes found threatening, belongs on the whole on the benign side of life. It is a situation in which the examiner feels an unusual sense of responsibility and takes unusual pains to establish rapport—unusual as compared to the average relationships of daily life. It is also an artificial situation in which success and failure do not have the kind of consequences they do in the real world. These circumstances are favorable for certain kinds of disclosure, but only for certain kinds. We who are interested in psychological tests should, therefore, modestly realize the things we cannot sample in personality, even while proudly pointing out how much more we can sample today than we ever could before.

REFERENCES

1. ALLPORT, G. W.: Personality: A Psychological Interpretation. New York, Henry Holt & Co., 1937.
2. BORING, E. G.: A History of Experimental Psychology. New York, Century, 1929.
3. GOLDSTEIN, K.: Human Nature in the Light of Psychopathology. Cambridge, Harvard Univ. Press, 1940.
4. HALSTEAD, W. C.: Brain and Intelligence. Chicago, Univ. of Chicago Press, 1947.
5. LEWIN, K.: A Dynamic Theory of Personality. New York, McGraw-Hill Book Co., 1937.
6. MUNROE, R. L.: Teaching the Individual. New York, Columbia Univ. Press., 1942.
7. MURPHY, G.: Personality: A Biosocial Approach to Origins and Structure. New York, Harper & Co., 1947.
8. MURRAY, H. A.: Explorations in Personality. New York, Oxford Univ. Press, 1938.
9. PHILLIPS, L.: Unpublished communication.
10. The Phrenological Journal and Life Illustrated. New York, Samuel R. Wells, publisher. Vols. *53, 54*, 1871–72.
11. RAPAPORT, D., et al.: Diagnostic Psychological Testing. Chicago, Year Book Publishers, 1945.
12. ROSENZWEIG, S.: Psychodiagnosis: An Introduction to Tests in the Clinical Practice of Psychodynamics. New York, Grune & Stratton, 1949.
13. SCHACHTEL, E.: Projection and its relation to character attitudes and creativity in the kinaesthetic responses. Psychiatry, *13*, 69–100, 1950.
14. SHAKOW, D., RODNICK, E. H., and LEBEAUX, T.: A psychological study of a schizophrenic: exemplification of a method. J. Abnorm. Soc. Psychol., *40*, 154–174, 1945.
15. THURSTONE, L. L.: The Vectors of Mind. Chicago, Univ. of Chicago Press, 1935.
16. WECHSLER, D.: The Measurement of Adult Intelligence. Baltimore, Williams & Wilkins, 1944.

2

DEVELOPMENT OF CLINICAL TESTS IN PSYCHOPATHOLOGY

By LOWELL S. SELLING, M.D., Ph.D.*

IT WAS THE writer's good fortune to substitute, during the summer of 1923 and 1924, for Miss Elizabeth Day, "psychologist" at the Bellevue Mental Clinic which, as some of you may know, was operated by volunteers from the Army Air Corps coming from nearby Long Island fields. This was one of the very earliest Mental Hygiene Clinics in the country, yet at Bellevue there were two distinct clinics.

One clinic was held for the purpose of examining feeble-minded children, serving as a certificating agency to send them to the institution at Randall's Island. Here the staff was relatively permanent, and it was operated by the New York Department of Public Welfare. I can recall that Dr. I. Broadwin and Dr. Glassberg were the psychiatrists serving at that time and that Dr. Emily Burr was psychologist.

The other clinic was the one which was serviced by the army medicos and performed what at that time was a very competent job, but one which we now would consider quite crude, in the general field of Mental Hygiene. I do not recall whether adults were serviced as well as children, but I know we examined a large number of children. At that time, the psychologist was merely a consultant, and certain cases were referred to her for the purpose of determing feeble-mindedness more quantitatively.

This latter clinic was the forerunner of the out-patient department which the Bellevue Psychopathic Hospital now has. In those days we on the Bellevue Psychopathic staff saw no out-patients. Miss Day, for whom I substituted, followed Dr. Leta Hollingworth who, I believe, founded the psychological service at Bellevue and, so far as I can find out, was the first psychologist to have a specific appointment to aid psychiatrists. Prison psychiatry with the assistance of psychological help was relatively unknown. Out-patient Mental Hy-

* Orlando, Florida.

15

giene Clinics for adults were only being started. Child guidance clinics under the Commonwealth Fund were beginning their post-war heyday, and due to the program set up by Drs. Healy and Bronner, the team of social worker, psychologist, and psychiatrist was already being developed in the Institute for Juvenile Research.

Dr. Hollingworth was appointed largely as a research person before the Stanford-Binet had come out. In the days before the Stanford-Binet, it was her job to try to fit the available tests into the psychopathological situation. Nobody knew just *where* the tests would be of value. Nobody knew *what* tests would be of value. And we must not forget that the program at Bellevue started before the Army program, and that the first sources of available material to Dr. Hollingworth were only those in Whipple's book on testing and Titchener's four-volume masterpiece which, as you know, were largely compilations of psychophysical measurements and specific introspective procedures.

The use of these materials left little upon which to build. I can recall opening a drawer in Dr. Hollingworth's desk and finding a mass of cards, some of which bore questions from the old Binet-Simon, some of which represented the individual tests from Whipple or Titchener, and others which I could not identify at all. I remember one card, about $3'' \times 3''$ square, which had on it nothing but a picture of an umbrella. I can recall a pile of solid ink blots, not shaded, nor with very much diversity like our Rorschach material, but apparently made by throwing gobs of ink on each card. Some tests which were the antecedents of parts of later group tests of intelligence, such as those of Otis, Haggerty, Baker, and others, were found on individual cards. They were made up of sentences with a word, two words, or more than two words replaced by dashes, and the patient had to guess what they were. One, which must have been for the superior adult, went something like this: "It ——— is ——— ——— ——— today." When we think in terms of the standardization of modern tests, the terrific variety of answers that would be possible in this primitive substitution test would be appalling, and certainly unscorable.

We all felt, in the early twenties, that the Otis group test and the Army tests, particularly the "scrambled alpha," were worthy of deep consideration and that we could stress their accuracy. Of course, we were willing to admit that the Stanford-Binet was more accurate than the group tests because the tester could observe the individual characteristics of the patient and pass upon the validity of important aspects of the test situation such as the subject's cooperativeness, his attention, his appearance of health or ill health, side remarks— which, particularly in psychotic patients, were very important—and other aspects of the test situation of similar ilk, which must remain unknown in the group situation. We were less confident about the non-language tests. We used the Army Beta and the Pintner-Patterson with some misgivings, but with more dependence than is now necessary with the plethora of similar tests which we have today.

I think that during the years of my interest in the Bellevue set-up from 1923 to 1930, we saw a distinct swing in the attitude of the staff toward the evaluation of psychopathology from the tests. During that period of time no standards had yet been set with regard to the qualifications of the person giving the tests. Anybody who called himself a psychologist could read off the questions, score them to the best of his ability, and his opinion and final score would be accepted. When we had rather poor examiners, the attitude of the staff was that the tests were unreliable. But later on during that period there were on the staff people who have since played an important part in the development of tests and their usage—particularly Dr. Clairette P. Armstrong, Dr. Elaine F. Kinder, and Dr. Harriet Babcock. (I was before Dr. Wechsler's time). The field was wide open, but most clinical psychologists had found that the better the standardization of the tests, the better was their acceptance. And it was surprising how well a skilled psychiatrist could extend the I.Q. and mental age into the evaluation of abstract traits. It was a matter of considerable amusement, when Dr. Gilbert Rich and I were doing some testing, that Dr. Samuel Feigin, the Assistant Director, could "guesstimate" I.Q.'s within plus or minus five points as a general rule, and this, after all, was the probable error of tests given under educational conditions in those days.

In the early twenties, the observation was made in various places that the passage or failure of certain tests, according to their nature, according to the trait involved, and according to the test year that they represented, offered in themselves an excellent diagnostic procedure, beyond what the test represented. In an intelligence test, which might be considered invalid because of the patient's psychotic condition, one could nevertheless observe by noting the errors and failures, certain characteristic traits of the schizoid or schizophrenic patient. The depression of the manic-depressive was often first established by a broad and consistent type of scatter, and the first observable symptoms of the psychasthenic were often revealed in the vocabulary test, or one or more of the definitions which were part of the old Binet.

At the same time that early clinical psychologists were becoming somewhat discouraged because of the lack of consistency in the I.Q. of psychotic and psychoneurotic patients with the psychiatrist's estimate of their intelligence, the school testers and the child guidance clinics were developing a "religious" attitude toward their accuracy. It was going to be ten years or more before the guidance or school psychologists would consistently look askance at the results of the intelligence test in the problem child, rather than consider the intelligence test results as a diagnostic entity. No one today will raise a question about the placement of a child in a school grade based entirely on an intelligence test, provided the tester is assured that emotional and environmental factors are not entering into the final score. But ground work was being laid in the late twenties for a period of great resistance on the part of many competent clinical psychologists to the idea that intelligence test results were nothing but fixed characteristics which would be unchanged during the life of the patient.

When these diametrically opposed schools of thought about psychological tests confronted each other, as groups were doing throughout the country—the psychopathology group working in a University Psychopathic Hospital versus the psychologists in the School of Education in the same University—it was quite obvious that the reason for the conflict should be studied. Why were the psychopathologists of the opinion that "in mental cases tests are no good," when the educators said, "The I.Q. is valid in all cases unless there is something wrong with the tester"? Of course, deviations were known even within the educational group. No one could be too sure of test results when they had an experience like mine: I tested a child from Randall's Island, which revealed him to be in the imbecile level, only to have him tested by Dr. Louise Poull, who found him to be twenty points higher. Fortunately, the patient still should have been committed, and it was obvious to the psychiatrist who checked on my test that he was defective, but the discrepancy was most embarrassing to me and due entirely, I am sure, to my lack of experience at that time.

The first reason for discrepancy in test findings lay in that factor—inexperience. It was during the year 1929 that a number of us got together to see what could be done about certifying testers. There was much debate upon whether psychologists, who at that time were mostly psychometricians with some additional knowledge of interpretations, were to be considered professional persons.

Probably our most serious problem was the fact that there were really no clinical psychologists at all. Even such experts on tests as Terman and Pintner were not, in a true sense, clinical psychologists. Their interest was in test-making and a creation of tools which would be of value to those who were actually in the field. Poffenberger and Hollingworth, although very practical psychologists, had their academic tasks. This left in the field only a very small number of persons, most of whom were not too well qualified to be examiners, and they, in turn, used very few tests although with each month the amount of testing material was expanding. Most of those who were doing tests for social agencies and school systems were not qualified by clinical experience in the sense that we ask for qualifications today, and for that reason a small group who got together in New York at that time tried to determine whether or not properly qualified people in the field of psychology were available.

The first question that came up in the discussions of this self-appointed group of qualifiers was, "Is a Ph.D. necessary for clinical psychology?" And, of course, the corollary to that was, "Is everyone with a Ph.D. in psychology qualified to give tests?" In general, we felt that the answer to the first was "Yes"—that a person who did not go far enough in psychology to get a Ph.D. should not be administering tests and should not be interpreting them. We left out of the question the personality factor, for it was quite obvious even in those days that there were a number of people who were going into psychology to correct some personality difficulty of their own, rather than to do a good systematic clinical job.

Of course, the field today has become so complicated that we have all sorts of queer people who call themselves clinical psychologists. I still cannot see how a person lacking some sort of standard degree equivalent to the M.D. can call himself a full-fledged clinical psychologist. I can accept the fact that a person trained for only a few months can *give* tests, but these tests must be given under supervision and, unfortunately, the supervision required today is much greater than most supervising clinical psychologists are willing to give.

Tests, particularly the individual intelligence test, must be given under standardized conditions. Examiners have no more right to change the inflection of a question than a laboratory man working for the physician has the right to change the meaning of a blood count.

If we cannot give our tests under standard conditions, we have no right to claim authenticity for them. Merely giving a plus or minus ten to our test result does not make that result any more accurate than it was before, and raises in my mind the question whether we need to give the test at all. As I pointed out before, many psychiatrists can guess within plus or minus five points the result of an intelligence test.

When achievement tests became more common to us, they changed the picture greatly, particularly in the growing field of child psychiatry. The psychiatrist, with relation to the psychologist, was the key man at the beginning of development of the field of child psychiatry. Since then we have had all sorts of medico-political upheavals. There have been clinics which have been headed by social workers, surely an anomaly, and some clinics headed by psychologists who used the psychiatrist only as consultant. And this, I think, deserves some discussion.

As I visualize it, clinical psychology, no matter how much it is liberalized, is a field of precision work. It has the same relationship to psychiatry that the clinical pathologist has to the field of medicine. A clinical pathologist can, himself, be an M.D. He may be able to make a diagnosis and may be able to do therapy. But basically his ability and specialty lie in precision examinations in certain routinized activities: the placing of pieces of tissue on a slide to make a diagnosis which is certainly more accurate than the diagnosis made by the clinician; so, in the same way, the clinical psychologist's accurate test or measurement, if he has proper background, proper training, and a proper attitude toward the field, may be far more accurate than the guesswork of the psychiatrist.

While nobody can say that intelligence, as measured by tests, is an exact numerical entity, the millions of tests which have been given and the successful outcome of the predictions made on the basis of these tests have proved that, in the main, they are accurate, useful, and valuable tools in child, and to a lesser extent, adult guidance and therapy. For instance, when there is a discrepancy between the intelligence of the child and his obvious ability to do school work, the clinician is given a clue that he must look into the emotional background of the youngster to see why the intelligence test does not measure up to what he is able to do. Or, if the achievement is less than the intelligence test result, the psychologist and psychiatrist are led into various fields of investigation directed toward therapy. For instance, if on the intelligence test the obvious difficulty lies in reading, a clinic can make diagnostic reading studies; if the difficulty lies in some other sphere, a clinic can make studies of the emotional reactions of the child. The staff can look into the home situation to determine the tensions there which may keep this child's intelligence out of keeping with the achievement or other test results.

But, basically, the most useful test in the field of clinical psychology with relation to psychiatry is the intelligence test. Discrepancies between the achievement tests and the child's actual achievement may be rectified by tutoring and other help. Distorted psychological mechanisms, those which have to be investigated before therapy can be attempted, are oftentimes revealed merely with the intelligence test, coupled with the psychiatric examination.

The confusion between what the psychologist can do and what the psychiatrist is able to do is becoming more and more noticeable. In the early days, the psychologist in the clinical field was well able to accept himself as an ancillary, rather than a surrogate of the psychiatrist. Even today, the difference between the clinical training of the clinical psychologist, under an accepted program, and that of the psychiatrist is evident to the detriment, I believe, of the clinical psychologist. I cannot see how, without the medical background which the psychiatrist has and the experience acquired through medical training, the psychologist can do the same job. He has only a specific knowledge of the quantitative tools at his disposal, which he attempts to extend into the field of mental and nervous diseases.

One realizes that the training in most psychological clinics is not complete when the student has worked only with a clinical psychologist who possesses no medical background. The key to the proper treatment and control of the individual medical case lies in the internship, where preparation for the potential private practice of medicine or one of the medical specialties, such as psychiatry, gives the psychotherapist the equipment he needs. During the 1930's, psychologists were trained to work as part of a team. Although the psychologist may not have needed to have a social worker to take the history of the case or to do home therapy, it is my considered opinion that the clinical psychologist cannot work alone and make a complete evaluation without the help of the psychiatrist. Too often psychologists have, to my knowledge, made bizarre diagnoses or have held up their reports pending more and more tests, until the patient has gotten out of control.

I am frank to admit that a thorough knowledge of surgery, gynecology or other medical specialty besides psychiatry, is not necessary for the clinical psychologist. A psychiatrist, on the other hand, must have some knowledge of these things. One cannot forget the tragedies that have occurred through the work of the lay analyst; the cases of tetanus or some other disease which were diagnosed as conversion hysteria, with the result that therapy, which could have been the difference between life and death, was delayed. So one can see that this little group which got together in the late 1920's was the forerunner of today's American Board of Examiners in Professional Psychology and other similar certifying bodies whose tasks are still incomplete and still not defined as thoroughly as the public deserves. I am firmly of the belief—and I think that psychiatrists with clinical psychological training will agree—that there are no tests as yet which can diagnose the psychosis or accurately evaluate the symptomatology of a psychoneurosis, with a recommendation of specific treatment, rather than just any type of psychotherapy that happens to be the psychologist's preference.

I suppose that technically we can consider achievement tests part of the clinical psychologist's armamentarium. They are simply tests of knowledge, after all, and the only reason why a competent psychologist should give them rather than a school counsellor is merely to be sure that the patient's state of mind, emotion, and attitude are properly evaluated. Since a majority of these tests are self-administered, such an evaluation is difficult. In some ways, the self-administered tests of intelligence have the same drawback. They do represent something more than learning, however, and a careful evaluation of specific type questions may reveal weaknesses in special areas of intelligence, such as reasoning, arithmetical judgment, and bizarre scores may suggest individualized examinations. Probably no test has yet been devised to measure accurately a patient's ability to respond to an emergency situation and do the needed thing, and it is the emergency situations which scientific psychopathology demands be evaluated before one can treat.

The problem of judging psychopathological factors and making a psychopathological diagnosis is not the sole possession of the psychiatrist, but, as I have pointed out, there is no question that with his repetitive experience in dealing with all types of psychopathy under training and experiential conditions, he is better able to evaluate the psychopathological picture. Again and again reports will come into my hands from very capable clinical psychologists in which lists of traits are very ably named and detailed evaluations of their relationship to one another are given, without, however, presenting any kind of unified clinical picture to justify a treatment program.

In the early part of the decade of 1930–1940, the clinical psychologist became more and more interested in tests of personality. His interest, I am afraid, was premature because the Rorschach, the Thematic Apperception, with the Minnesota Multiphasic Personality, and, later on, the Szondi, did not measure up to what we expected in terms of a quantitative evaluation of the facts of mental life. They did provide a more detailed description. They provided a broad picture, just as the handbooks on how to conduct a psychiatric examination provide a list of questions which must be covered in order to be sure that every facet of the patient's mental life is touched upon. And when the ink blot test was made into a group test by Harrower, the valid individual quantum-like nature of the Rorschach disappeared into exactly the same kind of fog as that into which the accurate individual test disappears whenever it becomes "self-administered."

I have no fault to find with the creators of our vast number of tests, and it certainly is true that as new tests were devised, standardized, and proved to have certain types of accuracy, we learned more about evaluating the pathological human mind. But by the time clinical psychology reached the 1940's, simple useful testbooks of test administration, like Garrett's, were out of date, and the conscientious psychological examiner had reached a horizon, hazy and bewildering, where there was a plethora of tests and measurements brought out biannually in the Mental Measurements Year Book. Here were hundreds of tests that had no chance for tryouts, yet many of them were used uncritically by "psychologists" giving us not even an impressionistic picture, but merely a palette of discrete blobs and commingling color blends without suggestion of form of personality or mental makeup.

At that time, clinical and consulting psychologists were casting the hawsers which had held them tightly to the docks of scientific psychology and filing their anchor chains to accepted and standardized tests and measurements, so that they floated, unguided and unpiloted, in the seas of non-directive interviewing. If the final test of an interview or series of interviews is the recovery of the patient or the aiding of the patient to come to some conclusion to solve his own problem, one must grant that patient-centered, non-directive psychotherapy, although uncharted and only vaguely marked, has served some purpose.

In my own hands, and in the hands of those who are as oriented as I am, i.e., who accept the value of Freudian methods and some Freudian psychopathological interpretations, who accept at the same time a physiological background for many mental disturbances, and who are unable as yet to see that there is much difference in results between non-directive psychotherapy, extensive psychiatric interviewing and interpretation, and psychoanalytic study and interpretation, which take about the same length of time, the value of these procedures, or better, the superiority of any of these procedures, remains to be proved. There is no question, though, that when the psychologist casts his tests aside and goes into the field of the unstandardized interviewing, he leaves much to be desired.

Having worked with psychologists over a period of years, it is obvious that the properly trained and experienced clinical psychologist can stand on his own feet, make his own diagnosis, be accurate, and have a value to his patient only if:

1. He uses a standardized test, an accepted test, and one which he knows thoroughly.

2. He knows every possible angle from which that test can be interpreted.

3. He stays away from the purely psychiatric technic of free-floating interviewing, although, of course, there is nothing to prevent his asking questions which are not in the test if he needs additional information.

4. He brings his facts together so that they represent a description of either a phase of personality or of the total personality. A psychologist, after all, must know his limitations. He cannot, for example, diagnose an attack of manic-depressive psychosis and prescribe for it in terms of psychotherapy when shock treatment is also available. As yet there is no psychological tool for this purpose.

5. He either has additional medical training or accepts the limitations of his psychological training. He cannot, as I have known psychologists do, make physiological or medical diagnoses. For example, a clinical psychologist working in a child guidance clinic under my supervision tested a 16-old boy. The boy was very large and had a refreshing amount of facial fuzz. The psychologist put among his summarizing statements the following: "This boy is large (gigantism) and has an excessive amount of hair (hirsutism). He probably has an adrenal tumor."

6. He realizes that there are many spheres for which the clinical psychologist working without psychiatric supervision can be trained: vocational guidance, educational direction, even marriage counselling, but when it comes to the evaluation of psychopathology he must either duplicate the training of the psychiatrist or accept the psychiatrist as being his supervisor or co-worker, in order to produce the best diagnosis and treatment.

3

THEORETICAL BASES FOR PSYCHOMETRIC TESTS

By LAURANCE F. SHAFFER, Ph.D.*

DIAGNOSTIC psychological testing often has been described as an empirical art that suffers from the lack of a solid theoretical foundation. In one sense, the criticism is just, for no systematic and comprehensive theory underlies all that psychometric testing tries to accomplish as an aid to psychiatric diagnosis. Yet in another sense, psychological testing does rest upon certain assumptions. Every use that is made of a psychometric score implies that postulates are held concerning the nature of the test and concerning the human behavior that it samples. The trouble is that many such assumptions are unformulated and implicit. If they were explicit, perhaps they would not stand the light of critical scrutiny or of experimental study. It may be a constructive step to state a few of the more obvious assumptions openly, and allow them to be examined.

INTELLIGENCE TESTS IN DIAGNOSIS

With few exceptions, the psychometric tests now used with psychiatric patients were originally "intelligence tests." They were constructed for one central purpose, the estimation of general intelligence, and were based upon assumptions quite appropriate to that intention. Operationally, individual intelligence tests have adopted the general factor theory of Spearman, although their authors have varied somewhat in their willingness to admit the allegiance. Wechsler (42) plainly espoused the Spearman two-factor theory, as modified by Alexander (1) to include "broad factors" such as verbal and practical (performance) ability. Terman and Merrill (38) did not state their assumptions as clearly, but the operations that they performed in constructing the Revised Stanford-Binet Test, and the interpretations that they make of the M.A. and I.Q. scores point strongly to a belief in *g*. Although other theories of intelligence have been developed,

* Teachers College, Columbia University.

such as Thurstone's multiple factor theory (39), no test so constructed has had wide clinical use. The Wechsler-Bellevue and the Stanford-Binet, which are used in the overwhelming proportion of all clinical psychometric examinations, were conceived as measures of a unitary intelligence. Any other applications are beyond the scope of the authors' original designs.

The concept of an intelligence test was implemented by the application of a number of subsidiary propositions used in test construction. One assumption is that intelligence shows increments from year to year during the growing period of childhood. Accordingly, items that showed such year-to-year improvement were retained, while others were discarded. Another assumption holds that "good" intelligence test items correlate positively with common-sense evidences of success in intellectual tasks, such as progress in school or advancement in an occupation requiring verbal or symbolic work. These two postulates were used consciously in selecting items for the Stanford-Binet. Similar assumptions seem to have operated in the construction of the Wechsler-Bellevue, although the full process underlying the item selection for that test has never been made public.

Largely because of the clarity of their theoretical foundations, and of the merit of the experimental steps used in their construction, the individual intelligence tests have been highly serviceable for the limited purposes intended. While by no means free from faults and errors, they are irreplaceable aids in much of educational and vocational guidance. In clinical practice, we know that a "mere I.Q." is far from a complete diagnosis, yet we would never want to be without it. Not only does an I.Q. help to understand a mentally deficient child, but it is also an aid in planning therapy for a psychoneurotic adult, and has other important uses.

During the past ten years, clinical psychometrics have become elaborated beyond the global use of intelligence tests. The new practices have mainly employed the Wechsler-Bellevue Scale, which lends itself to detailed analysis because of its eleven subtests. The interpretation of inter-subtest variability, or of "profiles," implies a number of assumptions that may seem questionable when they are examined in detail.

One assumption underlying the use of subtest profiles might be stated in this way: the component subtests of a scale are reliable measures of distinguishable traits or aspects of human ability. Another basic assumption might be: various traits or aspects of ability are impaired differentially in various mental disorders, as in organic damage to the central nervous system, in the functional psychoses, and in various psychoneurotic conditions. Only if reason and evidence favor both of these postulates can we place great confidence in the interpretation of profiles.

Let us examine the first assumption, that the component subtests measure distinct traits. A primary requirement of an independent test is that it be sufficiently reliable to yield a dependable score. Until quite recently there was little information about the reliability of the separate Wechsler subtests, but now several studies are available (6, 16, 40). They agree that the median reliability of a subtest is about .75, and that the several subtests range from a satisfactory reliability of about .90 for vocabulary, to unsatisfactory low reliabilities in the vicinity of .60 for digit span, arithmetic and picture arrangement. For a typical reliability of .75, an obtained subtest score of 12 might indicate a true score of from 9 to 15, which is a great range on a scale that extends only from 0 to 18. The evidence, therefore, does not favor an assumption that most of the subtests satisfactorily measure distinct traits.

The second postulate, that various profiles of ability traits characterize different forms of psychiatric disorder, has evoked a large number of studies especially within the past five years. Rapaport's (33) extremely detailed study seemed to find affirmative results, but present opinion believes that his work was received with premature enthusiasm. His groups were too small, too specialized, and too poorly controlled with respect to age, sex and education, to permit wide application of the results. A survey of many studies between 1945 and 1950 seems to confirm a statement made by Garfield (9) in an article summarizing his own work and that of others, "there does not appear to be any clear cut psychometric pattern which can be labeled 'schizophrenic.' " Some researches, it is true, showed tempting traces of results that were just significant statistically (20, 24), but never to a degree useful in practical diagnosis. The preponderance of research on Wechsler profiles in schizophrenia has brought forth only negative or contradictory results. Studies of psychoneurotics' scores (11), and of alleged signs of anxiety obtained from the Wechsler scale (37), have fared no better. Alas for our hopes, the conclusion seems inescapable that Wechsler-Bellevue subtest scores seem to offer little prospect of helping to diagnose functional behavior disorders.

Persons suffering from organic pathology of the nervous system seem to make somewhat more distinctive patterns of Wechsler-Bellevue scores than do those with functional disorders. The "organic" category is a strange mixture, of course, including cases of concussion, multiple sclerosis, encephalitis, CNS syphilis, alcoholism, grand mal epilepsy, and other conditions. In spite of this heterogeneity, a survey of a half dozen recent studies shows some agreement. In this group, scores on the digit-symbol test are especially impaired, and digit span, arithmetic, block designs and object assembly tend to fall below the individual's mean score. Vocabulary, comprehension, and information scores are likely to remain relatively high; studies disagree as to the remaining three subtests.

The work of Hewson (17), who devised a series of ratios of Wechsler scores to aid the diagnosis of organic conditions, seemed promising because of the methods of analysis used and because of the large number of cases, but could not be evaluated immediately, for the lack of cross-validation on an independent group. Gutman (14) has now reported a small cross-validation, showing that 60 per cent of an independent group of 30 organic cases were identified correctly by Hewson's method, and that only 17 per cent of 30 normals were misdiagnosed as organic. For further comparison, I have applied Hewson's ratios to the records of Rapaport's first 20 schizophrenic cases (33, p. 516), and have found that 30 per cent of them tested "organic." To identify 60 per cent of a nosological group at the cost of misidentifying 30 and 17 per cent of two other groups may seem a modest accomplishment, but it perhaps represents the high water mark of our progress.

Hewson's study raises another theoretical question concerning the diagnostic interpretation of test profiles. All seven of her most discriminative ratios contain the digit-symbol subtest, on which other studies also have shown that organic cases do poorly. Furthermore, Hewson demonstrated that a valuable supplement to the Wechsler scale is the Woodworth-Wells substitution test, which is practically an alternate form of the digit-symbol. Four of her ratios contain information and comprehension subtests on which organics do not perform poorly. Much of the discrimination is therefore based on three subtests, with special stress on one of them. In a critical statistical article, Wittenborn (44) demonstrated from Rapaport's data that as much diagnostic value can be obtained from observing two or three subtests that are conspicuous instances of success or failure, as from the entire profile. One wonders, therefore, how much of the recorded success in discriminating organics is due to the digit-symbol test alone.

A patient may perform poorly on the digit-symbol test for more than one reason. Like most other psychometric tasks, it is a complex performance psychologically. A low digit-symbol score may mean a failure to perceive simple forms accurately, inefficiency in immediate learning, inability to sustain attention, aversion to working with numbers, slowness of sensorimotor coordination, or a tendency to become confused in a highly speeded task. It is not unlikely that patients with organic disorders may suffer from any one of these disabilities, from any combination of several of them, or even from all. A low score, however, does not identify the function that is impaired, but is only a blunderbuss empirical tool. More penetrating research, using specially constructed tasks rather than intelligence test items, will be needed in order to make finer discriminations.

Two other proposals for theoretical approaches to the diagnostic use of tests may be mentioned briefly. Schafer (35) has argued rather cogently for the correlation of test "signs" with characteristics of thinking and behavior, rather than with diagnoses. Unfortunately, this good recommendation has been hard to carry out. An example may be drawn from some theorizing about the comprehension subtest. Wechsler (42, p. 81) terms it a test of "common sense," of "a general ability to evaluate past experience." Rapaport (33, p. 111) describes comprehension as measuring "judgment" . . . "the emotionally relevant use of one's assets in regard to the reality situation." Yet both of these workers find that the comprehension score is not severely impaired in many cases of schizophrenia. If you were to follow the armchair reasoning alone, the schizophrenics would be showing good "common sense," and good "reality testing,"˙ which your own common sense indicates is just what schizophrenics do not have!

Several students of psychometric measurement, notably Wechsler

(41, 43) and Jastak (21), have remarked that many conative, non-intellective and "character" factors influence test performances. A patient's score is determined not only by what he knows and can do, but also by his interest, docility, persistence, and zest to succeed, which may be described as aspects of his temperament and personality. It is quite true that intelligence test *tasks* evoke these factors, but intelligence test *scores* do not show them in useful isolation, but only tangled with the many other determiners present. The separation of the nonintellective factors from test performances remains a worthwhile project for future research.

In summary, the promise felt a few years ago that intelligence tests would contribute new strengths to psychiatric diagnosis has been most meagerly fulfilled. Intelligence tests are designed to measure global intelligence, and are based on theory and on operating principles explicitly directed toward that end. The tests cannot be blamed if they fail also to accomplish the alien task of psychiatric diagnosis, for which they were not intended originally.

PSYCHIATRIC CONCEPTS IMPLEMENTED BY PSYCHOMETRIC TESTS

Another psychometric approach has laid aside the conventional intelligence test, and has tried to implement psychiatric concepts with the aid of specially constructed measuring instruments.

One of the oldest psychiatric concepts is that of dementia, of progressive intellectual deterioration associated with mental disorder. That concept has been applied not only to organic disorders characterized by cerebral incompetence, but also to the commonest group of the functional psychoses as evidenced by Kraepelin's category of dementia praecox. The measurement of deterioration would seem to be an obvious field for the application of psychometric tests. The direct measurement of intellectual deficit is rarely possible, however, since few patients have been tested in their premorbid state. Babcock (2) opened a period of attempts to measure deterioration indirectly, by postulating that some psychometric function, usually a vocabulary score, represented the patient's original level to which other test performances could be compared. Several other tests, including the Shipley (36), the Hunt-Minnesota (18) and the deterioration index of the Wechsler-Bellevue, have been based on essentially the same theory.

The testing of the senile and of clearly deteriorated organic patients has tended to confirm the positive aspect of Babcock's hypothesis; they do indeed make higher scores on vocabulary than on other tests involving new learning, attention, and motor speed. With respect to differential diagnosis, troubles have arisen because of the relatively large proportion of normal persons and of undeteriorated patients who also test as if deteriorated when they really are not (22, 27, 28). These numerous "false positives" throw doubt on the usefulness of the method. Further studies have found low correlations between deterioration tests based on the same rationale (10, 26), and irregular relationships between deficit and age (32). A research (4) using premorbid and postmorbid test scores of a group of multiple sclerosis patients, found statistically significant relationships between direct and indirect measures of deficit, which were, however, too low to be of practical value. A similar study (34) of a small group of schizophrenics, tested before and during their illness, found that the supposedly nondeteriorating test scores were not a good index of premorbid intelligence, and that loss of intellectual efficiency in schizophrenics is more closely related to lack of attention and concentration than to any real mental loss. The hypothesis that dementia can be measured psychometrically receives only weak support from the consensus of current research.

Another psychiatric hypothesis which has developed into a psychometric technic is that abnormal persons are unable to perform abstract conceptual thinking. Normal people are capable of behaving both concretely and abstractly, but the abnormal person is confined to one mode, the concrete, and cannot shift to the other. First applied to the study of organically damaged persons, as by Goldstein and Scheerer (12), the method also has been used with schizophrenics by Kasanin (23) and others. The measures of the abstract versus the concrete attitude mainly involve the sorting of test objects into categories, and their re-sorting to form different conceptual groups. Descriptively, the results seem promising, but the findings have been reported in qualitative rather than quantitative terms; the proportions of organics, psychotics, neurotics, and normals that might fall below some defined point on the abstract-concrete continuum are not yet known. Until the technic is quantified sufficiently to permit statistical tests of significance, an evaluation must be withheld.

One new method for comparing the behavior of psychotics and normals has its roots in both of the concepts just described: in that of psychological deficit and that of abstract-concrete behavior. In an earlier critical article, Yacorzynski (45) questioned the theory that vocabulary does not deteriorate. He postulated that the type or quality of the definitions of words does improve during the growing years, and deteriorates in senility and dementia. Only the crudeness of the vocabulary scoring procedure, which allows as much credit for a poor definition as for a good one providing the word is recognized at all, makes the test seem unaffected by age and deficit. Recently Feifel (7) tested this hypothesis by examining the qualitative character of the responses of normal and psychotic subjects who had been matched with respect to crude vocabulary score. The abnormals showed a lack of abstraction in their responses, tending to define words by use, description, and other inferior modes, in contrast to the normals' selection of the synonym type of response. The study opens the possibility that a test of deficit may be constructed, which will also in a sense be a test of abstract-concrete behavior, by comparing the number of words known with some score based on the quality of the definitions.

Many years of giving tests to normal and abnormal subjects have led to the discovery of several other differentiating technics which, while first based on empirical observations, lend themselves to the formulation of theoretical postulates.

The Porteus Maze Test (29) was first developed as a device for classifying the mentally deficient, but thirty-five years of experience with it has pointed to many other values. From the outset, Porteus conceived the maze test as measuring qualities of planning and foresightedness, as against irresolution and impulsiveness. Subsequent research studies have shown its superior correlation with life-adjustment criteria. It is one of very few tests whose scores are radically lowered by the immediate effects of prefrontal lobotomy, and which shows gains proportional to postoperative improvement (31). The theoretical rationale of the test corresponds closely with descriptions of the behavior of lobotomized patients. Finally, a quantification of qualitative characteristics of maze test behavior has differentiated successfully between delinquents and normals, at both adult and juvenile age levels (30). Because of its theoretical basis as well as because of its empirical results, the Porteus test deserves wider use in psychiatric settings.

An empirical finding not yet anchored in theory is the relationship between the inability to reproduce geometric designs and the diagnosis of organic brain damage. The effect was first noted in the memory-for-drawings items of the Binet and other scales, and has resulted in the development of several recent tests (13, 25). Abnormal behavior in the copying of geometric figures and in their reproduction from memory is characterized by poor closure, misperception of form, perseveration, and especially by the rotation of the figure. The scoring of such faults can identify about 50 per cent or organic cases, while misidentifying only a negligible number of normals. Feeble-minded persons of organic etiology are also differentiated from endogenous defectives (5).

The psychometric applications of psychiatric hypotheses have only begun to realize their potential usefulness. Even with the meager beginnings of the present time, they have yielded more fruitful results than have the intelligence test scores. They emphasize the value of a theoretical foundation that is consonant with the tasks that are presented.

FUTURE DIRECTIONS

It is always presumptuous to predict the future, but present trends may at least be projected a bit, and present unused resources invoked that might contribute to progress. Three new approaches to the psychometric study of behavior disorders seem to offer promise.

One path of advance may lie in quantifying the qualitative. Much recent discussion of clinical testing has emphasized the value of the qualitative differences in test responses that often reveal more than the test scores as they are obtained at present. An excellent example has been given by W. A. Hunt.

In response to the question, "How far is it from Paris to New York?" a subject may answer "About 3,000 miles"; but I have had another subject say, "Unfortunately I cannot be as exact as I would like to. No, I don't know exactly. For an approximation—about 3,000 miles. Sorry I can't answer more definitely." Both these answers are correct and count the same in the scoring system, with the numerical symbols concealing the diagnostic richness of the second answer.

In response to the question, "Where is Egypt?" a subject may answer "In South America"; but I have had a schizophrenic answer "In a manner of speaking it may be said to be in an oasis—plenty surrounded by sand." Both answers are wrong and in scoring are represented by the same symbol—zero. Not only is the pathological significance of the second answer lost, but I would submit that a real difference in intelligence is overlooked (19, pp. 311–312).

Because of such observations, it has been urged that the real measuring instrument is the clinical psychologist rather than the test, and that the truest scoring key is his educated judgment. It is agreed that a trained human mind is a more complex and powerful instrument than the Mark III electronic computer, but it still has its faults. Our present tests were designed to avoid the very errors of subjective judgment to which it is advocated that we should return. There is, however, an intermediate solution between the horns of the too rigid test and the too errant human judge. That solution is the product scale. In this day of creative and progressive education we are likely to forget that scales for scoring children's compositions, handwriting, and drawing once existed. Such scales are quantified specimens of very qualitative performances. At least, we are all familiar with the scoring specimens in many test manuals by which we assign full, half, or no credit to vocabulary responses and to drawn designs. A constructive direction for research may be to discover many questions that tend to evoke qualitatively different answers from, say, schizophrenics and normals. The responses could be reduced to quantitative form by a compendious manual giving many scaled specimens of answers.

Another possible way to improve our clinical psychometrics might be to borrow a well-developed and pertinent technic from industrial psychology. Let us, for example, develop an aptitude test for being a schizophrenic. The suggestion may sound shocking, but it is worth a trial. The steps of the method are not simple, but they are well-defined. To develop an aptitude battery for airplane pilots (8), one analyzes the nature of the task, seeks critical abilities that define the differences between success and failure, and then constructs tailor-made tests for empirical trial. If the resources for pilot prediction had been limited to a manipulation of the subtest scores of intelligence tests such as the Wechsler-Bellevue, the effort would have been doomed to failure. Only by freeing ourselves from past conceptions of tests, and by compiling new tasks that tap the phenomena to be described or predicted, are we likely to achieve the desired goal. Of course, the construction of new tests for broad diagnosis might be only an initial and limited goal. Greater challenges lie in the prediction of the course of the disorder, of the selection of a therapeutic method, and of the outcome of treatment.

Both of the suggestions made so far are perhaps more akin to human engineering rather than human science. Even more needed than technics is the basic understanding of the nature and process of mental disorder, which, once achieved, will point the way to improved practices. There is all too much temptation to do nothing while we await the eventual genius, the Newton of psychopathology, who will furnish the spark to clarify our theoretical orientations. Newtons are unpredictable, however, and while waiting we might forge ahead as best we can. There are promising beginnings on which to build. The work of Halstead (15) on the psychology of brain damage has demonstrated a method for combining theory, experiment and statistical analysis. It is a basic research, not yet ready for clinical application, but ready to be built upon by further research programs. New theories, such as Cameron's (3) biosocial interpretation of behavior disorders, offer points of departure for the formulation of quantifiable hypotheses that can develop into more effective types of measurement.

In the past, one of the greatest obstacles to psychometric progress has been the separation between theory and practice. Conscious efforts toward bridging that gap promise great rewards, both to the depth of our understanding and to the quality of our service.

REFERENCES

1. ALEXANDER, W. P.: Intelligence, concrete and abstract. Brit. J. Psychol. Monogr. Suppl., *6*, #19, 1935.
2. BABCOCK, HARRIET.: An experiment in the measurement of mental deterioration. Arch. Psychol., N. Y., *18*, #117, 1930.
3. CAMERON, N.: The Psychology of Behavior Disorders. Boston, Houghton Mifflin, 1947.
4. CANTER, A. H.: Direct and indirect measures of psychological deficit in multiple sclerosis. J. Gen. Psychol., *44*, 3–50, 1951.
5. CASSEL, R. H.: Relation of design reproduction to the etiology of mental deficiency. J. Consult. Psychol., *13*, 421–428, 1949.
6. DERNER, G. F., ABORN, M., and CANTER, A. H.: The reliability of the Wechsler-Bellevue subtests and scales. J. Consult. Psychol., *14*, 172–179, 1950.

7. FEIFEL, H.: Qualitative differences in the vocabulary responses of normals and abnormals. Genet. Psychol. Monogr., *39*, 151–204, 1949.

8. FLANAGAN, J. C.: The aviation psychology program in the Army Air Forces. AAF Aviation Psychology Program Research Reports, Report No. 1. Washington, U. S. Government Printing Office, 1948.

9. GARFIELD, S. L.: An evaluation of Wechsler-Bellevue patterns in schizophrenia. J. Consult. Psychol., *13*, 279–287, 1949.

10. ——, and FEY, W. F.: A comparison of the Wechsler-Bellevue and Shipley-Hartford scales as measures of mental impairment. J. Consult. Psychol., *12*, 259–264, 1948.

11. GILHOOLY, F. M.: Wechsler-Bellevue reliability and the validity of certain diagnostic signs of the neuroses. J. Consult. Psychol., *14*, 82–87, 1950.

12. GOLDSTEIN, K., and SCHEERER, M.: Abstract and concrete behavior, an experimental study with special tests. Psychol. Monogr., *53*, #2, 1941.

13. GRAHAM, FRANCES K., and KENDALL, BARBARA S.: Performance of brain-damaged cases on a memory-for-designs test. J. Abnorm. Soc. Psychol., *41*, 303–314, 1946.

14. GUTMAN, BRIGETTE.: The application of the Wechsler-Bellevue scale in the diagnosis of organic brain disorders. J. Clin. Psychol., *6*, 195–198, 1950.

15. HALSTEAD, W. C.: Brain and Intelligence. Chicago, Univ. of Chicago Press, 1947.

16. HAMISTER, R. C.: The test-retest reliability of the Wechsler-Bellevue intelligence test (Form I) for a neuropsychiatric population. J. Consult. Psychol., *13*, 39–43, 1949.

17. HEWSON, LOUISE R.: The Wechsler-Bellevue scale and the substitution test as aids in neuropsychiatric diagnosis. J. Ment. Nerv. Dis., *109*, 158–183, 246–266, 1949.

18. HUNT, H. F.: A practical, clinical test for organic brain damage. J. Appl. Psychol., *27*, 375–386, 1943.

19. HUNT, W. A.: The future of diagnostic testing in clinical psychology. J. Clin. Psychol., *2*, 311–317, 1943.

20. ——, et al. The clinical possibilities of an abbreviated individual intelligence test. J. Consult. Psychol., *12*, 171–173, 1948.

21. JASTAK, J.: A plan for the objective measurement of character. J. Clin. Psychol., *4*, 170–178, 1948.

22. JUCKEM, HARRIET, and WOLD, JANE A.: A study of the Hunt-Minnesota test for organic brain damage at the upper levels of vocabulary. J. Consult. Psychol., *12*, 53–57, 1948.

23. KASANIN, J. S. (Ed.): Language and Thought in Schizophrenia. Berkeley, Univ. of California Press, 1944.

24. LEVINE, L. S.: The utility of Wechsler's patterns in the diagnosis of schizophrenia. J. Consult. Psychol., *13*, 28–31, 1949.

25. LORD, ELIZABETH, and WOOD, LOUISE.: Diagnostic values in a visuo-motor test. Amer. J. Orthopsychiat., *12*, 414–428, 1942.

26. MAGARET, ANN, and SIMPSON, MARY M.: A comparison of two measures of

deterioration in psychotic patients. J. Consult. Psychol., *12*, 265–269, 1948.

27. MALAMUD, RACHEL F.: Validity of the Hunt-Minnesota test for organic brain damage. J. Appl. Psychol., *30*, 271–275, 1946.

28. MEEHL, P. E., and JEFFERY, MARY.: The Hunt-Minnesota test for organic brain damage in cases of functional depression. J. Appl. Psychol., *30*, 276–287, 1946.

29. PORTEUS, S. D.: The Maze Test and Mental Differences. Vineland, N. J., Smith, 1933.

30. ——.: Qualitative Performance in the Maze Test. Vineland, N. J., Smith, 1942.

31. ——, and PETERS, H. N.: Maze test validation and psychosurgery. Genet. Psychol. Monogr., *36*, 3–86, 1947.

32. RABIN, A. I.: Vocabulary and efficiency levels as functions of age in the Babcock method. J. Consult. Psychol., *11*, 207–211, 1947.

33. RAPAPORT, D., et al.: Diagnostic Psychological Testing. Chicago, Year Book Publishers, 1945. Vol. I.

34. RAPPAPORT, S. R., and WEBB, W. B.: An attempt to study intellectual deterioration by premorbid and psychotic testing. J. Consult. Psychol., *14*, 95–98, 1950.

35. SCHAFER, R.: The Clinical Application of Psychological Tests. New York, International Universities Press, 1948.

36. SHIPLEY, W. C.: A self-administering scale for measuring intellectural impairment and deterioration. J. Psychol., *9*, 371–377, 1940.

37. SHOBEN, E. J., Jr.: The Wechsler-Bellevue in the detection of anxiety: a test of the Rashkis-Welsh hypothesis. J. Consult. Psychol., *14*, 40–45, 1950.

38. TERMAN, L. M., and MERRILL, MAUD A.: Measuring Intelligence. Boston, Houghton Mifflin, 1937.

39. THURSTONE, L. L.: Primary Mental Abilities. Chicago, Univ. of Chicago Press, 1938.

40. WEBB, W. B., and DeHAAN, H.: Wechsler-Bellevue split-half reliabilities in normals and schizophrenics. J. Consult. Psychol., *15*, 68–71, 1951.

41. WECHSLER, D.: The non-intellective factors in general intelligence. J. Abnorm. Soc. Psychol., *38*, 101–103, 1943.

42. ——.: The Measurement of Adult Intelligence. (3rd Ed.) Baltimore, Williams & Wilkins, 1944.

43. ——.: Cognitive, conative, and non-intellective intelligence. Amer. Psychologist, *5*, 78–83, 1950.

44. WITTENBORN, J. R.: An evaluation of the use of Bellevue-Wechsler subtest scores as an aid in psychiatric diagnosis. J. Consult. Psychol., *13*, 433–439, 1949.

45. YACORZYNSKI, G. Y.: An evaluation of the postulates underlying the Babcock deterioration test. Psychol. Rev., *48*, 261–267, 1941.

Part One: Discussion I

By DAVID WECHSLER, Ph.D.*

I N READING through the three papers which have been presented today, I sought to find the common themes, if any, which might be said to run through all of them. There seems to be at least one; namely, an overall disappointment in the current theories, methods and results of psychometrics, and in the case of one of the reporters, a specific dissatisfaction with the persons who in the last ten years have been trying to utilize them professionally, namely, the clinical psychologists. I shall presently try to consider and summarize briefly these objections but I should like to say in advance that I myself am not so perturbed as some of the reporters about the limitations of clinical psychology or its achievements. Indeed, as I review the literature of our sister sciences including psychiatry, in the last decade, I am, on the contrary, greatly impressed by the contributions of psychometrics and clinical psychology. I feel sure that if the reporters had taken a comparative approach or even had been inclined to emphasize the areas of success rather than the areas in which psychometrics have failed, the picture presented would be much more correct as well as more optimistic.

In spite of this stricture, I would like to say that I am in considerable agreement with what two of the papers have to say. I am entirely in agreement with Dr. White that one must be selective in our research, that is, look for the manageable parts of our subject matter and deal with them first. There is, as he says, great danger in pretending that psychological processes are as simple as they are often assumed to be.

I suppose that when Dr. White detailed to us his excursions into phrenology he had in mind VonÜxküll's dictum that the science of today is often the myth of tomorrow. Only I could not help wondering why, in seeking historical backgrounds of psychometric theory, he did not choose Galton instead of Gall for his analogy. Perhaps it was because he had in mind some of the projective technics rather

* Chief Psychologist, Bellevue Psychiatric Hospital; Associate Clinical Professor of Medical Psychology, College of Medicine, New York University.

than the more modest, at least in some cases modest, claims of our more pedestrian clinical methods. Still his general conclusions are such as most of us would want to agree with. There is no doubt that few if any psychological tests ever measure a specific restricted function. In the broader sense they tap sample specimens of behavior and are only generally differentiated by the fact that they emphasize one or another aspect of this behavior. If we accept this proposition, we must, as he implies, also agree to a second, namely, that no secure appraisal of an individual's functioning can be based on a finding of a single test. I have myself often emphasized the danger of putting all of one's eggs in one basket, whether it be the Rorschach, Thematic Apperception, or even the Wechsler-Bellevue Test.

The revelance of Dr. White's proposition, that personalities are open systems is, however, not quite so clear to me. As a general statement is is quite true that the psychologist interacts with the subject as a person and that they reciprocally influence the testing situation. But, of course, the question is to what extent. My own view is that it would not be considerable except in the rare and special case. In such instance it may be assumed that the competent examiner will be aware of the situation and be able to appraise it. This does not in any way contradict the desirability of having multiple examiners for research purposes, but I hate to think of the day when one will believe it necessary to make systematic "corrections" for the testor's personality.

Dr. Selling's paper is a little difficult to discuss. From its title I expected some historical survey of what psychometrics has contributed, or for that matter, failed to contribute, to the understanding of psychopathological conditions. Instead, as you have heard, a great portion of the paper is devoted to an analysis of the failings of the contemporaneous clinical psychologist as a person and a colleague. Evidently Dr. Selling looks back with nostalgia to the halcyon days at Bellevue in the 1920's when the psychologist, to quote, "knew his own limitations." I can report, however, that psychology at Bellevue as in many other places has changed considerably since 1925 and that its present status there as elsewhere is more nearly as described in Dr. William Menninger's address at the APA Denver meeting last Fall.

One or two other points in Dr. Selling's paper require more detailed

comment. The first has to do with his appraisal of the relation between clinical psychology and psychiatry. His view is that clinical
psychology "has the same relationship to psychiatry that the clinical
pathologist has to the field of medicine." This statement represents
a point of view shared perhaps also by others as to what they should
like the relationship to be but certainly does not describe how clinical
psychology in point of fact functions. Here again Dr. Selling con-
founds clinical psychology with clinical psychologists. He is much
more concerned with *who does what* than with *what is being done*.
This is obviously an *ipse dixit* approach, which can only lead to an
authoritarian psychology that has neither social nor scientific jus-
tification.

Dr. Selling's second assertion which needs comment is "that there
are no tests as yet which can diagnose the psychosis or accurately
evaluate the symptomatology of a psychoneurosis which will enable
specific treatment rather than just any old kind of therapy that
happens to be the psychologist's preference." Obviously no single
tests can do precisely that and I do not know any competent psychologist who claims that it could; but if Dr. Selling merely means,
as he seems to imply, that psychological tests cannot be used as aids
in diagnosis, it again represents a misreading of the facts. I can see
no possible reason for the use of psychometrics in psychiatry if they
are not going to help in the classification and diagnosis of various
mental disorders. This does not mean that such classification is based
on psychometrics alone, and to what extent psychologists themselves
are aware of it you can judge for yourselves from the paper just read
by Dr. Shaffer.

This brings me to Dr. Shaffer's paper which is in some respects
the most challenging to me. I also agree most heartily with his general
approach. Having said this, I should like to come to grips with him
on certain points in which I think he is in error. Dr. Shaffer has dealt
some telling blows and I am sure he would not want me to pull my
punches either. First, I will deal with what he calls the limited purposes or possible fields of application of general intelligence tests.
While it is true that authors of intelligence scales have not always
explicitly expressed their theoretical bases, I do not think that the
field of application of a test can be determined a priori by its author;
that on the contrary, any claim as to what it measures must eventually

be determined by what application and experience shows it to measure. In the case of intelligence tests experience has shown that the fields of application is quite broad. Dr. Shaffer himself admits that these tests are irreplaceable aids in education and guidance. What others and I have only asserted is that they can be used profitably in clinical diagnosis as well.

But to come to the item which seems to trouble Dr. Shaffer most—the problem of making profiles from subtest scores from an assembled battery, like the Wechsler-Bellevue—I must concede that most of the studies published on what is euphemistically called profile patterning is not very encouraging, and I can understand Dr. Shaffer's disappointment in reading not only the published results but also the unpublished material which comes to him as an editor. I have myself gone through some of this ordeal. One needs to say, however, what one means by a pattern. If by a pattern one means a unique configuration, then I think nobody has as yet shown the existence of a single pattern on any test. Those who have read my chapter on "Clinical Diagnosis" will recall that I have nowhere claimed specific profiles or define any patterns. Apart from the question of test subtest reliabilities, it is obvious that the chances of obtaining a unique configuration for a battery of 10 tests in which scores vary from 0–18 is practically nil. Even if only a three-fold scoring classification such as "good," "average" and "poor" were used with the Wechsler-Bellevue Scale, one would obtain more than 65,000 possible unique patterns. Accordingly, the tables in my MEASUREMENT OF ADULT INTELLIGENCE only comprise an empirical statement as to the tests on which various clinical diagnostic groups tend to do well or poor.

The question that naturally arises is what use, if any, is such a list. The answer is the same as that of a list of any symptoms—a descriptive one. The table, for example, which I give is not intended as a key for diagnosis for every beginner student in psychology anymore than the symptoms in a textbook of medicine are intended to enable a third year medical student to diagnose all of the diseases in internal medicine. This brings me to a second point about which Dr. Shaffer seems unduly perturbed, namely, the recurrence of certain tests as a sign in a variety of disease entities. This does not mean that diagnosis can be made on the basis of these tests alone, anymore than the symptoms of high temperature and gastric distress occurring in a great many diseases can be used to the exclusion of all others. Dr. Shaffer is quite right when he says that one can perform poorly on the Digit Symbol tests for more than one reason, but so can high temperature occur for more than one reason. Nevertheless, poor performance on Digit Symbol, like the occurrence of high temperature can be significant. The question, of course, is when and where. On the one hand, I agree with Dr. Shaffer that this cannot be done with the type of statistics thus far produced. On the other hand, considering the many sources of error involved in diagnosis, I am, unlike Dr. Shaffer, encouraged rather than discouraged by the percentage of diagnostic successes as revealed by the technics of the authors he cites.

I should have liked to take up all the points Dr. Shaffer made but restriction of time prevents me from discussing most of them. I will, therefore, proceed at once to the last part of his paper in which he makes some very constructive suggestions. One of them is what he calls quantitating quality. I should say psychologists have been trying to do this for a long time although more could be done in this direction. But perhaps even more necessary at present is what I would call *qualifying the quantitative*. In clinical practice, the end product of a diagnosis is some verbal statement. Whatever the limits set for test performance, one eventually has to say whether it is good or bad, that the patient is a mental defective or of superior intelligence, that it shows neurotic or some other personality structure. Now this can best be achieved by what Dr. Shaffer calls the product scale, and which I prefer to call the matching method. The assigning of quantitative scores to qualitative material is useful. Numbers are of value in making computations, but the important thing is the validity of the match. Some of the tests on the Wechsler-Bellevue are essentially matching methods in such as answers on the Comprehension, Similarities, and Vocabulary tests and the numerical scores are only a simple means for appraisal.

Another suggestion made for improving our psychometric methods by Dr. Shaffer was that we copy technics employed by industrial psychologists. I admit I am not too familiar with their technics, but as far as I can see they would offer little to clinical psychology. Their statistics in my opinion are psychologically spurious and I should hate to see an aptitude test for schizophrenics like one for airplane pilots. In any event, I think Dr. Shaffer will agree that as deficient as our clinical methods are for diagnosing schizophrenia they are at least as good as the Army's experience in picking pilots.

In conclusion, I wish to add that in spite of my specific criticisms I was much impressed with Dr. Shaffer's paper as a whole and in particular by the thorough job he did in presenting the basic theoretical problem confronting us in applied psychometrics. Perhaps the main difference in our points of view is that I have been more impressed by how much psychologists have done than by how much they have failed to do. We may not be as good as some of us claim, but our claims are much better than we think.

Part One: Discussion II

By JEROME D. FRANK, Ph.D., M.D.*

FOR THE PAST three years I have been associated with a research
project in group psychotherapy in which we have used the Rorschach and Thematic Apperception Tests to help evaluate changes
in patients as a result of therapy, and also as a diagnostic aid. I
should like to devote this discussion to a consideration of one of the
problems we encountered in using the tests diagnostically because
we believe it to be a fundamental one which needs clarification in
any thinking about testing. A central problem in group therapy is
how to compose groups. Its solution requires a means of predicting
how patients will react to one another and to certain issues which
may arise in the course of therapy. In attempting to use the tests
as an aid in solving this very difficult problem we have come up
sharply against the limitations which Dr. White particularly has
noted. We believe that the essential problem lies in the fact so well
expressed by Dr. White—that the individual is only partly separated
from his environment; that is, different aspects of a person's personality are elicited by different situations.

Operationally in our psychological testing we are trying to predict
from a person's behavior in a standard set of situations how he will
behave in other situations, using various personality attributes as
the constructs on which the predictions are based. In order to be
able to predict how a patient will respond in a given interpersonal
situation, we must know what the major personal issues with which
he is concerned are, and what are his characteristic modes of responding to or perceiving situations. Psychological tests often give
us very helpful information on these two points. Behavior, however,
does not occur in a social vacuum but is constantly modified by the
responses of the other people in the environment. We must, therefore,
also know how to define those aspects of the situations in which the
patient is to be placed which are apt to activate certain issues for him
or elicit his characteristic patterns of response. We believe that the

* Associate Professor of Psychiatry, Johns Hopkins University Medical
School.

value of psychological tests as predictive instruments ·is limited by the limitation in our ability to define adequately situations in this way.

The way in which the responses of the others in a situation can modify behavior has been brought home to us very strikingly by observing the same patients in individual interviews and in a therapeutic group. With schizophrenic patients especially, several therapists have reported that, knowing the patient only from his behavior in the group situation, they are literally unable to recognize him from the account of his behavior given in his clinical history. A neurotic patient who in individual interviews was very deferential and made efforts to please, in the group assumed a superior attitude, advised the others, belittled their symptoms, and dissociated himself so completely from them that some of them thought he was another doctor who had been secretly planted in the group.

The problem is further complicated by the fact that every situation contains components which elicit different patterns of response, some of which may be conflicting, so that we must be able not only to single out these components but to know which will predominate for a patient or how he will resolve the conflict at a given time. That is, we must be able to predict just what aspects of the situation the patient will choose to respond to. For example, we knew before the group meeting that the neurotic patient just mentioned was not only deferential to authority but was very eager to be liked by his peers and also very contemptuous of and competitive with them. We knew that the group situation contained both authority and peer figures, which would be likely to create a conflict situation for him, but we could not-tell in advance which of these aspects he would respond to primarily. Actually he solved his conflict by offering advice to the others as he conceived a doctor might, thereby showing his deference to the doctor and his superiority to the others. At the same time he thought he was pleasing them by offering them good advice and was entirely unaware that the others felt his attitude was contemptuous. He suffered quite a shock when they told him so.

The first task in dealing with this problem with which we are now engaged and which we have by no means solved, would seem to be to try to single out and describe some important situations which might face patients in terms of the range of conflicts, issues or habitual patterns of response they might stimulate. We would then have to study how the situations so defined would affect individuals with differing personality attributes as determined in part by the tests.

One way of getting started on this problem would be, as Dr. White suggested, to use a large number of different tests so as to see how the patient would respond to different situations. This is only a partial solution because no matter how much the tests differ from each other they are still all tests and part of a test situation. A serious practical difficulty also arises. Dr. White's statement that ten to fifteen hours of testing per person are necessary if the test results are to have any sort of scientific validity is a counsel of despair for research in therapy. Outside of the problem of persuading patients (who, after all, come for help, not to be studied) to cooperate in such a program, this much testing is bound to get entangled in the patient's mind with his treatment, especially since, as has been shown by others, tests have important therapeutic implications. It might be quite a problem to evaluate how much of the change in a patient was due to the testing program, how much to the treatment being studied.

The test we found most useful for getting a lead on what situations may be important for a patient is the Thematic Apperception Test because in it the patient sets up and deals with interpersonal situations significant for him. We have also found very helpful an interview conducted by a social worker which is directly aimed at studying the patient's responses to a wide variety of interpersonal situations in his present environment.

We have wondered whether the test situation itself could not be exploited so as to yield more data on this point, through varying the total setting systematically and looking for corresponding changes in the results. Dr. David Levy at the American Psychiatric Association meeting in Detroit in 1950 stated that candidates for analytic training who were required to take a Rorschach as part of their admission examination turned in protocols which seemed to be consistently influenced by the purpose for which the test was given. This would seem to be a lead that is well worth following. Dr. White pointed out the value of using different examiners with the same patient. Could this perhaps be carried further by exploring whether there are any consistent differences in test responses of different subjects related to definable differences in the personalities of the examiners? One might study the differences in responses on projective tests elicited by an examiner with a lot of prestige in the subject's eyes as contrasted with one who had very little, by a cold "scientific" tester, and a friendly therapeutically oriented one, by a sexually seductive examiner, and a parental one.

We think it may be possible to predict how patients with certain personality attributes as determined by tests and interviews will resolve the conflicts set up by various group situations as we observe them. We are becoming able to single out, for example, those patients who may be expected to react by cutting out the group and addressing themselves exclusively to the doctor in a help-seeking way, as contrasted with those who have to put up a great front of adequacy before the other group members and become so anxious if this front is threatened that they tend to leave therapy. Patients who may have a hard time are those whose need to maintain a claim on the doctor's sympathy is as strong as their need to show superiority to the others. Some seem to resolve this neatly by implicitly claiming moral superiority through having withstood greater suffering than the others; thus managing to assert their need for help and their superiority to other patients at the same time.

Differences between the reaction stimulating qualities of group and individual sessions may also supply some clues. For example, with the doctor alone the dependency and help-seeking aspects of a patient are apt to be especially stimulated. He comes to the doctor for help, and the doctor is a figure of power and prestige. In the group, surrounded by people he may regard as peers or inferiors, with whom he feels he must struggle for the doctor's attention, a whole new set of issues—status seeking, proving his superiority or greater worthiness, and so on—may be stimulated. Other differences in attitude stimulation are offered by mixed groups as compared with those of the same sex, or by so-called educational groups, in which the leader tries to guide discussion from personal problems to general issues, contrasted with analytical groups in which conversely, discussion of general issues is discouraged and personal material is emphasized.

We are finding the Rorschach and Thematic Apperception Test a great help in approaching this crucial problem of how to predict how patients will react to specific therapeutic situations. In stressing what appear to be the limitations of these tests for this purpose, it has been my hope to stimulate thinking and discussion which might yield ideas as to how to make them more useful.

Part Two

DIAGNOSTIC USE OF PSYCHOLOGICAL TESTS

4

AN EXPERIMENTAL CRITERION FOR THE PROGNOSTICATION OF THE STATUS OF SCHIZOPHRENICS AFTER A THREE-YEAR-INTERVAL BASED ON RORSCHACH DATA*

By ZYGMUNT A. PIOTROWSKI, Ph.D., and NOLAN D. C. LEWIS, M.D.†

PURPOSE

OUR PURPOSE is to present a list of fifteen perceptanalytic Rorschach signs formulated to serve as a prognostic criterion in schizophrenia for a three-year-period. The signs were developed from data provided by Rorschach (19) examinations of 100 schizophrenics who were in-patients of the New York State Psychiatric Institute and who were followed and reexamined psychologically as well as psychiatrically after an interval of from three to fifteen years. We have found it very difficult to devise a perceptanalytic prognostic criterion that would be valid regardless of the length of time for which the prognosis is to be made. Consequently, we have limited the interval to three years since it is easier to predict for shorter than for longer periods.

With increasing psychiatric facilities and an increasing awareness of mental illnesses on the part of the public, more and more cases of mild forms of schizophrenia come to the professional attention of psychiatrists. Some of the milder cases even recover, although usually they are left with psychological scars (9). Many of them show an improvement which, if not permanent, may last for years. Hence, dependable prognostic criteria have become of urgent practical concern.

* This is part of an investigation supported by a research grant from the National Institute of Mental Health of the National Institutes of Health, Public Health Service. To our knowledge, this is the first communication in world literature which presents the prognostic perceptanalytic signs in such detail and for such definite, extended periods of time.

† New York State Psychiatric Institute.

METHODS AND SUBJECTS

The patients were diagnosed by one of us, Lewis, on the basis of personal interviews, Psychiatric Institute case histories, as well as on the basis of follow-up reports from hospitals and psychiatrists. The diagnoses were made in accordance with *Criteria for Early Differential Diagnosis of Psychoneurosis and Schizophrenia* (8). The great majority of the patients were first admissions at the Institute. The interval between the first Rorschach examination of each patient and the follow-up diagnostic interview was from three to fourteen years. The prognostic signs were developed by studying Rorschach records obtained at the time of the earliest hospitalization. The 100 schizophrenics were divided into four groups: an "improved" group including those patients whose level of personality functioning and socioeconomic adjustment was better at the end of the three-year-period than it had been in the period of life when they were first examined; the "unchanged" group, including nearly all of the well-preserved episodic cases as well as other patients who manifested no noticeable change, particularly no sign of having become worse in terms of personality possibilities and socio-economic adjustment; a "somewhat worse" group, including patients who manifested a definite change for the worse, being less able to take care of themselves and less able to maintain cooperative and constructive interpersonal relationships; and the "much worse" group, including patients who have become worse to such a degree as to require constant and special attention even within the hospital. Once the patients had been divided into these groups, a search was begun for signs which would best differentiate among the groups. This search was not limited to signs which, taken singly, appeared with greatly different frequencies in the four subgroups, or at least in the two larger subgroups. (The good group consisted of the combined improved and unchanged, and the poor group consisting of the combined somewhat worse and much worse group.) Six of the signs did not differentiate markedly between the groups. However, they have been retained because they add to the discriminatory power of the entire criterion. These six signs are: inductive perception; the animal percentage; the presence of form-color responses; the difference between the three sums, ΣM, ΣC, and Σc; and the difference between time per response and initial reaction time when the sum of shading responses is smaller than the sum of color responses. The Rorschach records were scored according to a revised system, published under the title *A Rorschach Compendium* (15).

DEFINITION OF CRITERION

Fifteen signs constitute the criterion. Twelve of these signs have been assigned positive values of 1 to 3 points because they correlate positively with improvement or absence of deterioration. Three of them have been assigned negative values of −1 point each because they were produced with a significantly higher relative frequency by schizophrenics who have become worse. The total score for each patient is the sum of his positive points minus the sum of his negative points.

Sign 1. IndP, or inductive perception, is given the value of plus one point. It consists of a gradual proceeding from small details to larger details or even to wholes, when the latter include the former as constituent parts (17). Examples of IndP are: "This is an eye, it's a head," the eye being an integral part of the head. "These look like a woman's shoes; it looks like a leg. It looks like a woman all dressed." The patient is credited with this sign only if he produces it spontaneously and not as a result of the examiner's inquiries concerning the patient's responses. A variety of IndP, also given plus one point, consists of seeing details which are integral parts of the same object although the object remains unnamed. For example: "An eye, long nose, a mouth." Such a response is scored IndP if the details are spatially so related that they could form integral parts of the same whole. In responses of this kind, the schizophrenic apparently is influenced by the image of a whole even though he fails to verbalize it.

Sign 2. hEvd, or high evidence, is given the value of plus three points. This is a more exacting sign than Evd (13). A patient is credited with this sign when he has demonstrated his capacity (a) to weigh the degree of correspondence between the objective form of the interpreted blot area and the form of the imagined object elicited by that blot area, and (b) to decide actively and independently what the correspondence is, implying explicitly or implicitly that the Rorschach plates are not reproductions of definite objects but merely vague forms which can correspond to the shapes of imagined objects only to a certain degree and rarely, if ever, perfectly. The intellectual trait measured by hEvd is the ability of a patient to evaluate by himself and with finality the adequacy of at least some of his scorable responses. A patient who can manifest such intellectual flexibility, independence, and differentiation between his own subjective visual images and his adequate perceptions of the objective stimulus material, has a well-preserved sense of reality. The reaction hEvd presupposes confidence in one's capacity for the retention, modification and evaluation of his own percepts. In hEvd, as in Evd, the patient must indicate his awareness that the same area can be interpreted in more than one way.

High evidence should not be confused with secondary associations. For example, a patient may respond with the image of a rare object and then recite everything he knows about the topic; these secondary associations, by themselves, are not hEvd. Only when some details of the patient's story are used by him spontaneously to estimate the degree of correspondence between the interpreted blot area and the shape of the imagined object, does hEvd apply. Counterindications of hEvd are inability to keep a percept (an imagined object) in the field of consciousness for any length of time, inability to separate visually from the interpreted area those details recognized by the patient himself as irrelevant, or manifestation of any trait implied by sign 3, i.e., by intellectual passivity. Also all perceptanalytic pathognomonic signs of schizophrenia—contamination (16), number and place responses (19), variable form level (19), and inconstant percepts of variable dimness (14)—are incompatible with hEvd and, consequently, negate the scoring of hEvd. The essential intellectual feature of the pathognomonic signs is a loss of self-criticism and of conscious control over the thought processes. The sign hEvd implies more than autocriticism or insight; it has been designed to record the patient's ability to act on the basis of his self-criticism and insight by evaluating the approximate degree to which his images correspond to the objective blot areas. Since hEvd is the only sign given the high value of three points, its presence should be ascertained with particular care.

A very good example of hEvd was provided by a patient who stated spontaneously that Plate I resembled very closely a flying bird, less closely an airplane, and very poorly, a map. Another patient said of Plate V: "When I first saw it, it looked like the wings of a butterfly, but they are not really; they are not soft like a butterfly's wings."

Other examples of responses which entitle a patient to hEvd credit are: "It looks like a bat; the wings, body. This is not in the bat (white spaces). Better a bat than a butterfly because of its size and colors." "Here inside could be a bug. It looks like a spider, not a bug. See his legs? More like a spider than a bug." "Could be a peacock. Head, legs, spread of feet here. Actually looks more like wings than feathers." An example of counterindication of hEvd is given in the following response to Plate V: "This is the head of a woman (near top middle) but these (meaning top middle extensions) look like horns; she would have to have horns." In this response the patient realized that the image of a woman with horns was a poor one, but he was unable to disregard the top middle extension.

Sign 3. IntelPas, or intellectual passivity, is given the value of minus one point. The complex intellectual trait which this sign has been designed to indicate is (a) the inability to produce a meaningful response, or (b) the inability to determine the degree to which a produced percept corresponds to the interpreted blot area, even though the patient feels an urge to give a response, or to determine the degree of the adequacy of a given response, or both. IntelPas should not be applied to color responses nor should it be mistaken for a color shock; it is applicable to form, shading, and movement responses. IntelPas implies that the patient is not certain of his percepts and that he cannot compare independently and actively the shape of the imagined object, i. e., the percept, with the shape of the blot area to which the percept refers. In most instances of IntelPas the patients leave the issue undecided. Sometimes the patients ask the examiner for help but rarely with a genuine interest in obtaining real assistance. In this respect, IntelPas is different from Plx, or perplexity (10). The latter sign is almost pathognomonic of organic diseases of the brain (20). It means that the patient is incapable of judging the adequacy of his response, being impelled by anxiety to ask the examiner for help, and showing immediate and marked relief when the examiner reassures him. In the present study, Plx is considered as one kind of IntelPas. Of course, most cases of IntelPas are not Plx because few schizophrenics are sufficiently concerned over their Rorschach performance to solicit the examiner's approval or to seek his reassurance. All perceptanalytic pathognomonic signs of schizophrenia are included as indications of IntelPas.

IntelPas and hEvd are mutually exclusive as far as our prognostic criterion is concerned. IntelPas is given priority in scoring; when both hEvd and IntelPas appear in the same record, which is a rare occurrence, only IntelPas is scored. A third possibility exists—that of producing neither sign. Patients with IntelPas have a very weak sense of reality. The sense of reality can not be satisfactory unless there is intellectual flexibility, conscious control over ideas, and ability to check one's thoughts against empirical evidence. Whenever a patient demonstrates that he is incapable of producing a distinct visual image and of retaining it in his mind for any length of time, his sense of reality is seriously affected, particularly if his consciousness is not clouded and he is not evasive.

Examples of IntelPas are found most frequently in records of intelligent schizophrenics who have become much worse. "When you give me these pictures, they suggest so many things. They look so blurred but they are something, they suggest something. I couldn't very well make out what this could be. I would be guessing unless I had some sort of clue." "It's very hard to be definite about this because it's not distinct enough to be able to say anything about it though it might have something to do with some portion of the body." "I don't want to guess because I might have forgotten this particular part." "I've never seen anything like that. I don't recall anything like that. Doesn't look familiar at all. May be some sort of a fly. May be a fly, I don't know exactly what it is." "This is one thing I can't get, this thing that sticks out. I don't know what it is." "I'm thinking what this one might be. I'm afraid I don't know." "Look at those things here. What could they be? Animals? I don't know what they look like." "Birds flying. I don't know whether they are meant to be attached or separate." "I don't know what a chicken looks like. It looks like a chicken." "Looks like a man. They aren't exactly men. These pictures don't mean anything to me. I'm just guessing."

At times the examiner must exercise some initiative in order to ascertain the presence or absence of IntelPas and hEvd. If at the end of the examination the patient is asked which Plates he liked best and which least, his reply usually brings forth remarks bearing on the two signs without direct questioning.

Sign 4. FC = 1 or 2. This sign is given the value of plus one point. The form-color response is assumed to indicate a type of emotional interest in other people which makes for adequate social adjustment and is associated with consideration for others (19). Every patient who has either 1 or 2 FC responses is credited with this sign.

Sign 5. FC > 2. Every patient producing more than two FC responses is credited with plus two points.

Sign 6. M = O. This sign is given the value of minus one point. Inability to produce an M, or a human movement response, is a sign of marked personality weakness in healthy as well as in sick adults.

Sign 7. (M + ΣC) / (M − ΣC) > ±2. This sign is given the value of plus one point. A patient is credited with it if the sum of his human movement and his color responses is more than twice the difference between his human movement and his color responses; the credit is given regardless of whether the ratio is a positive or a negative one, provided it is larger than two. In computing the ΣC, there should be assigned a value of one-half point to every FC, a value of one point to every CF, and the value of one and one-half points to every C. The sign is computed by taking the sum of human movement responses and adding to it the sum of color responses. This sum is then divided by the difference resulting from the subtraction of the sum of color responses from the sum of human movement responses. It does not matter whether the quotient thus obtained is a plus or a minus value. What matters is that the quotient be a number larger than 2.0; if it is, the sign is credited. This sign is not credited if both M and ΣC are zero.

Sign 8. If W+ = 3 or 4, and if M > 1, the patient should be credited with plus one point. Only the good whole responses are considered and they must number either 3 or 4. Also, the number of human movement responses must be more than one. Thus, both conditions must obtain for the sign to be applied. A W+ response is a whole response having a good form. The F−, F±, CF, C, c, etc., responses with poor or vague forms do not qualify. Examples of W+ are W M+, W FM+, W F+, W FC+, W Fc+, etc.

Sign 9. If W+ = 3 or 4, M = 2, and Σc ≥ ΣC, plus two points are given. All three conditions must obtain before the sign can be credited to the patient. The Σc, or the sum of the bright shading responses, must be as large as or larger than the ΣC. The strength of the shading responses can be computed in a manner analogous to that which Rorschach devised to calculate the sum of color responses. The bright shading responses should be computed separately from the dark shading responses, Fc′ and c′, because these two types of chiaroscuro reactions indicate two different ways of alleviating anxiety and of controlling the outward manifestations of anxiety (15). The following procedure is suggested: give one and one-half point for each c; give one point for each Fc; and one-half point for every two chiaroscuro responses ascribed to movement or color responses. In this way every two responses of this kind, Mc, CFc, mc, etc., would contribute one-half point to the Σc.

Sign 10. If W+ = 5 or 6, and M > 5, the patient is credited with plus two points.

Sign 11. If the difference between any two of the following three sums, ΣM, ΣC, and Σc, is smaller than two, the patient is given one plus point; the difference between the highest and the lowest of the three values should not exceed 1.5. However, if any two sums are 0, the sign is not applied and no credit is given.

Sign 12. If both Σc < ΣC, and (T/R − IntRT) > 30″, the patient is credited with plus one point. T/R means total time of the examination proper (excluding the inquiry) divided by the total number of scored responses. IntRT signifies initial reaction time or the time elapsed between the handing of a Plate to the patient and his beginning to give the first scorable response to that Plate. The IntRT is the average of the IntRTs for each Plate. If the patient fails to give any scorable response to one or several Plates, these Plates are omitted from the computation of the IntRT.

Sign 13. h% = 0. If a patient fails to produce any response with a human content, he is given minus one point. In this investigation anatomy and sex responses have been set apart from other human content responses. We have classified responses as anatomical when they contained parts of human or animal bodies that can be seen only as a result of dissection. We have limited the category of sexual responses exclusively to genital responses; secondary sex characteristics, such as breasts, buttocks, thighs, lips, have been scored as human content. Responses were classified as human if they contained the whole human body or those of its parts which can be seen without anatomical dissection, regardless of whether the body is clothed or not. We intended to free the human content categogory from psychological associations such as are frequently attached to anatomy. Pictures of human beings, statues, mythological figures, etc., were classified as human content.

Sign 14. h% between 1 and 20. This sign is given the value of plus two points.

Sign 15. a% < 35. This sign is given the value of plus one point. Every response with animal content is classified as an animal response; however, there are two exceptions. Animal genitalia should be scored as sex responses. Parts of animal bodies which can not be seen without dissection of the animal should be scored as anatomical responses.

MEANING OF SIGNS

All but the first three of our signs consist of conventional Rorschach scoring symbols. Sign 1, inductive perception, has been found with somewhat greater frequency in records of schizophrenics who either maintained their level for at least three years or who have improved in this interval, than in records of schizophrenics who have become worse (17). Since this sign is very rare in Rorschach records of patients suffering from demonstrable lesions of the cortical and subcortical areas of the brain, it indicates a perceptual habit which is associated with a relatively well-preserved intellectual ability. Sign 2, high evidence, is a still stronger counterindication of marked intellectual regression. It can not be produced unless the patient consciously and keenly exercises a basic quality of the human mind: the need to check one's ideas against empirical reality. Every patient with hEvd demonstrates his faith in objective reality criteria, and his rejection of autistic thinking.

In contrast, the third sign, intellectual passivity, denotes not only that the patient does not actively try to determine how well his image fits its respective area (as is implied by sign hEvd), but also that the patient is unable to decide independently and definitely whether or not there is adequate correspondence between the visual image and the interpreted area although he wishes to have his doubts resolved on this point. In other words, intellectual passivity implies that the patient is aware of a serious impairment in his fundamental intellectual capacity of testing his imagination and ideas by empirical observations. Any patient demonstrating this impairment in such a degree as to earn the negative sign of IntelPas is assumed to suffer from marked intellectual regression.

Signs 4 and 5, FC = 1 or 2 and FC > 2, derive their favorable prognostic significance from the high correlation between the number and quality of the form-color responses on the one hand and an effortless and adequate emotional adjustment to conventional life situations on the other. It is unlikely that patients with several FC would behave in a manner that would be socially conspicuous and undesirable. The presence of a number of good FC seems to exclude a marked personality deviation from the healthy norm.

Signs 6 to 11 have to do with the numbers of human movement responses and their relationship to other Rorschach symbols. Absence of human movement responses points to lack of creative imagination and lack of a systematized conception of the world and of one's place in it. It is also significant that one of the most frequent results of cerebral pathology is the failure to produce human movement responses (10). Every patient with positive sign 7 must have at least some human movement responses and these must approximately equal the number of color responses. This conforms with the general rule that, other conditions being similar, individuals with approximately equal numbers of human movement and color responses can handle interpersonal relationships more easily than those with unequal quantities of these responses. Sign 11 has about the same implications, but it differs from sign 7 by the inclusion of the sum of bright shading responses. If the Σc is about equal to the ΣC, the control of emotional impulses, indicated by the ΣC, causes less tension and requires less conscious effort than is the case when these two sums are unequal (15). Therefore, patients who produce sign 11 can make a social adjustment with greater facility and thus are less likely to be disturbed by environmental influences.

Moreover, in the absence of noticeable personality disturbances there is a positive correlation between the human movement responses and the accurate or good quality whole responses. This finding was incorporated into signs 8, 9, and 10. Patients who show this positive correlation between W+ and M are rewarded with positive points on their prognostic scale. The biological truism that health is not possible if the principle of proportion is violated finds an expression in these three signs. Since the W+ is a measure of the capacity for a realistic planning of one's activities in order to accomplish a constructive purpose which, in turn, would lead to recognition by others; and, since the M measures, among other things, creative imagination and indicates that the individual has some conception of the world and of his role in it, based on deep and lasting experiences—it is understandable that there should be a proportion and a positive correlation between these two important personality traits.

Sign 12 measures a capacity for conscious control over thought processes. However, it applies only to patients whose Σc is below ΣC, that is, to patients whose automatized and easy control over motor impulses (symbolized by the Σc or the bright shading responses) is inadequate (15). Such inadequacy is indicated by the numerical dominance of C, or color responses, indicators of a spontaneous emotional responsiveness to the environment, over the Σc, indicators of the control over this emotional responsiveness. Notwithstanding the weak conscious control over his emotions, a patient is credited with the positive sign 12 when he takes his time, at least thirty seconds per response, to deliver his responses. Patients who rush their responses do not get credit. IntRT, or the initial reaction time to each Rorschach plate, tends to be long in schizophrenic records. Therefore, many schizophrenics who fail to qualify for sign 12, delay interpreting Plates (probably as a result of intellectual blocking), but once they begin interpreting, rush through without sufficient conscious control.

Signs 13 and 14 deal with human content responses. A complete absence of responses with human content usually denotes a lack of interest in other people as distinct individuals. In most such instances, it is hostility that is responsible for the diversion of interest from others. In most schizophrenic cases, the absence of human content may be an effect of their autism and emotional flatness. It is an unfavorable sign. On the other hand, the presence of human content is prognostically favorable, provided it is not excessive. We found it expedient to place the upper limit of the h% at 20. When the h% exceeded 20, it did not add to the differentiation between the good and the poor groups. A possible reason for this may be that the high h% is frequently a reflection of hypochondriacal ruminations and somatic delusions of the psychotics. The animal world, referred to in sign 15, has such a wealth of forms that it is easy to give animal responses to

Rorschach Plates. High animal percentages manifest a lack of visual imagination. Low animal percentages indicate a greater ability to visualize a variety of forms than do high animal percentages. Thus a low a% is an intellectual asset.

RESULTS

The frequency with which each sign occurs in every subgroup is shown in Table I. The differences in the percentages of incidence between the good group (the combined improved and unchanged groups)

TABLE I. PERCENTAGES WITHIN EACH GROUP FOR EACH OF 15 SIGNS USED TO PREDICT THE STATUS OF SCHIZOPHRENICS AFTER A 3-YEAR INTERVAL

Group	No. Pts.	Sign Number														
		1	2	3	4	5	6	7	8	9	10	11	12	13	14	15
Improved	42	14	43	17	33	19	24	45	26	14	10	33	14	7	69	24
Unchanged	20	10	45	15	25	5	15	25	10	—	—	20	15	—	70	15
Worse-Somewhat	28	4	—	46	32	4	43	21	4	—	—	21	4	29	43	18
Worse-much	10	—	—	60	10	—	90	—	10	—	—	10	30	40	40	20
Improved and Unchanged	62	13	44	16	31	15	21	39	21	10	6	29	15	5	69	21
Worse	38	3	—	50	26	3	55	16	5	—	—	18	11	32	42	18
Percentage Difference		10	44	−34	5	12	−34	23	16	10	6	11	4	−27	27	3

and the poor group (the combined worse groups) were the basis for assigning a positive or a negative value to a sign, and for determing the weight of each value.

For ninety-one of our one hundred schizophrenics we have not only a three-year but a seven-year follow up. Fifty-six of our three-year good group were followed for seven years; of these, twenty-six continued to improve or maintained their status, not getting worse, while thirty became worse. Thirty-five patients of the three-year poor group were followed for seven years; all of them were still classified as worse in relation to their psychological status at the time of the first Rorschach examination. By comparison with the period of the earliest hospitalization and Rorschach examination, the one hundred schizophrenics were divided into sixty-two good and thirty-eight poor cases at the end of the three-year-period, while at the end of the seven-year-period ninety-one of the one hundred were divided into twenty-six good and sixty-five poor patients. This marked increase in worse patients between the third and the seventh year demonstrates not only the deleterious effect of the schizophrenic psychosis but also the necessity of setting a time limit if prognosis in schizophrenia is to approach a degree of precision.

These changes in the status of the schizophrenics have a bearing upon the value of the signs. Six of the signs, i. e., signs 1, 4, 9, 10, 14, and 15, showed practically no difference in the degree to which they discriminated between the good group and the poor group at the end of both the three-year and the seven-year-intervals.

Six of the signs, 2, 3, 5, 6, 7, and 13, grew weaker in their discriminatory power after a seven-year-interval. The decrease in discrimination can be measured in terms of the differences in the percentages of the occurrence of the signs in the good and in the poor groups at the end of both intervals, the three-year one and the seven-year one. The following were the respective percentage differences: for sign 2: 44 and 21; for sign 3: −34 and −28; for sign 5: 12 and 10; for sign 6: −34 and −4; for sign 7: 23 and 13; and for sign 13: −27 and −17. Sign 12 occurred more frequently in the good group in the three-year follow-up, the percentage difference being 4, and more frequently in the poor group in the seven-year follow-up, the percentage difference being −9.

The remaining two signs, 8 and 11, both positive, heightened their discriminatory power as the length of the follow-up period increased, the percentage difference changing form 11 to 21, and from 16 to 26 respectively. A patient is credited with sign 11 when the numbers of human movement, color, and bright shading responses are almost equal. Since sign 11 shows the greatest rise in discriminatory power as the length of the follow-up period increases, while sign 7, based on the ratio between the human movement and the color responses alone loses its discriminatory power after the third year, it can be concluded that it is the presence of the sum of the bright shading responses that is significant. Sign 8, $W+ = 3$ or 4 with $M > 1$, is credited when the number of human movement responses per good whole responses is relatively high. This sign indicates restraint in the planning of activities for the achievement of a difficult purpose that would strengthen the patient's position among his fellow men. Both signs 8 and 11 imply a good capacity for energy control, and consequently a decrease in the chances of clashing with the environment and its attendant problems of adjustment.

Table II presents the distribution of the total criterion scores in each of the four subgroups. It also gives the average criterion score of each subgroup, and the group averages of the good group (improved and unchanged) and the poor group (somewhat worse and much worse). It is evident that there is a definite and positive correlation between the schizophrenic's criterion score and his chance for improvement during the three years following the Rorschach examination, which was used to compute his prognostic criterion score.

TABLE II. PROGNOSTIC CRITERION SCORES FOR 3-YEAR INTERVALS WITHIN FOUR SUBGROUPS OF 100 SCHIZOPHRENICS

Group	Criterion Score															Single Group Ave.	Two Group Ave.
	11	10	9	8	7	6	5	4	3	2	1	0	−1	−2	−3		
Improved	2	4	2	2	3	4	4	3	10	4	—	3	—	1	—	5.00	
Unchanged	—	—	—	—	4	—	3	4	3	3	1	2	—	—	—	3.75	4.59
Worse-Somewhat	—	—	—	—	—	—	2	2	3	2	7	4	1	4	3	.79	
Worse-much	—	—	—	—	—	—	—	—	—	—	3	3	2	2	—	−.30	.50

None of the schizophrenics who have become worse earned a score higher than 5 points. Thus, a score of more than 5 justifies the expectation that the patient will improve, or at least that he will remain basically unchanged, when his capacities and adjustment in the period preceding his Rorschach examination are compared with his capacities and adjustment three years later. One-third, 21 out of 62 good patients, earned a score of more than 5 points. A minus criterion score on the other hand, points rather definitely to the possibility that the patient will grow worse. Twelve out of thirty-eight worse patients, and only one out of sixty-two good ones, received minus scores. This sole exception in the good group was a patient who had deviated from the healthy norm very markedly when she was admitted to the hospital. Her modest but definite improvement still left her at a very low level of personality functioning. This patient was not a first admission but had a long history of schizophrenic behavior. This same patient was the only patient in the good group to produce all three negative signs. In the poor group, there were six out of thirty-eight patients with all three negative signs.

Following are the main conclusions of this investigation:

1. A schizophrenic producing a criterion score of two points or more has 55 chances out of 64, or 86 out of 100, to be improved at the end of a three-year-period following the administration of the Rorschach examination which was used for the computation of the criterion score.

2. A schizophrenic producing a criterion score of one point or less can be expected to become worse at the end of the three-year-period, the probability being 29 out of 36, or 81 out of 100.

3. Predictions based on the rule that a criterion score of two points or more indicates an improved or unchanged status at the end of a three-year-period, and that a criterion score of one point or less indicates a further deviation from the healthy norm at the end of a three-year-period, would have been correct in 84 out of the 100 cases of schizophrenia.

4. Predictions for a seven-year-period, made in the same manner as predictions for the three-year-period, would have been correct in only 60 per cent, or in 55 out of 91 cases of schizophrenia.

VALIDITY

According to the statistical chi-square test, the association between high criterion scores and improvement at the end of a three-year-period, as well as between low criterion scores and getting worse at the end of a three-year-period, is valid. We obtained four groups by dividing both our good group and our poor group into two, separating the schizophrenics with scores of two points or more from the schizophrenics with scores of one point or less. The chi-square, calculated with the Yates correction, amounted to 40.46, implying that the chances for the positive association between criterion scores and status being accidental are far below 1 in 100. However, it is important to keep in mind that the chi-square and other statistical formulae aid in determining the significance of an association between phenomena only if the phenomena continue to be observed under essentially the same conditions as those in which the formula was originally calculated.

The most essential condition which must be kept constant to obtain results similar to ours is the diagnosis of schizophrenia since our prognostic criterion applies only to schizophrenics. The diagnosis of early and mild cases of schizophrenia can be very difficult (8). Many diagnostic disagreements disappear when patients are rediagnosed after long follow-up periods and accurate catamneses. Another essential requirement is that the manner of evaluating the schizophrenics' personality status not be significantly different from ours. In evaluating the status we paid the greatest attention to the patients' subjective feeling of psychological comfort, their proved capacity for useful work, their interest in meaningful relationships with others, and their capacity to maintain these relationships. The system of scoring the Rorschach records is another fundamental factor because it determines directly the criterion score. Differences in the scoring of the records would obviously cause differences in results.

We are not certain of the effect of the patient's intellectual level, his training and his age upon the prognosticating power of our criterion. More than two-thirds of our patients were in their twenties when first examined. In general, intellectual capacity and mental work habits affect the Rorschach findings and, consequently, the criterion score. At the time of the first Rorschach examination, our schizophrenics' average intelligence quotient was between 110 and 120. Only five patients had I.Q.'s below 90 (but above 80) and all of them became worse seven years after the original examination, but four were either improved or unchanged after three years. It remains to be seen whether another schizophrenic group with an I.Q. distribution significantly differing from that of our patient population would yield an equally high degree of positive association between the criterion scores and the course of the psychosis.

DISCUSSION

Any schizophrenic may exhibit sudden and marked personality changes at almost any time. Many of these personality fluctuations are of short duration. A schizophrenic's personality status on a particular day may not be typical of his usual behavior. For this reason, our estimates of status were based not merely on each patient's social behavior and subjective feeling manifested at the end of the follow-up period, but also on the frequency and acuity of personality variations during the entire period. In this manner we have been able to ascertain whether the general trend of personality development has been towards improvement, towards increased deviation, or towards oscillation around an essentially unchanged personality level.

The passage of time has a considerable influence upon the personality of most schizophrenics. The most important factor in evaluating prognosis is the duration of the illness: complete agreement exists among all investigators that there is an inverse correlation between duration of the illness and improvement or recovery (2). The question arose as to how the inexorable and deleterious effect of the schizophrenic disease process influences the validity of our prognostic criterion. A follow-up of seven or more years furnished a partial answer to this question. We have found that the criterion continues to be of aid in indicating patients whose prognosis remains unfavorable: thirty-one schizophrenics out of thirty-three with criterion scores of 1 point or less, or 94 per cent of this group, became definitely worse at the end of the seventh year. The criterion is not helpful if the score is above one point because then the chances are about even that schizophrenics with a score higher than one point will fall either into the good or into the poor group at the end of the seventh year. Our average criterion scores continued to differentiate significantly between the two groups but this differentiation was less marked than it had been for the shorter period. The average scores in the seven-year follow-up were 6.2 points for the fifteen improved, 3.7 points for the eleven unchanged, 2.3 for the fifty-five somewhat worse, and .7 points for the ten much worse psychotics; the good group averaged a score of 5.14 points, while the poor group averaged a score of 2.05 points.

Signs 8 and 11 were the only ones which gained in their predictive value as time progressed. They deal with the ratio of good whole responses to human movement responses, and with the mutual relationship of human movement, color, and bright shading responses. The good whole and the human movement responses revealed their prognostic value also in short-term prognosis when the immediate outcome of insulin coma treatment was studied (11). These two components apparently measure personality traits that are essential for the schizophrenic's adaptability to life, and they may therefore be indispensable in setting up any perceptanalytic prognostic criterion.

We have not evaluated the effect of treatment, either somatic or psychological, upon the patients' status. Nearly all of our patients received some form of shock treatment, especially the electroshock. Many were treated with unspecified forms of psychotherapy. We have abstained from estimating the influence of treatment upon the personality development of the schizophrenic because of the great difficulty of this problem. It has been impossible to obtain sufficiently complete and reliable information concerning the length and the quality of the various forms of treatment that were administered to our patients. Nevertheless, there is some evidence that schizophrenics with higher criterion scores respond more positively to treatment, particularly to appropriate psychotherapy, than do patients with lower scores. Psychotherapy in the form of attempts to understand the personal problems of the patients, of suggestion, and of personal encouragement is a general practice and frequently yields tangible results (5). A survey of our data has disclosed that our poor group and our good group received about the same relative amounts of treatment. Consequently, there is reason to believe that the criterion scores were not affected by possible differences in the quantity and quality of treatment.

Most psychotic reactions are an attempt to regain equilibrium and are composed of both regressive and progressive trends (5). A concatenation of adverse circumstances may disturb any balance gained by the adaptive forces of the partially deficient individual and may precipitate a psychosis or cause a greater deviation form the norm (5). Thus the effect of environmental pressures upon the personality status and upon the validity of the criterion scores should be investigated. We consider our estimates of the degree of environmental pressure as tentative. Among our patients, nineteen had to contend with heavy environmental pressures during the follow-up period. Of these only one had a criterion score of less than 2 points; four had the highest scores of 10 and 11 points; and the remaining fourteen had scores of between 2 and 6 points. Apparently, then, at least some schizophrenics with high criterion scores are capable of resisting adverse environmental conditions rather well. It is possible that severe environmental pressures have lowered the criterion scores in our good group, but we have no way of verifying this conclusively. Nearly all patients in the poor group had been exposed to minimal environmental pressures. They had been hospitalized throughout virtually the entire three-year follow-up period. Hence, they were spared the necessity of competing with others in earning their living.

It was reported in 1938 that those schizophrenics who derived the greater benefit from insulin coma therapy had produced, even before treatment, Rorschach records indicative of a higher intellectual and emotional level than had schizophrenics who benefited less from the insulin treatment (11). Furthermore, the report stated that the patients who improved much had displayed, before treatment, not only a higher degree of emotional responsiveness to the environment but also a higher capacity for controlling and stabilizing their emotional reactions because of their relatively better developed inner life (creative imagination) and their more efficiently functioning intelligence. Available evidence indicated that the reverse was also true: Rorschach records of many unimproved patients resembled records obtained from patients with organic brain diseases (11). Additional evidence presented in 1940 (1), and in 1941 (13), confirmed these conclusions.

Nonetheless, the proposition that the closer the similarity of a schizophrenic's Rorschach record to that of the healthy adult, the better his prognosis—and that the greater the similarity of his Rorschach record to that of the organic cerebral patient, the poorer his prognosis—does not provide a sufficiently high percentage of correct predictions. It needs to be complemented by the following principle: Schizophrenics who function noticeably below their potential level and who are inefficient, inaccurate, and poorly controlled, as shown by their Rorschach records, are more likely to improve, either as a result of treatment or spontaneously, than those schizophrenics who do not reveal any noticeable difference between their actual and their potential psychological functioning (12). This 1939 finding that patients who improve following insulin shock treatment had manifested during their pre-treatment Rorschach examinations a noticeable disproportion between potential and actual functioning, was corroborated three years later (3). In other words, if a schizophrenic functions as well as could be expected on the basis of his Rorschach findings, he does not seem to benefit from shock treatment; however, he may remain unchanged for a number of years.

The present study supports the soundness of these general psychological principles of prognosis in schizophrenia. Its results are in close agreement with conclusions reached by clinical psychiatric observations as well. For example, it has been noted that the form of the schizophrenic psychosis is of great importance prognostically. Statistics frequently demonstrate the efficacy of insulin therapy in the paranoid and catatonic forms, and its relative ineffectiveness in the hebephrenic and simple forms (2). Similarly, Rorschach records of paranoid and catatonic schizophrenics display personality potentialities superior to those found in records of the hebephrenic and simple schizophrenics. The fact has been emphasized that atypical forms of schizophrenia have a much higher rate of improvement than do typical forms (4). The majority of our patients with high criterion scores could be classified as atypical. They differ in many respects from the classic forms of schizophrenia described by Kraepelin and Bleuler. They were early and mild cases of the psychosis and failed to produce strikingly psychotic symptoms.

Since shock therapy does not change the matrix of the schizophrenic psychosis, but only the secondary features (7), it is not surprising that fundamentally the same prognostic criteria apply to treated and non-treated schizophrenics. Although the new shock treatments have modified the conclusions regarding patients recovering spontaneously, the basic prognostic factors seem to remain the same (2, 6). Obviously time is a most pertinent element in prognosis. Measurable personality changes in schizophrenia continue to take place for at least twenty years. A study of five hundred schizophrenics disclosed that the percentage of improved patients dropped from 35 per cent at the end of the ninth year following admission to 27 per cent at the end of the twentieth year (18). We were unsuccessful in developing an adequate prognostic perceptanalytic criterion when we disregarded the interval of time for which the prognosis was to be made. It was necessary to keep the time interval constant for all schizophrenics in order to construct a satisfactory prognostic criterion. Thus, while essentially the same factors are used in making any prognosis in schizophrenia, a specific prognostic criterion for a definite period of time or for a definite condition (various forms of treatment, sudden changes in life conditions, etc.) requires its own special arrangement of the prognostic factors.

SUMMARY

We have presented a prognostic criterion based on a revised perceptanalytic Rorschach method. The criterion is designed to predict personality changes in schizophrenics for a period of three years. It has been developed as a result of a follow-up; ninety-one of the one hundred schizophrenics were psychiatrically re-evaluated and rediagnosed at least seven years after the administration of the Rorschach tests which were used in the construction of the prognostic criterion; the remaining nine patients were rediagnosed three to six years later. Catamneses covering these rather long follow-up periods bolster the validity of the diagnoses. The great majority of our one hundred schizophrenics were young adults, both male and female, of average and superior intelligence. The criterion differentiates between the sixty-two improved and unchanged schizophrenics and the thirty-eight schizophrenics who have become worse with an accuracy of 84 per cent.

REFERENCES

1. HALPERN, F.: Rorschach interpretation of the personality structure of schizophrenics who benefit from insulin therapy. Psychiat. Quart., *14*, 826–833, 1940.
2. KALINOWSKY, L. B., and HOCH, P. H.: Shock Treatments and Other Somatic Procedures in Psychiatry. New York, Grune & Stratton, pp. xiv ff. 294, 1946.
3. KISKER, G. W.: A projective approach to personality patterns during insulin-shock and metrazol-convulsive therapy. J. Abnorm. & Soc. Psychol., *37*, 120–124, 1942.
4. LANGFELDT, G.: The Prognosis in Schizophrenia and the Factors Influencing the Course of the Disease. London, Oxford U. Press, pp. 228, 1937.
5. LEWIS, N. D. C.: Research in Dementia Praecox. New York, Natl. Comm. Ment. Hyg., 320, 1936.
6. ——: The prognostic significance of certain factors in schizophrenia. J. Nerv. & Ment. Disease, *100*, 414–419, 1944.
7. ——: Shock therapy of psychoses: evidences for and against damage. Bull. N. Y. Acad. Med., *21*, 673–685, 1945.
8. ——: Criteria for early differential diagnosis of psychoneurosis and schizophrenia. Amer. J. Psychotherapy, *3*, 4–18, 1949.
9. ——, and BLANCHARD, E.: Clinical findings in 'recovered' cases of schizophrenia. Amer. J. Psychiat., *11*, 481–492, 1931.
10. PIOTROWSKI, Z. A.: The Rorschach ink blot method in organic disturbances of the central nervous system. J. Nerv. & Ment. Disease, *86*, 525–537, 1937.
11. ——: The prognostic possibilities of the Rorschach method in insulin treatment. Psychiat. Quart., *12*, 679–689, 1938.
12. ——: Rorschach manifestations of improvement in insulin treated schizophrenics. Psychosom. Med., *1*, 508–526, 1939.

13. ——: The Rorschach method as a prognostic aid in the insulin shock treatment of schizophrenics. Psychiat. Quart., *15*, 807–822, 1941.
14. ——: Experimental psychological diagnosis of mild forms of schizophrenia. Rorschach Res. Exch., *9*, 189–200, 1945.
15. ——: A Rorschach compendium, revised and enlarged. Psychiat. Quart., *24*, 543–596, 1950.
16. ——, and LEWIS, N. D. C.: A case of stationary schizophrenia beginning in early childhood with remarks on certain aspects of children's Rorschach records. Quart. J. Child Behavior, *2*, 115–139, 1950.
17. ——: An experimental Rorschach diagnostic aid for some forms of schizophrenia. Amer. J. Psychiat., *107*, 360–366, 1950.
18. RENNIE, T. A. C.: Follow-up study of 500 patients with schizophrenia admitted to the hospital from 1913 to 1923. Arch. Neurol. & Psychiat., *42*, 877–891, 1939.
19. RORSCHACH, H.: Psychodiagnostics, A Diagnostic Test Based on Perception. Berne, Switzerland, H. Huber, 226, 1942. (First edition, 1921.)
20. SANDERS, J., SCHENK, V. W. D., and VAN VEEN, P.: A family with Pick's Disease. Kon. Nederland. Akad. Wetens., Verh. (2nd sect.), *38*, 1–124, 1939.

5

THE DIAGNOSTIC USE OF PSYCHOLOGICAL TESTS FROM THE PSYCHIATRIST'S STANDPOINT

By OSKAR DIETHELM, M.D. AND CHARLES A. KNEHR, PH.D.*

THE STATUS OF psychological procedures in the field of psychiatry cannot be evaluated merely by a consideration of the tests and methods themselves but must be considered in relation to the individual psychopathological problem which needs to be studied and treated.

Dynamic psychiatry stresses the importance of the longitudinal character of etiological factors. In his therapeutic progress the psychiatrist works with the longitudinal dimensions in order to find and affect the dynamic factors. It is an interesting observation that most of our psychological test procedures are cross-sectional in nature. The results of these tests in psychiatric practice have limitations in which they are of value primarily in the field of diagnosis with only incidental usefulness in therapy. It happens frequently that psychiatrists, with an insufficient understanding of the tests, expect results which the tests were never intended to offer. In consequence, such psychiatrists either follow uncritically far-reaching interpretations and conclusions or reject psychological tests altogether. In the opinion of the authors, every psychiatrist should, during his training, become acquainted with the theoretical background of psychological testing, and through actual practice, become familiar with some of the more widely used technics. Such training will permit him to understand the value and limitations of tests and the indications for their use in clinical psychiatry.

There is a large number of psychological procedures available to the psychiatrist. Many different psychometric instruments may prove to be of value' under different circumstances in his clinical practice. One of the chief problems is the decision as to what psychometric

* New York Hospital and the Department of Psychiatry, Cornell University Medical College, New York; the Department of Psychology, Hunter College, New York.

procedures should be used in a particular case. For example, there are over forty intelligence tests which may be used for adults. There are many tests of mental ability and achievement for children. Personality inventories and psychodiagnostic procedures probably number in the hundreds. There are rating scales and tests of attitudes. A number of measures have been designed to test the level of conceptual thinking. Many aptitude tests of all kinds are available, and to these may be added the specialized technics that may be developed as the result of a specific research program. Because of his specialization, the psychologist, if well-trained, is able to aid the psychiatrist in the choice of test procedures to be applied to a given problem. Even though it is desirable for the psychiatrist to be familiar with many psychological procedures, it is generally advisable for the psychiatrist who wishes a patient tested to consult with the psychologist who is to do the work so that the proper procedures may be applied with a minimum of time and effort. There does not seem to be much point in what might be called "shotgun" test procedures, and it would appear that no more testing should be done than is required to answer the particular problem to be solved. On the other hand, one should not fail to do as much examining as necessary where such examining appears advisable.

I. INTELLIGENCE TESTS

In the case of intelligence testing, for example, there is no one test that yields all the information one might desire. There are times when a twenty-minute paper and pencil test is adequate for the particular problem. On occasion, one may wish to be relatively clear of a particular cultural background, and for this, the use of several recently developed tests is advisable. These seem to test functions of the kind presumably met with in the Stanford-Binet or Wechsler-Bellevue tests and may or may not be performance tests in the usual sense of the word. Tests such as the Weschsler-Bellevue have a wide variety of test items, both verbal and non-verbal, and offer promise of the usefulness of the differential scores obtained from the various subtests. Because it is widely used and well-known, we consider it desirable to discuss the Wechsler-Bellevue test (1) from the point of view of psychodiagnostic procedures in psychiatry.

In using the Wechsler test, as in the case of any psychometric procedures, the limitations as well as the advantages should be considered when interpreting the results. The literature reports conflicting evidence regarding the diagnostic effectiveness of differential signs based on subtests of the Wechsler-Bellevue test. This test has two forms with eleven subtests each and these main batteries of tests may be divided into performance and verbal scales, yielding a number of possible inter-comparisons. The evidence from studies of the last few years makes one cautious in the use of clinical signs turned up in the course of testing with the Wechsler-Bellevue test. For example, there are studies which report that the mental deterioration index does not pick out organic defect (2), or that the deterioration index does not differentiate between schizophrenic and psychoneurotic groups (3). Another example is that where there is no clinical evidence of deterioration in mental deficiency, one may find deterioration indicated in the test scores (a ratio between what has been called the "hold" versus the "don't hold" tests) (4). The results reported in the literature tend to confirm our own observations in which differential signs obtained during psychometric examinations have been checked against the ultimate picture of psychopathological findings. Perhaps the most extreme case we could cite in this connection is that of a patient, P. D., who underwent a radical lobotomy for treatment of intractable phantom limb pain. The patient had already undergone excision of a small portion of the right postcentral parietal cortex and, and at the time of lobotomy, the operating surgeon reported considerable atrophy of the brain. Since, in this case, we had no preoperative tests, we were much interested in the deterioration index. The index comprises four tests which seem to stand up with age and with some psychopathological changes, and four which apparently do not. The ratio between them gives a percentage loss or increase as the case may be. In the patient just cited, the index turned out to be a gain of 18 per cent.

In general, our experience shows the scatter patterns or other differential signs to be too variable for general use in reports on individual cases. While particular signs may be incorporated into a report as suggestive, the applications of typical intelligence tests would seem, at the moment, to continue to be most useful in terms of the usual need for intelligence measures as such, to evaluate educational retardation, to determine the level of insight to be expected in particular cases, to evaluate sources of difficulty in the patient, and to provide evidence on such problems as the lack of native endowment versus possible deterioration.

Persons using tests such as the Wechsler-Bellevue come very soon to the realization that a number of factors alter test performance. Anxiety, for example, is indicated to alter the digit span of a patient and may alter his performance on a test such as the block design. A patient showing some sort of schizophrenic process may show certain rigidities or peculiarities in his thinking which cause unusual changes in his performance when compared with the normal on a test such as the similarities test. Organic involvement is presumably related not so much to changes on the verbal tests, but has been indicated by Wechsler to be particularly noticeable on tests such as the digit symbol and the block design. If the patient with extreme anxiety were to show differential changes in subtest scores consistent with the changes shown by other patients with the same difficulty, then the search for diagnostic signs would be considerably closer to success. The fact that such effects are not consistent from one patient to another first of all makes the use of such signs questionable with an individual patient and at the same time does not allow one to state very much concerning the effect of anxiety or the concreteness of schizophrenic thinking as it affects the test scores. A recent study attempting to discern a test pattern in cases of anxiety indicated that the loss on the digit span forward and backward was not as good an indicator of anxiety as the general distractibility during the total test procedure. This suggested that temporary inefficiencies on the block design test in anxious patients may be a better sign than the digit span (5). When testing is repeated after clinical improvement, the digit span shows up in relation to anxiety in clear-cut fashion (6). In general, since over-all diagnostic patterns are founded on the same assumptions as, for example, the more limited search for evidence of the effects of anxiety upon test performance, it becomes clear that at the present time one is unable with any great degree of confidence to make definitive statements from the configuration of test scores from a single examination.

An investigation which was carried out by Diethelm and Jones demonstrated the influence of anxiety on some routine psychological tests which are used by psychiatrists (6). The findings included decreased span of digits in the presence of anxiety, mistakes in the serial subtraction of 7 from 100, decreased general grasp and recall of a story (Cowboy Story). The reliability of these tests had been established previously. Anxiety also unfavorably affected learning and retention, studied by means of a maze test. Although anxiety significantly decreased the score of the Kohs Block Test with most patients, there was a small group which was influenced only slightly. The conclusion that the influence of anxiety was not uniform in every patient is most important. It is possible that one or another of the functions of attention, learning, retention, immediate memory, and thinking is affected very little. At the same time, the majority, or all, of the remaining functions may be affected to a pronounced degree.

The intricate relationship between strong emotions and intellectual functions is not understood as yet. Psychological tests should offer the basis for an explanation of the ready anger outbursts, frequent illusions and misidentifications in manic excitements of feeble-minded persons, of the perplexity and unreality experiences in depression, of the anxious, perplexed, paranoid reactions with thinking disorders in states of anxiety. There has been too ready a tendency to explain such psychopathological behavior in damaged brains, for instance after accidents, operations, or in cerebral arteriosclerosis, by specific histopathological changes. The psychopathological reactions in oligophrenia force one to review tests critically as well as the conclusions drawn from their findings.

II. RORSCHACH TEST

Among the projective technics, the Rorschach experiment deserves to be considered first as a diagnostic tool. As in all tests, it is important that the test be administered correctly and the protocol taken down accurately. In addition, the interpretation should be undertaken by someone familiar with the broadest aspects of dynamic psychiatry. The most reliable results are obtained if the psychiatrist is both able to administer and evaluate the test. On the other hand, since satisfactory validation of the procedure has not yet been possible (7, 8), some skepticism may rightly remain in the minds of those to whom the scored and interpreted protocol is given. Perhaps the excellent results reported for Rorschach examination in the hands of clinicians may be due in part to observations made during the administration of the test which may aid the subjective interpretation of the patient's responses. The psychiatrist who is skilled in the administration and interpretation of the Rorschach test is aware of these subjective factors.

In many fields of clinical psychiatry the Rorschach test seems to be a valuable diagnostic tool, not only for diagnosis of clinical entities, but also for specific psychopathological reactions; for instance, pathological emotional reactions. The diagnostic evaluation of psychiatric illnesses is of doubtful value if one considers their uncertain and changing definitions and delimitations. Most work published relates to nosologic entities which clinicians have subjected to critical scrutiny for many years with resulting modifications, or partial or total rejection. This same criticism applies to studies in deterioration and the application of other psychological tests to the field of psychopathology.

The well-trained clinician who takes sufficient time to study the patient will have little need for projective tests to establish the diagnosis. He will prefer to do so by examination because every psychiatric diagnostic study constitutes a certain amount of therapy. All diagnostic tests must be considered desirable aids to the clinical diagnosis and not their substitutes. Diagnostic tests must be regarded the same way in psychiatry as in the other branches of medicine. Administration and interpretation of many tests is so time-consuming that to use such devices routinely would require an uneconomical and unjustified expenditure of time and money.

The Rorschach test may offer an experimental corroboration of a clinical diagnosis. In difficult problems the test is therefore indicated. In recent years, the test has been found of value in determining the role of emotions in a psychopathological picture. There are good reviews in the literature on the detection of anxiety. In studies not yet published, Oberholzer has also been able to determine the type and intensity of other emotions; for instance, tension and resentment. Anxiety can be recognized as neurotic anxiety with little content (corresponding to the French "angoisse") and anxiety in the sense of uneasiness (the French "anxiété").

III. Thematic Apperception Test

The Thematic Apperception Test is of value for the diagnosis of dynamic factors and not of psychopathological symptoms and illnesses. The test elicits interpersonal relationships of overt and hidden forms. The procedure is not well standardized, and the lack of scoring standards makes it markedly dependent on experience and clinical insight (9). Validation has not been adequate (10), and the estimate of its worth depends upon one's experience with it. In connection with a larger study in the Payne Whitney Psychiatric Clinic, the Thematic Apperception Test was included as part of the project. The test was administered after the patient had been studied by the psychiatrist in one to several hours of interviews. Detailed statements of the dynamic factors revealed in the test were checked against the data obtained in the diagnostic and therapeutic interviews. Out of thirty patients studied, seven were found to have given some dynamic leads which had not been obtained by the psychiatrist. In several patients the test revealed a relatively inclusive picture of the essential dynamic factors which were obtained later in therapeutic interviews. The test seems, therefore, to be a valuable tool for therapeutic guidance, especially in patients who are on the defensive and who may suppress dynamic material. However, some patients will fail to supply useful dynamic leads, particularly if the material is well verbalized and thus under control. It is, nevertheless, again obvious that the experienced clinician who obtains a good anamnesis and combines his direct examination with psychotherapy will have limited need for the test.

The study of handwriting, of drawing, and of painting are some of the many projective procedures which may give valuable information to the skilled investigator. The successful use of projective technics depends on many unknown quantities. The best results seem to be obtained when the tests are used by able psychiatric clinicians. The inadequacy of some of the particular measuring devices used in the study and treatment of psychiatric patients has been justifiably criticized by psychologists. However, it should be kept in mind that the psychiatrist is anxious not to overlook any technics which promise help in diagnosis and therapy. Such an attitude is acceptable if the psychiatrist is aware of the inaccuracies of the methods used. It should be the task of the psychiatric and psychological investigators to explore such method fsurther, thus offering the clinician increasingly more reliable and valid tools.

IV. Minnesota Multiphasic Personality Inventory

As in the case of the projective tests, the literature presents conflicting evidence regarding the adequacy of the Minnesota Multiphasic Personality Inventory as an instrument of differential diagnosis (11). As with the Rorschach and the Thematic Apperception Test (and other test devices as well), the Minnesota Multiphasic Personality Inventory alone is not adequate to the task of diagnosis both because of the breadth of information required for adequate diagnosis, and because of the nature of typical diagnostic categories themselves.

The clinical usefulness of the Minnesota Multiphasic Personality Inventory was investigated on patients in the Payne Whitney Psychiatric Clinic (12). These studies indicate that the general psychopathological picture is, in most cases, reflected in the test profile. When improvement occurs, corresponding changes occur in the profiles. In those cases where the psychopathological changes become more severe, or where there is no essential change, the test profiles correspond with the clinical picture.

The test is a quantitative measure which depends little on interpersonal relations, and when interpreted in the light of more recent recommendations seems to provide a very reliable indication of the main psychopathological features. It is questionable whether the test can be used for the diagnosis of the psychiatric illness from which the patient suffers. It offers, however, apparently reliable information with regard to psychopathological syndromes. This result is to be expected when one keeps in mind that the test is based upon answers from the patient which are elicited by well-planned questions. Diagnosis in psychiatry cannot be based on anamnesis only, but includes direct physical and psychiatric examination of the patient. The test should be considered as a specific laboratory examination which may be used with all other information by the clinician in evaluating a given case.

There are patients whose profiles show significant elevations on the scales measuring depressive and schizophrenic features. There is no sure way of indicating from a profile alone whether we are dealing with a schizophrenic patient showing depression, or depressive illness with features of disorganization. So, while the test quantitatively yields a picture of the psychopathology involved in this example, it still does not allow one to make a valid diagnosis in the absence of all available data.

Thus, the Minnesota Multiphasic Personality Inventory seems to be a good instrument for indicating some of the chief psychopathological features and would seem valuable in checking doubtful long-term evaluations of a subtle variety. In those few cases checked where diagnosis has remained doubtful for some time, the psychopathology indicated in the final diagnosis has been in essential agreement with the indications of psychopathology on the Minnesota Multiphasic Personality Inventory.

V. DETERIORATION TEST

Quantitative differential testing would seem to hold real promise in the evaluation of relative amounts of deterioration in psychopathological conditions. The use of cross-sectional technics to determine previous and present levels of functioning should appear more possible at the present time than ever before. While much work has been done to show differences in mental functions in diagnostic groupings for large populations, the psychiatrist is interested in such evaluation as it applies to the individual. This immediately implies differential possibilities of response in the test situation or qualitative changes in performance compared to samples of responses of persons not known to be deteriorated. The Babcock test and the differential patterns provided by the comparison of subtest scores on the Wechsler-Bellevue test represent approaches of this kind. The Vigotsky test is an example of the approach using predominantly qualitative changes in performance. A good deal of work has been done in this area yielding conflicting results in the application of doubtful criteria (13).

The main criticism is that patients are studied as if they were static, suffering from a well-defined disease. There is insufficient understanding of the different forms of deterioration, or of the influence of obvious and suppressed emotions on dissociated functions. In deterioration, a longitudinal approach, involving retesting of the individual in similar and different situations, is essential if one wants to recognize phasic and cross-sectional changes and differentiate between fundamental and incidental changes.

An interesting example of disorders of conceptual thinking under the influence of anxiety was observed by Diethelm and Welch (14). In a small number of psychoneurotic individuals, anxiety produced a transient thinking disorder which corresponded to that frequently described as schizophrenic. This observation forces one to reconsider the concept of schizophrenic disorders of thinking and deterioration. Until the influence of emotions on thinking is better understood and individual patterns of reactions recognized, it seems questionable that diagnostic tests of such psychopathological disorders are valuable.

Deterioration implies a recessive or retrograde trend in psychological functioning. The term, as used in the clinical sense, does not imply that such recession in performance be permanent. What is meant is that the adequacy of functioning of the individual is now poorer than the standards for that person. Such altered levels of functioning may be due to a number of factors such as histopathological changes in the brain, the effect of toxic factors, transient neurophysiological changes, emotional interferences as well as well-defined psychopathological processes. More often than not in the clinic, it is not possible to obtain historical information of the kind required about a patient which has sufficient precision to be useful in any quantitative estimate of deterioration. The problem then becomes that of the reliability of such estimates from a cross-sectional approach such as offered by some present tests and some as yet untried psychometric methods. It would seem that the deterioration noticeable in a patient would preclude any reliable estimate of his performance or level of integrated psychological functioning prior to the present deterioration.

The psychological approaches to an evaluation of the deterioration which accompanies psychopathological processes are largely quantitative in character. Deterioration does not necessarily imply an actual loss in quantitative terms but rather may refer to some alteration in the integration of psychological functions which causes an individual to become less adjusted than when compared to his usual standards. In this sense, then, quantification does not necessarily imply that we are dealing with less of some particular, measurable characteristic of behavior.

As test procedures offering promise of evaluating deterioration are used and reports find their way into the literature, we find that one must be cautious in accepting results from any of these procedures at their face value. The work of Wechsler (15), Foulds and Raven (16) and others in studying the effects of aging factors on various psychometric measures is yielding a greater understanding of the problem of the measurement of deterioration. The results reported are apparently consistent with recent theoretical statements about intelligence and give us a clearer idea of what one is doing when examining for intellectual deterioration.

It has been suggested that intelligence as generally approached by testing can be viewed in two ways and may help us to evaluate better the problems of deterioration. Cattell (17) speaks of "crystallized" and "fluid" abilities and much of our typical adult intelligence testing seems to depend upon the peaks of these crystallized or already learned abilities for the scores which we obtain. He pointed to the problem of fluid ability which may be equated perhaps with the notion of Hebb (18) and Knehr (19) that intelligence represents basically the structural possibilities provided by the organism as particularly evidenced by "flexible" functioning, which may be interfered with at later development and adult ages by that which is already learned and habituated. These statements seem, by the way, to put an intelligible floor under Spearman's two-factor theory in which he provided statistical evidence for a general intellective factor, with specific factors in each task. If we are to estimate deterioration, we are not likely to gain these estimates necessarily from a study of habituated, crystallized abilities. It has been characteristic of many of the reports of studies of brain damage and of lobotomies and topectomies (20, 21, 22) that many functions involving well-practiced abilities may show little if any decrement due to such interference. There is the suggestion that alterations may rather show up in the factor referred to as fluid or flexible functioning, meaning what the organism can do in new and unusual situations. Following this assumption, we have been recently using Raven's Progressive Matrices (23), which is a nonverbal test with no time limit and seems to meet what one would suppose, on present theoretical grounds, to be the requirements for a good test of basic functional intelligence. Along with a good vocabulary test (which represents abilities which may persist relatively well with aging and through moderate psychopathological conditions), it seems to offer some promise of estimating present functional intellectual levels perhaps more reliably than the Babcock and the Wechsler tests. The Matrices is a test using items which apparently do not involve already well organized and familiar material although there is no test in which previous experience does not play a role. Some of the subtests on the Babcock and the Wechsler tests do use material of more familiar kinds. The Progressive Matrices is indicated to be heavily saturated with g (general factor of intelligence) which Spearman finally described by the term, "abstract neogenesis" (24). Even though it is a nonverbal test, it seems to involve integrative cognitive functioning at the highest level and is quite unlike many of the tests used, for example, by Halstead (25) in which little impairment was shown with organic damage.

So, while previous psychological procedures for assessing deterioration have not measured up to all we would like from them, the approach appears to be a sound one and it is possible that these cross-sectional procedures can be made more adequate to the task. There are innumerable ways of measuring deterioration that are not practical in psychiatry. Such procedures include repetitive testing, both before and after the occasion, for deterioration induced by illness or experiments and which are regularly used in studies of the psychological effects of drugs, fatigue, and altitude. Under these circumstances, it is not difficult to discern those procedures which do and do not provide measures of altered performance indicating deteriorated performance. However, in a hospital, control series usually cannot be done on the patient, and consequently these technics cannot ordinarily be used, leaving the approach discussed previously as the more probable procedure. Further work may well turn up measures which may be quite reliable indicators of the extent of deterioration in particular patients upon whom cross-sectional technics were used.

In planning and administering psychological tests for clinical purposes, the psychologist and the psychiatrist must consider their diagnostic and investigative aspects. It is of exceptional importance to the practice of psychiatry that understanding of behavior and its aberrations be pursued (26). In the field of clinical psychiatry, the psychologist should carry out fundamental research while using his skills in the evaluation of the total problem. As fundamental systematic knowledge is furthered, so probably will pathological processes be better understood with a consequent increase in effective therapeutic procedures. Psychology stands as one of the basic sciences underlying the practice of psychiatry and it is in the realm of research that the trained theoretical psychologist is peculiarly well equipped to make fundamental and lasting contributions both to theoretical knowledge as such and to the practical problems relating to psychiatric diagnosis and therapy.

SUMMARY

Many publications in the vast literature, with which our experience is in accord, emphasize the value of various procedures for differential diagnosis from test scores on intelligence tests, projective testing, and objective personality measures. Such tests, however, cannot be relied upon to provide the physician with a clear-cut diagnosis. In the discussion of psychological procedures we have indicated the undesirable ability of "shotgun" programs of psychological testing as a routine for psychiatric patients.

The psychologist's function in psychiatry lies in the fields of diagnostic evaluation and research in psychopathology. The practice of psychiatry provides many theoretical problems and at the same time offers a fertile ground for the testing of theory. With the acceptance of psychology as a basic science for psychiatry and with progress in psychopathology, psychologist and psychiatrist, separately or in close team work, will be able to develop valid diagnostic tests.

REFERENCES

1. WECHSLER, D.: The Measurement of Adult Intelligence. Baltimore, Williams & Wilkins, 1941. (2nd. edition.)
2. KASS, W.: Wechsler's mental deterioration index in the diagnosis of organic brain disease. Trans. Kans. Acad. Sci., *52*, 66–70, 1949.
3. SCHLOSSER, J. R. and KANTOR, R. E.: A comparison of Wechsler's deterioration ratio in psychoneurosis and schizophrenia. J. Consult. Psychol., *13*, 108–110, 1949.
4. SLOAN, W.: Validity of Wechsler's deterioration quotient in high grade mental defectives. J. Clin. Psychol., *3*, 287–288, 1947.
5. RASHKIS, H. A. and WELSH, G. S.: Detection of anxiety by use of the Wechsler Scale. J. Clin. Psychol., *2*, 354–359, 1946.
6. DIETHELM, O. and JONES, M. R.: Influence of anxiety on attention, learning retention, and thinking. Arch. Neurol. and Psychiat., *58*, 325–336, 1947.

7. ROTTER, J. B.: Present status of the Rorschach in clinical and experimental procedures. J. Personality, *16*, 304–311, 1948.
8. HUNT, H. F.: Clinical Methods: Psychodiagnostics. Ann. Rev. Psychol., *1*, 207–220, 1950.
9. WYATT, F.: V. Measurement and the Thematic Apperception Test. J. Personality, *17*, 169–176, 1948.
10. TOMKINS, S. S.: The present status of the Thematic Apperception Test. Am. J. Orthopsychiat., *19*, 358–362, 1949.
11. HUNT, H. F.: Op. cit., 213 ff.
12. WEST, L. J.: Personal communication. Study to be published.
13. HUNT, J. McV. and COFER, C. N.: Psychological Deficit. In Hunt, J. McV.: Personality and the Behavior Disorders. New York, The Ronald Press, pp. 971–1032, 1944.
14. DIETHELM, O. AND WELCH, L.: Effect of pathologic anxiety on inductive reasoning. Arch. Neur. and Psychiat., *63*, 87–101, 1950.
15. WECHSLER, D.: Op. cit.
16. FOULDS, G. A. and RAVEN, J. C.: Normal changes in the mental abilities of adults as age advances. J. Ment. Sci., *94*, 133–142, 1948.
17. CATTELL, R. B.: The measurement of adult intelligence. Psychol. Bull., *40*, 153–193, 1943.
18. HEBB, D. O.: The Organization of Behavior. New York. John Wiley & Sons, pp. 275 ff., pp. 294 ff., 1949.
19. KNEHR, C. A.: Intelligence as structural limitation and potential. J. Psychol., *29*, 165–171, 1950.
20. HALSTEAD, W. C.: Brain and Intelligence. Chicago, Univ. of Chicago Press, 1947.
21. METTLER, F. A.: Selective Partial Ablation of the Frontal Cortex. New York, Paul B. Hoeber, Inc., 1949.
22. HEBB, D. O.: Man's frontal lobes. Arch. Neur. and Psychiat., *54*, 10–24, 1945.
23. RAVEN, J. C.: Progressive Matrices. London, H. K. Lewis & Co., Ltd., 1938.
24. SPEARMAN, C.: Theory of general factor. Brit. J. Psychol., *36*, 117–131, 1946.
25. HALSTEAD, W. C.: Op. cit.
26. GUTHRIE, E. R.: The status of systematic psychology. Amer. Psychol., *5*, 97–101, 1950.

6

PERSONALITY AND INTELLIGENCE: INTEGRATION OF PROJECTIVE AND PSYCHOMETRIC TECHNICS*

By SILVAN S. TOMKINS, Ph.D.†

W E ARE IN THE process of testing a variety of hypotheses concerning the influence of personality on the development of the potential called intelligence. We assume that intelligence is but one of the components determining intelligent behavior. Motivation, incentive, training and practice are determinants of intelligent behavior no less necessary than basic intelligence.

Our focus in this investigation is the relationship between past learning and present learning ability. There is reason to believe that an individual who has learned enough to satisfy himself and his society for the first two decades of his life may or may not be able or willing to continue to learn at the same rate for the remainder of his life. Many investigators have reported a decline in intelligence test scores after the age of 20 or 25 years. The most recent and pertinent findings are those of Foulds (3) who compared the normal changes, with age in a person's capacity for intellectual activity and ability to recall information. The former was measured by means of Raven's Progressive Matrices, the latter by the Mill Hill Vocabulary Scale. The capacity to solve the Progressive Matrices "appeared to have reached its maximum by the age of fourteen, to remain constant for about ten years and then to decline." There is reason to believe that this decline in learning ability is the resultant of cultural and motivational factors rather than a symptom of biological aging inasmuch as the decline is smaller for the higher educational groups. But the recall of information tested by the vocabulary scale "appears to increase up to about the age of thirty and remains relatively constant up to the age of sixty." Adult deterioration has consistently been re-

* The writer is indebted to J. Kitay and C. E. D'Honau for the collection and scoring of data.

†·Associate Professor. Department of Psychology, Princeton University.

ported to be slight for vocabulary and information. It would seem, therefore, that what one has learned and one's ability or inclination to continue learning are somewhat independent variables. Societies differ significantly in the premium which they place upon continued learning after maturity. Among primitive, relatively stable societies, there may be, in fact, negative sanctions for new learning on the part of adults. More complex, relatively unstable societies may demand and reward continued problem-solving in some areas of activity— notably science, art and business, provided these solutions are not too revolutionary. There are nonetheless important areas in which free inquiry and experimentation suffer taboo when deeply rooted traditions are violated.

Although learning ability is limited by basic potential it is clearly dependent on learning experience. Thinking does not develop spontaneously but is the end result of a long learning process. Harlow (4) in a brilliant series of experiments on the learning ability of monkeys demonstrated that training on several hundred specific problems made the monkey "an adjustable creature with an *increased capacity* to adapt to the ever-changing demands of a psychology laboratory environment." When monkeys were first faced with a particular type of problem they learned by the slow, trial and error process. But as a monkey solved problem after problem of the same basic kind it learned each new problem more and more efficiently until eventually the monkey showed perfect insight when faced with this particular kind of situation, solving the problem in one trial. Harlow has called this process of progressive learning the formation of a "learning set." "The subject learns an organized set of habits that enables him to meet effectively each new problem of this particular kind. A single set would provide only limited aid in enabling an animal to adapt to an ever-changing environment. But a host of different learning sets may supply the raw material for human thinking." Particularly illuminating is the finding that the educated hemidecorticate animal is superior in learning ability to the uneducated full-brained monkey. Furthermore, after a lapse of a year or more, a monkey regains top efficiency in a few minutes or hours of practice on a problem that it may have taken him many weeks to master originally. This suggests not only that one "saves" learning ability but that one also loses some of it through disuse. If this is the case, the differential deterioration of vocabulary and progressive matrices and other tests of learning ability is not the whole story. One would have to test learning ability for many trials to determine what degree of learning ability had been permanently lost. The fact that the more intelligent and better educated show less decline in learning ability may well be a function of continued learning throughout maturity.

Hebb (5) has shown that some aspects of the rat's intelligence at maturity are a function of his early experience. Two litters were taken home to be reared as pets. They were out of their cages a good deal of the time and running about the house. While this was being done, 25 cage-reared rats from the same colony were tested. Hebb tested both groups on an "intelligence test" which he devised for rats. "When the pet group was tested, all seven scored in the top third of the total distribution for cage-reared and pets. More important still, the pets improved their relative standing in the last ten days of testing. . . . This means that the richer experience of the pet group during development made them better able to profit by new experiences at maturity—one of the characteristics of the intelligent human being." In the light of Harlow's results we cannot ascertain that this difference can be attributed to difference in early experience or to differences in amount of learning experience between the two groups. But whatever the case it is clear that learning experience plays a crucial role in the development of the potential intelligence.

It is our hypothesis that learning ability must be exercised to be acquired in the first place and continually practiced if it is to be retained. If this is true it means that the same set of laws describe capacity and achievement. It has long been recognized that unpracticed skills "decay" but the basic capacities underlying skills have been assumed to remain constant. Whether an individual continues to learn after maturity depends to some degree on the demands which are put upon him and also on what degree of curiosity remains after his formal education. In order to continue to learn a person must think and in order to think, after the external pressures of formal education subside, we believe he must derive some satisfaction from thinking itself. He must in some sense become "addicted" to thinking and an inner life. There are at least two kinds of personality in which the cathexis for symbol manipulation and a rich inner life never develops. One is the overly-impulsive individual who suffers too little delay between the appearance of his needs and their gratification. The other is the overly-conforming individual whose unquestioning acceptance of the dictates of convention make superfluous and somewhat dangerous any experimentation with the conventional values of the *status quo.* For both types of personality, life is accepted as it is experienced—one does as he wishes, the other wills the obligatory. There are, of course, many other types of personality structure meager in an inner life. There are a variety of ways in which a rich inner life and a cathexis for learning may develop. Their delineation is beyond the scope of this report. We mean by a rich inner life one that is complex and active in symbol manipulation. We do not mean to refer to the continual preoccupation with inner states such as anxiety, depression, hypochondriases, etc. Such states may either impoverish thinking or provide a fertile soil for the development of thinking.

We propose to test the hypothesis that young adults of approximately the same intelligence and history of past achievement would differ in their learning ability depending on whether or not they had developed an inner life. We administered a battery of personality and psychometric tests to a group of fifty-six Princeton seniors. We will report only the results of the relationships between the Rorschach test and the Guilford Zimmerman aptitude battery, tests I and V. Test I is a multiple choice vocabulary test. Test V is a test of spatial orientation, in which each item shows the prow of a motorboat against a background scene in two similar views. The examinee must report what directions the boat has moved in going from the first to the second of the two pictures. The boat may have turned right or left, may have risen or fallen and/or may have tilted right or left. We chose this as a test of learning ability for a special reason. Questioning of subjects revealed two rather different approaches to the solution of this set of problems. Some subjects solved each problem one by one and tended, for this reason, to get low scores since they could not solve many of the problems by this method. Other subjects, after a few laborious solutions saw that the problems were essentially variants of one problem and devised one general method of solving all of them and since this could be done rapidly, achieved high scores. In this particular test it happens that a general solution is more efficient than several specific solutions. It is, of course, entirely possible to devise a set of problems where a general solution would take more time and penalize those who tried to work it out. The value of this particular subtest of the Guilford Zimmerman battery for our purposes is that it is a somewhat unstructured learning task, solvable in piecemeal fashion and also solvable in a more general fashion. Too many psychometric tests are so structured that they do not reveal much of the person's basic mode of intellectual function. What we usually learn from them is whether, under explicit instructions to solve a problem, he can solve it. Exactly how he achieved the solution we cannot always tell. These tests were designed to be factorially pure. Only in the case of the vocabulary test has this been achieved. This test has approximately zero correlation with the other subtests. The spatial orientation test is significantly correlated with spatial visualization and general reasoning (.63 and .39). We would expect an even higher correlation between this test and the test of general reasoning except for the fact that the latter presents a series of unconnected problems in which there is little possibility of achieving gains from transfer.

The vocabulary test correlated .01 with test V, spatial orientation. Since there was no relationship between spatial orientation scores and vocabulary scores, and since this group was fairly homogeneous both in basic intelligence and academic achievement, we supposed that the differences between scores in vocabulary and spatial orientation was essentially a difference between past learning and present learning ability. Vocabulary tests in general have proven to be the best single measure of basic level of intelligence. We believe this to be the case because language is something which all individuals have had high motivation to acquire, because language has been overlearned through daily practice, because language is perhaps the most standardized skill we acquire, and finally because all have been given instruction in the use of language. The flaws in vocabulary as a test of intelligence stem from the limitations and exceptions to these generalizations. Not all have had the same motivation to acquire the same vocabulary. Although all have had sufficient motivation to learn to communicate for the purpose of satisfaction of basic needs, lower class children, in particular, have had no strong and consistent sanctions to apply themselves to acquire expertness in language in the school room or elsewhere beyond what is necessary for immediate communication. Second, though all have had great practice in language, it has not been practice in the the use of the same words. Third, although language is well standardized, not all have learned the same number of word meanings. Fourth, although all have been given instruction in language not all have been exposed to the same level of language usage, nor if exposed have had the same motivation to learn. Although these considerations limit the validity of the vocabulary test as a single indicator of intelligence level it is probably the best single indicator we possess.

Our hypothesis predicted that those with rich inner life would have greater learning ability on the spatial orientation test than those whose inner life was undeveloped, but that in our particular sample there would be no systematic difference between these groups in what they had learned in the past as measured by vocabulary scores. We used the Rorschach M score as our criterion of inner life, converting it to $M\%$ to correct for differences in number of responses. It is our impression that this conversion is useful only in the event that the total number of responses is more than 10 and less than 100. If responses are less than 10, a single "easy" M gives a spuriously high $M\%$, and if responses are over 100, the $M\%$ is spuriously low. Since we had no records with excessively few or many responses this measure was more useful than the uncorrected M score.

Our findings were in the expected direction. We found no significant relationship between $M\%$ and vocabulary scores, but did find a correlation between $M\%$ and scores on spatial orientation significant at less than the 5% level of confidence, of .29. The average score on the spatial orientation test was 23.49, with a standard deviation of 10.75. Those with zero $M\%$ average 17.5 on spatial orientation, those with the highest $M\%$, from 20–31, average 34.6 on spatial orientation. These differences are accentuated when we examine our more specific hypotheses. The coarcted group, 0 $M\%$ and zero Sum C has a mean spatial score of 10.6. The impulsive group, 0. $M\%$ and high CF and C with 0 FC, has a mean spatial score of 12.2. The vocabulary scores do not differ significantly either from the average or from each other.

While this group is too small to place great reliance on these preliminary findings we should like to discuss findings of other investigators which tend to point in the same direction. Altus and Thompson (1) reported a significant correlation between the M score and the

Ohio Psychological Examination. Wittenborn (11) reported "a general tendency for the number of Human Movement responses to be positively related with mental ability measurements. This tendency is not wholly due to the fact that mental ability is slightly related to total number of responses; this is indicated by the consistent positive differences between the groups in per cent Human Movement responses." However, none of the differences proved to be significant at the five per cent level. In the California study of prejudice, Reichard (7) reported a difference in M score bordering on statistical significance between the prejudiced and unprejudiced, the latter having a higher number of M responses. Taken in conjunction with Rokeach's findings (8) that the latter are less rigid in thinking, these results support our findings. Hertz (6) reported a significant correlation between I.Q. and M responses. Wishner (10) reported a significant correlation between M and block design on the Wechsler-Bellevue, in a group of neurotic subjects, but failed to find a correlation with I.Q. Two of the most interesting sets of findings which, taken together, suggest some generality for our hypothesis are those of Werner (9) and Cassel and Danenhower (2). Werner reported that exogenous brain-injured children, when compared with endogenous feebleminded children, show a reduction in the number of Human Movement responses. Cassel and Danenhower reported that a group of endogenous and exogenous feebleminded children who were matched for total Mental Age by the Thurstone Primary Abilities Scale showed a verbal score higher than mean score and a space score lower than mean score for both groups. In terms of Mental Ages the mean for both groups was 6.4. Verbal mental age was 6.7 for endogenous, 7.2 for exogenous. The space mental age was 5.9 for endogenous and 4.7 for exogenous. The endogenous profile is, in general, much more uniform than the profile of the exogenous child matched for total mental age. The mental age on spatial is lowest for both groups, but the endogenous child is no more than half a year lower than his mean total mental age on the spatial test and .8 years lower than his verbal mental age; whereas the exogenous child is on the average 1.7 years lower on space than total mental age and 2.5 years lower on space than on his verbal mental age. When the M score is depressed there is also a greater depression of the spatial score.

If the Human Movement response indicates an active inner life than we should expect to find some relationship with learning ability and intelligence. We should not expect this relationship to be particularly strong in the case of intelligence as measured by the I.Q., since this represents past achievement as well as present ability. We should expect the relationship to be somewhat stronger with present learning ability. We should not expect the relationship to appear when groups are heterogeneous in intelligence. The relationship should be stronger the more homogeneous the intelligence of the individuals being compared.

It is not certain that the Rorschach M score is the best index we might use for the kind of inner life in which we are interested. In fact, we have very little theoretical basis or experimental evidence for saying exactly what the M score does mean. If Human Movement responses do indicate an inner life, we should expend considerable effort in finding out just why. Wittenborn's (12) analysis revealed that "Human Movement responses comprise functionally similar behavioral elements and quantification of them is an appropriate procedure. The consistency among groups of human movement responses (as well as their relative independence from groups of color responses) may be taken as evidence that the total Human Movement response score could bear a valid relationship to an important feature of the personality which could not be predicted from a knowledge of the individual's color responses." An immediate problem which needs solution is whether it is the fact that the response is human, empathic or movement, or some interaction between these elements that is important. Then we need to know to what extent the significance of this response depends upon the specific degree of ambiguity of the Rorschach test. In preliminary experimentation with the Levy movement blots where the plates are more structured and the instructions more explicit, we have found that the relationships reported in this paper are reversed, with significantly negative correlations between the M score and flexibility of thinking. We should subject individuals distinguished for particularly high and low M scores to careful clinical and experimental study to determine whether there is any personality characteristic which consistently distinguishes one group from the other. If and when we are certain of what the Human Movement response means, our efforts should be directed toward a theoretical explanation of the basic mechanisms involved. If we do not, clinical practice will continue to muddle through on a trial-and-error empirical basis.

REFERENCES

1. ALTUS, W. D., and THOMPSON, G. M.: The Rorschach as a measure of intelligence. J. Consult. Psychol., *13*, 341–348, 1949.
2. CASSEL, R. H. and DANENHOWER, H. S.: Mental subnormality developmentally arrested: The primary mental abilities test. The Training School Bulletin. Fall, 1949.
3. FOULDS, G. A.: Variations in the intellectual activities of adults. Amer. J. Psych., *62*, 238–247, 1949.
4. HARLOW, H. F.: The formation of learning sets. Psychol. Rev., *56*, 51–65, 1949.
5. HEBB, D. O.: Organization of Behavior. New York, John Wiley & Sons, 1949.
6. HERTZ, M. R.: Rorschach norms for an adolescent age group. Child Develop., *6*, 69–76, 1935.
7. REICHARD, S.: Rorschach study of prejudiced personality. Amer. J. Orthopsychiatry, *18*, 280–286, 1948.
8. ROKEACH, M.: Generalized mental rigidity as a factor in ethnocentrism. J. Ab. and Soc. Psychol., *43*, 259–279, 1948.
9. WERNER, H.: Perceptual behavior of brain-injured, mentally defective children. Genet. Psychol. Monog., *31*, 55–110, 1945.
10. WISHNER, J.: Rorschach intellectual indicators in neurotics. Amer. J. Orthopsychiatry, *18*, 265–279, 1948.
11. WITTENBORN, J. R.: Certain Rorschach response categories and mental abilities. J. Appl. Psychol., *33*, 330–338, 1949.
12. ——: Statistical tests of certain Rorschach assumptions: the internal consistency of scoring categories. J. Consult. Psychol., *14*, 1–19, 1950.

Part Two: Discussion I

By JOSEPH ZUBIN, Ph.D.*

A CURSORY REVIEW of the development of psychiatry indicates that long before the introduction of quantitative testing procedures by Binet, psychiatrists had used informal testing procedures to great advantage. Bleuler, for example, would often require his students to determine whether a patient was "intelligent" or "unintelligent," but such determinations were based on common sense methods only. With the introduction of intelligence tests, the psychiatrist was provided with a more stable basis for evaluating intelligence. It is, therefore, of great interest to see what the team of psychiatrist-psychologist represented by Drs. Diethelm and Knehr have to say about the use of psychological tests in their clinic. They point out that psychological tests at the present time are used in cross-sectional studies primarily and therefore can be of value only in the field of diagnosis and only of incidental value in the field of therapy. This is, however, a criticism of the users of tests rather than of the tests themselves. There is no reason why suitable tests cannot be applied from time to time from the beginning of therapy, during the process of therapy, and after the end of therapy to determine the status of the patient with regard to important aspects of his personality as well as important details of his condition. Actually, such longitudinal studies of patients with mental disorder became possible with the introduction of fever treatment for general paresis, and have been applied since to most of the other available therapies. To be sure, the number of experiments in which such monitoring of the therapeutic process was made by means of tests are still few in number. The use of such tests for the evaluation of current somatotherapy is still new and there are many problems to be solved before the tests can be applied to the individual case with precision and accuracy. The patient cited by the authors who showed an actual gain in performance after a lobotomy for intractable phantom limb pain, is a case in point. Reduction of pain and anxiety had led to many an

* Psychiatric Institute, Columbia University.

96

improvement in psychotic patients undergoing psychosurgery. There is no reason why the intractable pain case should not show a similar rise. This gain, of course, is only apparent since, by removal of tissue, one can hardly hope to increase the level of performance. The assumption must be made that the initial performance was considerably below the actual capacity of the individual, and when the morbid pain was removed, a return to the pre-morbid level occurred.

Since the presence or absence of deterioration is of great consequence to diagnosis and treatment, many proposals have been made for measuring the presence of deterioration in patients by means of test-score patterns. Perhaps the most trenchant criticism of such patterns is that they can be no more reliable than the individual subtests on which they are based, in the same way that no chain can be stronger than its weakest link. The only way to establish more valid patterns for differentiating various degrees of deterioration is to develop more reliable tests in the first place. Another factor which interferes with measurements of patients' progress is the fact that on repetition of a test, practice effects enter, which may themselves be influenced by the therapeutic process. For example, although it was possible to demonstrate that no losses occurred following operation in the Columbia-Greystone I patients, it was clear that a definite although not reliable lag in benefit from practice occurred in the operative cases. Just how to control this differential practice effect becomes a very important issue. It is apparently not due to lack of learning ability since experiments directed towards the specific testing of learning ability, not only failed to reveal losses, but instead, produced actual gains. Perhaps this failure to gain from practice may be attributed to the apparent loss of familiarity for learned material which many patients exhibit after the shock therapies and also after psychosurgery.

The use of the Rorschach which is by far the most popular test in the clinic today is subjected to severe scrutiny by the authors. It is the belief of most workers that the rather striking results of blind analysis of the Rorschach are no longer of either heurestic or scientific values. Instead, only open-eyed interpretations of Rorschach protocols including all the information that one can get from interviews and other tests is far more useful for an understanding of the patient. Though the usefulness of projective technics in the field of psychopathology is limited, their use with normal human beings or in comparative culture studies is still less developed, since there are no objective criteria for validating the many personality characteristics which these tests allegedly reveal. This is unfortunate, since it sets off projective technics as a field apart from the rest of psychology without much communication with the rest of the science from which it sprang. It is to be hoped that as the theoretical formulation of the structure of personality and its variables are discovered, the proper place of projective technics in normal personality analysis will become more defined.

Regarding the use of the Minnesota Multiphasic Personality Inventory, and similar inventories, it is surprising to note that these tests are as useful as they have come to be. It had once been thought that the primary usefulness of such tests was for screening purposes only. With the increased usefulness of such tests in the clinic as aids in diagnosis and in evaluation of therapy, it becomes important to realize that they suffer from a basic though remediable deficiency. At the present time, scores on these tests credit only deviant responses; that is, a score is given only for those items which differentiate a given psychopathological group from the normal group. Items which the allegedly deviant individuals answer in a way similar to normals, are not counted. Furthermore, the construction of the test by the usual methods of item analysis eliminates such items entirely. This is unfortunate since both the liabilities as well as the assets of an individual are important in determining his status with regard to psychopathology or normality. The pressure of certain normal trends may offset or keep in check an abnormal trend. We already have available methods of pattern analysis which give the total response pattern of individuals. It would be well to develop these methods further to the end that a balanced indicator of the individual's status would be available in which both his liabilities as well as his assets would be included.

It has sometimes been argued that psychological tests cannot help basically in evaluating disease processes or determining diagnosis because the disease by its very nature is dynamic, never stationary, whereas tests can only catch the momentary status of the individual and hence lack the dynamic quality which would make them useful in measuring a dynamic entity. This argument is valid insofar as tests sometimes fail to vary comitantly with alterations in the disease status. Nevertheless, for any given moment, even the dynamic disease process is stationary, and a static representation of the traits and behavior of the individual at the moment in which he is tested may be of value in determining the subsequent course of the disease. For this reason, it is quite possible that despite the static nature of test scores, they may still be useful in the evaluation of the patient.

The importance of anxiety in producing deviations in performance in such tests as the Vigotsky and other conceptual thinking tests is, according to the authors, independent of the type of disease. They wonder, however, whether the influence of emotion on thinking in general is comparable in the schizophrenic and in the neurotic. Since it is possible to induce deficiencies in behavior under states of cerebral anoxia in normal individuals, it becomes even more apparent that underlying thinking deviation is probably a biochemical imbalance in the brain. That this biochemical imbalance is independent of specific tissue function is demonstrated quite clearly by the Columbia-Greystone I study in which removal of tissue actually enhanced conceptual thinking in some patients. The problem, as the authors state, requires much further analysis and will yield a clearer resolution when the biochemical functioning of the brain in neurotics, schizophrenics and normals becomes clear.

Regarding the problem of deterioration, it is important to realize that many individuals suspected of deterioration may be showing only apparent deterioration. It is necessary to differentiate between the senescing process which characterizes everyone with advancing age, and the deteriorating process, which characterizes only those individuals who suffer an accelerated senescence because of some organic or unknown cause. The problem is still further complicated by the fact that the individual curve of growth and decline is quite different from person to person, and only a longitudinal study of the single individual can reveal whether he is growing or declining at the proper biological rate, or whether he is exhibiting a sudden onset of deterioration over and above that to which he is entitled from the sheer process of senescence. This whole problem needs much further investigation. The studies which have already appeared indicate that there are many functions in which the senescent not only holds his own against the younger man, but actually excels him. On the other hand, there are some functions in which the senescent individual seems to be below the younger man. Until proper age norms are developed the problem of deterioration will remain unsolved. Furthermore, the entire notion of deterioration in relation to schizophrenia has been disturbingly reopened by the recent results of psychosurgery. In the Columbia-Greystone studies, patients who show what is ordinarily called deterioration improve either after operation or after "total push" procedures. On the other hand, patients who do better on the tests and show less deterioration, or none at all, fail to benefit from psychosurgery or "total push." It seems as if the patients who performed better on tests are the ones who are actually "deteriorated" from the point of view of their illness. Individuals who are still struggling with their psychoses have a chance for improvement, whereas those who can perform well on the tests despite their psychosis may already have reached the point of no return in their chances for improvement. Another suggestion that has emanated from these psychosurgery findings is that conceptual thinking is more severely disturbed by emotional or conflicting elements than is perceptual observation of the immediate environment. It may be that patients who are conceptually confused but perceptually clear, are the ones who may eventually show an improvement, while those who are, on the other hand, conceptually clear but perceptually confused, have passed beyond the point of reversibility, at least under present methods of treatment and therapy.

The paper by Drs. Piotrowski and Lewis promises to become a landmark in prognostic work with psychological tests. It must be pointed out, however, that the study is not prognostic in the real sense of the word. True prognostic studies in which prediction is made at time of testing or examination are very rare in psychiatry. Most so-called prognostic studies are in reality retrospective studies in which the initial test scores or traits of the patient are analyzed in the light of subsequent outcome. It would be well to coin a new term for such studies—perhaps "hysterognostic" would be suitable—in order to differentiate them from studies in which the outcome is actually predicted at the time of testing, and not postdicted at the time of outcome. Two problems arise to vex the prognostician. First, the time interval for which the prediction is made. This is discussed by the authors and it is pointed out that their prediction for the seven-year follow-up, based on their three-year hysterognostic study, was not very successful. (A statistical analysis of the actual outcome after seven years indicates that the prediction was not statistically significant.) The second point that needs to be borne in mind is that the test performance and the predictions based upon it depend upon the stage in the disease process where the test is applied. Heretofore, most prognostic studies have tacitly assumed that the better the score, the better the prognosis. Generally, this holds true, but several studies have appeared in the literature in which the reverse held true, poor test performance being prognostic of good outcome, while good test performance was prognostic of poor outcome. This was especially marked in the studies of O'Connell and Penrose (1) and Schnack, Shakow and Lively (2), who found a negative correlation between test performance and outcome for metrazol patients and a positive correlation for insulin therapy. More recently, the hysterognostic studies of the Columbia-Greystone I patients have indicated that in their case, too, a negative correlation existed between test performance and outcome. The hypothesis that suggests itself is that for recent mild cases such as those who are selected for insulin therapy, a positive correlation is to be expected, while for more chronic cases such as those who are selected for psychosurgery, a negative correlation may be found. Why poor performance should be related to good outcome remains an unsolved question. Perhaps the authors' suggestion that the disparity between basic capacity and apparent ability is the measure by which prognosis can be achieved, may explain this dilemma. It may be that at a certain stage in the disease process, ability is depressed beneath capacity, but as the disease process continues, ability may return and approximate more the level of capacity exhibited by the patient. Another way of looking at it is that the disease process itself may set up emotional disturbance of such intensity that the patient is incapable of dealing with the problems and tasks which he would otherwise be capable of dealing with. It is quite possible that the patient who had a criterion score of minus 2, and nevertheless improved, belonged to the chronic group who are characterized by low scores but good prognosis. It is clear, then, that for a prognosis to be successful it is necessary to know the stage in the disease process at which the patient has arrived, and the interval for which the prediction is made. Thus, in subsequent validation studies, it will be necessary to study groups similar to the present group not only in age, sex, diagnosis, etc., but also with regard to stage of disease process. Unfortunately, mere duration of hospitalization or interval since first symptoms appeared is not always trustworthy as an indication of the duration of illness. Furthermore, mere duration itself is not sufficient, since the disease process may advance at different rates in different patients.

The need for a cross validation study on similar patients becomes clear when it is realized that chance alone may often produce a statistically significant difference. Thus, if 100 indices had been compared in this study, one would expect 5 of them to meet the level of statistical significance even when no real relationship existed. The authors do not state how many comparisons they made before arriving at their final prognostic criterion. Only by cross validation can the *truly* significant be separated from the *apparently* significant.

Coming now to the actual indices developed by the authors for prognosis, it becomes quite clear that only by scoring rigorously according to the authors' system can any comparability be attained. Unfortunately, the degree of reliability of the authors' scoring system, while no doubt high for their immediate colleagues, has never been established in other clinics or other laboratories, and the discrepancies in scoring sometimes are quite high. Some type of standardization in this respect is urgently needed.

The authors have demonstrated that neither tradition nor clinical practice need bind one to any conventional approach when such questions as the prognostic validity of a test is raised. They, therefore, examined the Rorschach test from old as well as new angles and emerged with new approaches which seem to be more suitable than the old ones. It is necessary, however, to indicate that their new indices or signs derive from the old even though they may be superior to them. For example, inductive perception is probably a legitimate derivative of the DW or DdD scoring of Rorschach protocols, and adds to such scoring a rationale which makes it quite clear and more specific. Regarding sign no. 7, which relates the sum of the movement and color responses to the differences between these two types of responses, it is difficult to understand why such an innovation was necessary. Simple arithmetic would indicate that the new index is nothing more than the old well-known ratio for the Erlebnistypus. If you let r represent this ratio, then the new sign proposed by the authors is identical with $(r + 1)/(r - 1)$. Whenever such a direct relationship exists between the old and the new, the burden of proof for introducing a new index ought to fall on those who introduce it. There may be ample reasons for the needed change. Perhaps the difficulty of dealing with zero values for M or for ΣC lies behind this introduction. But this improvement is obtained at the cost of producing a ratio of infinity when $M = \Sigma C$. It would be well for the authors to point out the basis for the change.

Another needed clarification ought to be made with regard to the change in differentiating power of each of the fifteen signs from the 3 year follow-up to the 7 year follow-up. Only the *changes* in per cent differentiation between the good and the poor groups are given. The statistical significance of these changes is not referred to. One wonders whether a change from 15 per cent to 21 per cent is sufficiently important to mention, without mentioning its significance.

In summary, the authors are to be congratulated on the splendid attempt at providing us with new indicators of the possible course of the disease in milder forms of schizophrenia. This is the group of patients that are now inundating our clinics and hospitals and it is very important to be able to separate them from those who have progressed much further in the disease process and for whom different types of therapies are essential. It is to be hoped that others will provide the necessary corroborative evidence to establish the validity of the proposed procedures.

Dr. Tompkins attempts to find relationships between such factors as the M response on the Rorschach and psychometric measures of intelligence. The chief purpose of this integration is to discover the reasons why some individuals, though possessed of a relatively high I.Q., fail to continue to develop their learning abilities or to achieve success in life while others maintain a continuous interest in learning new things throughout life. This problem is especially important in psychopathology since it is possible that the factor which determines continued growth and development through learning ability may be crucial for such psychopathological conditions as psychopathic personality on the one hand, and character neurosis of the inhibited variety on the other. The author then postulates that individuals of approximately the same intelligence or same history of past achievements differ in their learning ability depending on whether or not they had developed an "inner life." The degree of inner life is to be measured by the M response. The degree of learning ability on the other hand is to be tested by an orientation test in which learning ability is involved.

The author concludes from the reliable correlation between the orientation test and the per cent of M responses in the Rorschach record that there is a relationship between inner life and learning ability. This is a suggestive hypothesis but it is quite apparent that the existence of the correlation between these two factors does not necessarily indicate the presence of an inner life in the individual as the primary factor. The correlation between the orientation test which is dependent upon perceiving a direction of the prow of a ship in two successive positions and the proportion of movement responses may both reflect a perceptual factor which may be entirely divorced from such considerations as inner life. It is also interesting to note that all attempts to provide a rationale for the meaning of M in terms of inner life or creativity have failed to produce positive results. This has held true not only of the M response on the Rorschach but of attempts at measuring the capacity for movement through such tests as the Levy movement blots.

REFERENCES

1. O'CONNELL, J. J. and PENROSE, L. S.: Tests of psychomotor efficiency in patients treated with metrazol. J. Ment. Sci., 87, 183–191, 1941.
2. SCHNACK, G. F., SHAKOW, D., and LIVELY, M. L.: Studies in insulin and metrazol therapy. J. Personality, 14, 106–149, 1946.

Part Two: Discussion II

By JOSEPH F. KUBIS, Ph.D.*

IT IS INDEED A PLEASURE to discuss the implications of the three papers just presented at this meeting because they illustrate with compelling authority the bold promises, discerning caution, and fond hopes inherent in the contributions of psychological research to psychiatric practice. Dr. Piotrowski's consistently accurate clinical intuitions hold out the bold promise for even greater possibilities among the projective technics psychology has been developing. Dr. Knehr's presentation illustrates the basic cautions that must be manifested in the interpretation of psychological test results—a trait universal among good scientists and one that inspires confidence among the allied professions that have to depend upon test results, often without too much knowledge about their value. Finally, Dr. Welch's paper brings into focus the fond hopes that can be realized in the development of procedures relatively uninfluenced by the personal biases of the research worker.†

This panel also points up the broad scope of the methods psychology has been applying to problems of interest to the psychiatrist. This is a healthy sign in the growth of psychology indicating youthful flexibility and ingenuity rather than rigidity and sterility, often the forerunners of "advanced maturity." Among the widely divergent procedures discussed today, each meets a definite need in psychological and psychiatric research and helps form an integrated control system of checks and balances. The projective tools offer the clinician an opportunity for the free exercise of his intuitions in a complicated life-space where the interactions of all forces cannot be controlled by exacting experiment. Though more restrictive, standardized psychological tests present the functioning individual side by side with a norm, thus enabling the psychologist or psychiatrist to evaluate this specific behavior in a more objective light. There is, finally, the experimental procedure, uncompromisingly rigid and assuming the double

* Fordham University, New York.

† Dr. Welch's paper appears in Part Five (pp. 271–289) of this Volume.

role of alert sentry and discerning skeptic with respect to all claims demanding entrance into the citadel of science. It is clearly apparent that these diverse approaches to scientific truth are closely inter-related and often merge into a productive pattern well illustrative of the scientific method. Promising clinical insights are temporarily molded into a working tool, such as a projective test or questionnaire. These are, sooner or later, thrown into the experimental furnace and with the impurities dissolved, the remainder is often molded into a standardized form, a psychological test. Note here the tortuous paths science compels clinical intuitions to take so that (ultimately) they may emerge in a purified form, independent of their creator and his special abilities.

Although my main interest is in the experimental areas, I cannot neglect the papers read by Dr. Piotrowski and Dr. Knehr. In the field of projective testing there are few clinicians, too few, in fact, who are willing to test the instruments of their faith by means of what has come to be known as Blind Diagnosis. Dr. Piotrowski has never hesitated to work under these conditions which are so challenging and so threatening to the security of many clinicians. His diagnoses have been uncannily accurate and his success has kept alive the dwindling hopes of experimenter and psychometrician alike that such technics are basically amenable to the confining restrictions of experimental control. Among his more rigid experimental confreres he is much respected for his frank admission that projective interpretations possess different levels of validity, and that the specification of such levels in any clinical report is a binding obligation on every serious clinician. Finally, when the individual indices on the Rorschach failed to fulfill earlier promises, he clearly and correctly expounded the necessity of considering the various components and the interpretations therefrom as interdependent. This helped give proper meaning and greater clarity to Rorschach interpretations.

There are, however, several persistent questions that arise in the minds of the experimental scientists when confronted with the work so successfully completed by Dr. Piotrowski. How much of the success can be allotted to the Rorschach Test and how much to Dr. Piotrowski? Can we train other clinical psychologists to approach this degree of accuracy? Will Dr. Piotrowski's outstanding ability prove detrimental to the careers of many young budding clinicians who may be expected to do as well? The point herein stressed concerns objectivity and standardization, factors not readily congruent with the art of Rorschach interpretation.

Dr. Knehr, on the other hand, laid greater stress on the more objective psychological test technics. The psychologist finds it easier to handle and to interpret such tools if they are not impressed into service beyond the limits of their effective operation. Dr. Knehr wisely cautions us against the indiscriminate and untested use of variegated segments of test performance as critical signs of behavior abnormalities. In the psychiatric and neurological clinics, the syndromes of patients as described by the psychiatrist or neurologist must remain the criterion against which to judge the value of the test in ultimately determining pathological diagnosis. Admitting that diagnoses may lack the depth and warmth some psychologists would desire, and that in some instances they may be inaccurate and inadequate insofar as underlying dynamics are concerned, it is still difficult to see how tests can do better and how psychologists can give accurate and objective psychiatric diagnoses in the present state of test development. Such reminders, as implied in Dr. Knehr's paper, are needed to confine the enthusiastic energies of young psychologists within more realistic bounds. They are also invaluable in prodding the psychiatrist to sharpen his own diagnostic tools and to postpone early hopes for easy victories in the grim battles we've been waging for centuries.

In advising professional people to become acquainted with the tests upon which they depend, Dr. Knehr suggests something easier to do in theory than in practice. Most psychologists are too busy to become acquainted with all the tests available in clinical practice. Psychiatrists are busier still. The primary need is a small core of basic tests and an adequate description of them to the medical profession either through a series of formalized conferences or through the informal means available in well conducted case conferences.

The final paper is that of Dr. Welch whose fertile imagination and ingenious experimentation is clearly apparent in the well-conceived and integrated series of studies emanating from the laboratories of the Payne Whitney Psychiatric Clinic. Objectivity is the goal and experimentation the method in arriving at definite and specific signs of mental abnormality. Pavlovian conditioning has been the inspiration in devising a procedure to measure the excitation threshold relative to potential threat. Homeostasis, unbalancing forces and return to emotional equilibrium are the underlying concepts forming the theoretical structure of these experiments. The results seem fruitful and are most encouraging with respect to clarifying many hopeful insights concerning the diagnoses and perhaps even the therapy of anxiety states.

Dr. Welch's experimental work culminates in a series of association, concentration, reasoning and psychogalvanic tests with specific application to pathological conditions. From the point of view of dynamics, it might have been profitable to study the quality of the associations elicited from the various syndrome groups. Similarly, it might have been instructive to study the performance of anxiety patients on the concentration test in view of the various clinical opinions concerning the insistent intrusion of non-relevant anxiety processes during attempts at concentration. However, Dr. Welch clearly demonstrates the deleterious effect upon reasoning of anxiety states when such are present in the various psychopathological disorders.

The papers presented today are basically project reports involving teamwork between the two disciplines of psychiatry and psychology. Team projects minimize irrelevant and insignificant research because of greater availability of "brain power" and because of the inevitable and continual internal criticism during the planning, execution and interpretation of the study.

There is, moreover, a critical need for such an integrated approach to evaluate the tools and the proper use of such with human organisms insofar as adjustment is concerned. There is something radically wrong with our training procedures when students are more concerned about knowing the test than knowing the patient. Equally disconcerting is the tendency for psychologists to propound psychiatric diagnoses after giving one or two tests or, worse, to present an involved but fascinating description of possible dynamic interplay on the basis of one or two courses in projective technics. Psychiatrists cannot escape from responsibility in these matters for they have often encouraged the psychologist along his semi-psychiatric career without proper guidance or control. It is pointless to remind you of the responsibility of the psychiatrist to know thoroughly the tool *his* science has developed, for with adequate knowledge, effective and intelligent control of its use is the natural outcome.

Even more critical is the need for an integrative approach between psychologists and psychiatrists in the planning and conduct of experiments since this is much more difficult and intricate and often consumes such considerable time and energy that one person or one group would hesitate before undertaking even a minor project. Serious ethical considerations and the rights of patients are always involved and these are better evaluated, controlled and protected under combined planning. It is my feeling that many advantages inherent in team work have not been fully exploited by our professions. The material is there; ingenuity always sparks more readily from intellectual interaction; time never presents a problem when worthwhile projects are undertaken. No animal laboratory can match the ideal conditions available to us in working with mental patients. Such interpretive fallacies as humanizing the brute or animalizing the self are eliminated. No animal laboratory possesses the significant knowledge of patients and the effective control over them that is ours.

The final link in the integrated research chain, namely, statistical control, often was the weakest and one that posed serious ego-threats to psychiatrist and psychologist alike. Statistical technics were given lip service only; they were dragged in at the last moment to resuscitate mutilated data; or they were quietly disregarded when measurement did not conform to intuition. Gone is the day when we can be forgiven for disregarding the statistical model until we are in difficulties. Mathematical models are available or can be developed to coordinate the various phases of an experimental or testing program so as to elicit maximal information at minimal expenditure of time and effort. Such available technics should be welcomed. They are guaranteed to increase security by dissipating fear.

These comments, and especially my urgent call for the closer integration of the work of psychiatrist and psychologist in coordinated research, may create the impression in some quarters that no such integration exists. Such an inference is not true. It has been my good fortune to work in coordinated research projects with a number of psychiatrists who had appreciable knowledge of the psychological tools and technics we were using. From a creative point of view this proved a most effective mental stimulant throughout the course of the planning and the evaluation of the project. While furnishing a gentle check on my unbridled enthusiasm, these men never failed to provide genuine inspiration.

Part Three

PRESIDENTIAL ADDRESS

7

THE PHILOSOPHY OF SCIENTIFIC COOPERATION

By WILLIAM B. TERHUNE, M.D.*

THIS MEETING is devoted to discussions of methods by which psychology can further implement psychiatry, together with the implied corollary: how the principles and technics of psychiatry contribute to psychology. It is, therefore, appropriate to examine and define the philosophy of scientific cooperation as applied to these disciplines. The Greek derivation of philosophy is "love and wisdom," virtues essential to science. Webster further defines it as "a systematic body of general concepts or principles, ordinarily with implications of their practical application." By reasons of necessity and good will, there has evolved a philosophy of cooperation in science which transcends personal and national aggrandizement, uniting scientists into one brotherhood working for the advancement of mankind.

Strange as it may seem, clinical psychology crept up on psychiatry and took it unawares. Since World War I, psychiatrists have given lip service to psychology and recognized its usefulness, but through lack of realization of its potentialities they accredited it only in a subordinate position. With World War II, psychiatry and psychology suddenly found themselves united by a military wedding. Although this union is a logical eventuation and not wholly unexpected, nevertheless when a dominating, spoiled bachelor marries a younger, vigorous spouse, misunderstandings occur. Disagreements arose at once as to who was to take care of their most cherished possession, the patient. The physician considered this his inalienable and sole right, but the psychologist insisted on sharing this privilege. As long as the psychologist remained in the home, that is, in an academic setting, there had been little disagreement, but when the psychologist essayed to enter the realm of sick people, friction arose as to areas of re-

* Medical Director, Silver Hill Foundation, New Canaan, Connecticut; Associate Clinical Professor of Psychiatry, Yale University, New Haven, Connecticut.

sponsibility for patients. This situation has been improved by closer association.

The period of relative isolation in science is terminated. Although individuals will continue to make further contributions to scientific knowledge, it will be through team play and cooperation that the volume of ultimate facts will be acquired and employed. Experience shows that the practical application of team play and cooperation is fraught with difficulty. We, whose work lies in the sphere of interpersonal relationships, should analyze our particular predicament, and formulate a workable philosophy to enable us to assimilate into one body of knowledge the divergent opinions of neurophysiologists, psychologists, psychoanalysts and other psychiatrists.

Professor William Burnham in his book, *The Normal Mind*, states that a fundamental concept in good human relationships is that of "a normal democratic group, one where each member has freedom for initiative, and where the special abilities of the different members are integrated for the common purpose; therefore, a group where individual differences are not accentuated and the occasion of discord, but contribute to the common purpose in a cooperative activity" (1). This defines our purpose: we, as scientists with a strong tendency to be individualists, must work together in reasonable harmony, and socialize our individualism.

Psychologists and psychiatrists are struggling disciples of two new sciences and before the factual patterns of these can be clearly established, we must evolve through four stages, as follows:

1. There must be within the two groups an outer fringe of dissatisfaction relative to existing conditions.

2. Each must undergo an extensive period of exploration in search of factual information and must relate new knowledge to the established facts of other sciences.

3. There must be a period of intensive selectivity of facts applicable to our present purposes.

4. An adaptation of these facts on the basis of those already current, which have become ingrained because they meet the needs (practical, emotional, and aesthetic) of a particular science, must take place.

These phases of scientific growth apply to the present situation between psychiatry and psychology. Neither side is satisfied; each is tentatively experimenting with different procedures in an effort to find a workable plan acceptable to both. Unfortunately, a program of association was forced into action before extensive exploration had been completed. Psychologists were put into clinical service in World War II before they were ready for this new role, and before the psychiatrists were prepared to accept them on this basis.

To bring about a true spirit of cooperation, psychologists must lose much of their defensive attitude developed as an overcompensation for lack of medical training, and be willing to learn from the older discipline. Psychiatrists, in turn, must learn more about psychology, particularly psychological testing. Then they will be in a position to help the psychologist adapt to psychiatric use the particular tests psychiatrists need, especially those in connection with differential diagnosis and evaluation of the results of treatment. As a doctor of medicine, I feel that no one except a physician is equipped to diagnose, treat, and prognosticate for a sick person, but I do believe that psychology is in a position to render great supplementary assistance in all three of these fields. We would do well to consider the ideas of a number of psychologists and psychiatrists who have been studying this situation. I shall quote from several of these.

Dr. William C. Menninger says: "The problem is becoming more acute. Whether psychiatrists like it or not, many psychologists are doing treatment quite outside any medical group. We have two choices: (a) We can solidify our relationship, clarify our misunderstandings, and work closer together. Or, (b) assume a condemnatory, do-nothing policy" (2).

"Since the two disciplines are concerned not with academic disputes, but with the health and welfare of people, our mutual obligation is to clarify misunderstanding and disagreement, to clarify interpersonal and working relationships. Ignorance and criticism within each group concerning the other give rise to varying degrees of insecurity and fears. Until recently a large percentage of psychiatrists had never associated with a clinical psychologist, and psychologists had never worked in a clinical setting.

"Clinical psychology must still map out domain in relation to pre-existing professions. Psychiatrists who had courses in psychology in pre-medical school in 1910 or 1915 or 1925 have little understanding and many misconceptions of present-day clinical psychology; many psychiatrists underestimate diagnostic testing done by modern clinical psychologists.

"The probabilities are that the physician will never accept any non-medical individual who attempts to provide treatment for sick people without the safeguards provided through scientific medical knowledge" (3).

Dr. Lawrence S. Kubie has said: "The general medical attitude toward psychology tends to be uncomprehending; psychiatry is often grudging, reluctant, suspicious, excluding. If medical education fails to accept the responsibility for training psychologists, in twenty-five years there is likely to be a development of clinical psychologists in competition with and in opposition to medical psychiatry. This would set back the hands of the clock, and be a grave loss to both science and the community as a whole.

"Anything that is inevitable should be recognized and dealt with. If we fight against it blindly, we will fail. If we succeed, success would only stunt the development of clinical psychology. First-rate men would avoid the field of clinical psychology, or else defy medical biases and develop quite outside medical auspices. It is wiser for medical schools and teaching hospitals to train clinical psychologists to be competent and skillful psychotherapists, offering them those elements of medical education which are essential for their scientific development, as well as for the protection of patients" (4).

Dr. Laurance F. Shaffer has written: "The feeling tone of the relationship between clinical psychology and psychiatry has varied greatly in the past fifty years. This relationship is not always harmonious. The mutual suspicion, distrust, and antagonism is of psychological interest—evidence of a family feud, with sibling rivalry resembling that of two middle-aged sisters engaged in a lawsuit over the father's will. The patients, psychology and psychiatry, are not yet entirely cured of their aggressions, but some progress has been made. Rapport has been established and mutual counseling has taken place in a most permissive atmosphere. Dependencies and aggressions have been recognized, accepted, and even reflected! Considerable extinction of old anxieties has taken place. The prognosis is hopeful, and with further treatment, the patients may look forward to the expectation of a happy and useful life together" (5).

David Rapaport states: "There is a determined effort being made to standardize the professional practice of clinical psychology. This is being carried on in consultation with the American Psychiatric Association, in order to ensure the harmonious relations of these two closely related professions, and in order to plan jointly the combating quackery and malpractice. Standardization is, however, a slow affair, studded with grandfather clauses and tolerant to a fault. In such a period a profession is best judged by the strongest and not the weakest links in the chain" (6).

Professor David Shakow, of the University of Illinois, expresses this view of the situation: "Instead of dichotomy in thinking and method, there should be a team approach that offers the patient a type of service that will be contiguous, collateral, ancillary, articulative and integrative. The essence of true team activity is coordinated thinking of persons with different points of view growing out of different training. Controversy is based on old complexes of terms: supervision, direction and guidance versus collaboration, association and cooperation" (7).

The statement of Professor Robert I. Watson on the broad subject of working together in science, is significant. "Dissension and strife, agreement and mutual respect do not take place between sciences; they take place between persons" (8).

From these expressions of opinion it is evident that science develops as a series of stepping stones progressing to a paved highway that is constantly being widened and straightened so that it leads more directly to the destination men seek. To those who travel this road the philosophy of science should be one of encouragement since it gives praise and credit where they are merited and looks vigilantly for opportunities to use every contribution. The scientist must be willing to live and work in an unsettled world, knowing that with the multiplicity of scientific discoveries it will constantly become more unsettled. It would be foolish for any one branch of science to take a fortified stand against another; such a position indicates inherent weakness and impedes progress. Just as in the end fortifications are overcome, abandoned or by-passed, so rules and regulations in the field of science are of only temporary value.

Sources of Friction Interfering with Scientific Cooperation

Psychopathologists, interested in the mechanisms of interpersonal relationships, have extended their studies to inter-racial and transnational relations. We have long been interested in group and mass psychology and it is hoped that in time these reactions may be carefully studied in the light of our present knowledge of psychodynamics. For example, we need a better understanding of the factors underlying public reaction to mental disease. What are the underlying mechanisms of these attitudes? What may be done to correct erroneous and harmful attitudes? How can public interest and energy be mobilized to better the health of all people?

We are especially concerned to ascertain the psychodynamics underlying the difficulties encountered in scientific cooperation. What is the nature of the resistance and how may it be dealt with? The difficulties are much the same in science as in other human endeavors. Scientists are usually individualists who, having considerable drive, do not find it easy to work with one another, but recognizing the value of cooperation, attempt to be tolerant and generous.

The following factors complicate scientific cooperation:

(a) *Scientific Doubt.* Scientists are taught to beware of enthusiasm and to inspect all new findings critically. Criticism is one of the responsibilities of science, but it generates a certain amount of friction and difficulty in interpersonal relationships. Many who are engaged in scientific work are not altogether scientifically minded; they do not subject their own work to sufficient criticism before they announce their findings. The result is that in all divisions of science, and particularly in new ones such as psychiatry and psychology, unsubstantiated claims of scientific discoveries are announced daily. Many of these ideas appear in the press before the material has been presented to scientific confrères—who are almost immediately questioned by the public as to the validity and importance of the new discoveries. This puts the scientific man on the spot with the result that he has a tendency to take a position of scientific doubt in order that the public may not be misled and also perhaps as an excuse for his own uninformed state. Consciously or unconsciously he resents being placed in this position and his resistance is aroused against both the individual involved and the so-called facts which have been prematurely announced.

This source of difficulty could be eliminated if scientists were careful to test their data more thoroughly and to submit findings to their confrères for approval before announcing them publicly. This would entail the cooperation of the press but in the long run humanity as well as science would benefit.

(b) *Possessiveness.* Men have a tendency to say: "This is mine. Keep off! This I have earned or else do possess. I will share it with no one except insofar as I wish." Psychiatrists are familiar with this tendency in young children and when continued into senility it is sometimes exhibited as miserliness. To a moderate extent this tendency is good since it encourages people to value and guard what has been entrusted to them or earned by their own efforts. However, possessions, whether tangible or intangible, will depreciate unless shared with others. In the insecure individual possessiveness is marked. This tendency sometimes extends to a wish to encompass more and more. One who owns a valuable piece of land protects it by buying more; the person with a fortune strives to accumulate more; the dictator attempts to control the world. People who are more or less successful in the exercise of possessive tendencies sometimes acquire the Jehovah complex: "I know best. What I say is right; anyone who disagrees with me is wrong." Psychopathologists understand the dangers of this complex. As scientists we know that it is based on erroneous conceptions and yet we find that this tendency continues to operate in all of us in spite of our efforts to overcome it. Possessiveness militates against the attainment of the cooperative attitude in science.

(c) *Aggressiveness.* Another factor interfering with scientific cooperation is aggressiveness, the instinctive drive to assert oneself. The more dynamic the person, the more marked is this tendency. It frequently attempts to overcome others, to place them in the wrong, to be sure that they remain in a subordinate position that the aggressive individual may retain his position as chief. Notwithstanding the fact that the aggressive individual may have learned to act courteously and give the impression of tolerance, a strong tendency to rise above others, to dominate and control, promotes friction in the world of science.

(d) *Sense of Inferiority.* All normal human beings at times doubt their ability and competency. This is particularly true of the young scientist as he discovers the magnitude of his chosen profession and develops modesty in regard to his own contribution. Although an undue sense of inferiority may be detrimental to the individual himself, it is not this feeling *per se* which creates friction but the unfortunate ego tendencies which the individual builds up in compensation. Over-aggressiveness and self-assertiveness make cooperation difficult.

(e) *Fear.* We know that fear, one of man's strongest affective reactions, interferes with good interpersonal relations. This emotion is exhibited as fear of failure, of loss of prestige, of being considered ignorant, of having someone or some group interfere with one's progress and ultimate attainments. When an individual or a science tends to encroach on another's activities, fear binds together those engaged in similar undertakings in a concerted effort to maintain their own status.

(f) *Maintenance of Privilege.* In the past fifty years we have been aware that the general population attributes to science more power and privilege than perhaps is justified. Once attained, it is hard for those who enjoy privileged position to risk the possibility of losing any portion of it.

Through working for the betterment of mankind, medicine has won a superior status and many important privileges. No other profession is as highly respected. Psychiatry, aided by the fact that it is a branch of medicine, has attained a high status in its own right, no part of which does it intend to surrender—but does rightly expect to improve. It fears that its field is being invaded by the clinical psychologists. This condition came to pass without most psychiatrists being aware that it was happening. When in World War II, clinical psychologists proved their value in a psychiatric setting, not only did they make a unique contribution as psychologists, but due to the shortage of psychiatric personnel, they were assigned to duties that the psychiatrist had considered his own. Thus we see that the maintenance of status and privilege, a deterrent to scientific cooperation, is particularly likely to be a source of friction in the medical world.

(g) *Hedonism.* Throughout life man is influenced by the pleasure-pain, satisfaction-dissatisfaction factor. Much as we invite change and progress, we are nevertheless resistant to it, inherently disliking anything that might unduly complicate our lives.

Intellectually we welcome the opportunity of broadening our scientific knowledge and usefulness, but even in this we are ambivalent, for we dread the complications inherent in the process. So, as we accumulate facts, we have a natural resistance to the acceptance of new facts and situations which might complicate the practice of science as we have known it.

(h) *Scientific Isolation.* The nature of their work and inherent individualism contribute to the isolation in which scientists work. Although learned men, as far as their own field is concerned, many of them are ignorant in regard to other spheres, even those of closely related sciences. Practical measures for overcoming this lack of knowledge of the achievements in such allied sciences as psychiatry and psychology should include publication in the Journal of Psychology of a yearly bulletin of progress in psychiatry, and a similar bulletin of progress in psychology to be published in the Journal of Psychiatry. Interlocking committees and joint meetings at local, state and national levels would do much to smooth out misunderstandings and causes of friction in controversial areas.

(i) *Resistance to Group Pressure.* Being an individualist, the scientist, more than the average individual, is resistant to group pressure. Neither psychiatrists nor psychologists want their colleagues to dictate what they should or should not do. They are even less receptive to suggestion from outside groups, and stand together against any form of apparent coercion. While, in a modified form, this resistance to group pressure may be a desirable quality, when carried to extremes, it does not promote good professional relationships.

This superficial estimate of the difficulties encountered in scientific cooperation indicates that these lie in the individual, rather than in the body of science itself, and leads to a consideration of the ethics involved.

CODES OF ETHICS

In the consideration of a program for scientific cooperation, we have for guidance the tradition and practice of medical ethics. For two thousand years the medical profession subscribed to the Hippocratic Oath and handled its ethical problems on the basis of the Greek tradition of good taste and personal honor. There was no formal codification of ethics or "rules"; emphasis was upon the spirit and not the letter. In England, in the eighteenth century, there developed a situation not unlike that which we now face. At that time there were three groups of medical practitioners: physicians, surgeons and apothecaries. The physicians, having the best training and cultural background, enjoyed a superior social and professional standing. Surgeons were practical men interested in advancing their specialty to a respectable footing. Apothecaries acted as doctors to the poor, calling in a physician when a patient was beyond their skill. They served a five-year apprenticeship, and were fairly capable of dispensing medicine. As a group, apothecaries were on good terms with physicians and did not abuse their privileges. Physicians relied upon them and found them helpful.

This was the medical situation when Thomas Percival was born in Warrington, Lancashire, in 1740. His grandfather was an apothecary and his uncle a physician. At his death, this uncle left Percival a modest income and a valuable medical library, which influenced his choice of a career.

From adolescence Percival was a scholarly and independent thinker, a dissenter and a Unitarian. Debarred from English universities because of his non-conformity, he matriculated at the University of Edinburgh, then took his medical degree at Leyden in 1765. That same year he was elected a Fellow of the Royal Society, the youngest member ever to be so honored.

Percival settled in Manchester and immediately attracted attention by his medical and philosophical writing. His friends and correspondents were many and varied, including David Hume, Benjamin Franklin, Voltaire, Diderot and D'Alembert. Outstanding ability, energy, social vision and personal charm enabled him to organize committees of physicians and influential citizens to enforce sanitation, enact factory legislation, build public baths, and participate actively in the Manchester Literary and Philosophical Society, of which he was president.

In 1778, Percival was appointed physician to the Manchester Infirmary which was then in a state of confusion attendant upon changes made in the staff and resulting dissension. Both parties to the controversy believed in Percival's fairness and good judgment, and he was asked to draw up "a scheme of professional conduct relative to hospitals and other medical charities." The immediate controversial issues and his intimate knowledge of the physician-surgeon-apothecary relationships doubtless influenced his formulation of the "rules" which became known as Percival's Code. This was printed for private distribution and circulated among distinguished medical men for criticism and revision before the completed work was published in 1803. A new edition with minor changes appeared in 1827 and a third revision in 1849. Thus came into existence what is known as "medical ethics." Although Percival would have deprecated the stressing of the letter rather than the spirit, codification of ethical principles into "rules for professional conduct" had this result. The Hippocratic Oath, previously the basis of medical ethics, has remained unchanged but since the publication of Percival's Code in 1803 continued revisions of it to meet changing conditions have been found necessary.

This is clearly illustrated by the Code of Ethics of the American Medical Association, based on Percival's Code and adopted in 1847, the year in which the Association was organized. In 1903, the Code was revised and renamed "The Principles of Medical Ethics." These Principles were again revised in 1912 and practically every year since it has been found that amendments are necessary. Changes occur most frequently in those sections concerned not with the principles of medical ethics, but with medical etiquette—"rules of conduct." Significantly, few persons, even physicians, know that Percival's Code of 1803 forms the basis for the medical ethics under which we now practice in 1950. It was, however, only recently that Professor Conant of Harvard proposed that all those professionally qualified for work in the natural sciences take the Hippocratic Oath, becoming members of the "One World of Science."

Man-made rules serve for a short time only. Scientific cooperation must be based upon ethical principles which endure. Our thinking is historically influenced by conditions obtaining over a century ago and, although the code of physicians has been modified with time and experience, it does not altogether reflect the needs of the present era.

As new sciences, psychiatry and psychology bring an understanding of human nature far beyond that which existed a hundred years ago and we should be in a position to map out a philosophy of scientific cooperation more in keeping with current needs.

That both psychology and psychiatry are attempting to do this is shown by the fact that the American Psychological Association and the American Psychiatric Association have interlocking committees for the purpose of studying this situation. Each committee has issued preliminary reports containing its definitions of the nature and functions of clinical psychology, which I bring to your attention since many psychiatrists are not familiar with these reports:

Training. On the professional level a four-year *doctoral program*, with curriculum that will prepare a clinical psychologist for his three functions: namely, diagnosis, therapy and research. Curriculum will include general psychology, psychodynamics of behavior, diagnostic methods, related disciplines and therapy. *Psychological research* is stressed throughout the program.

Certification of Clinical Psychologist at diplomate level by a *Board of Examiners in Professional Psychology.*

Licensing at state levels. In thirty-six states, bills for certification and/or licensing were being considered prematurely until action was postponed at the request of the American Psychological Association.

Internship or externship for one year is to be integrated with courses in theory, with stress on necessity for inter-disciplinary joint study and work in psychology and psychiatry. *Accredited training centers* must provide adequate contacts between psychologists and psychiatrists. Training programs should enable students to recognize problems with which they are not prepared to deal, and which require consultation or referral to a psychiatrist.

Clinical psychologists engaged in diagnostic or therapeutic work must maintain active, open channels for collaborative working relationships with physicians. It was pointed out that although some men with Ph.D. degrees consider themselves well enough trained to conduct therapy, the psychological profession as a whole does not. Practice on a post-doctoral level should be continued under supervision.

Research brought discussion on the following general issues: Training in specific methods (testing technics, statistics and so forth); the possibilities of joint research; uniform clinical records that can be used for further research; the need for systematic follow-up in clinical research; general agreement on the part of both groups that psychologists engaged in research should have some therapeutic training and experience.

In the 1949 meeting of the interlocking committees it was agreed that *professional relationships* are actually better than appeared in the abstract. Many of the problems arising between the two professions stem from the personal rather than the professional level and this also occurs intra-professionally. It is possible for both groups to find a core of agreement.

Professional interchange should take place on both the local and the national level.

In general, while both the associations are opposed to the independent private practice of clinical psychologists, "they do approve the practice of therapy by clinical psychologists with open channels to psychiatrists and other medical groups."

In the consideration of these reports it would be well to bear in mind a statement by Robert Oppenheimer of the Institute for Advanced Study, at Princeton, on the "Encouragement of Science." In "Science" for April 14, 1950 he writes:

"Discoveries in science and their application to practice have changed not only the material conditions of life, but many matters of the spirit. They have changed the form in which practical problems of right and wrong come before us; the focus of ethical issues for both individuals and groups. They have given us new methods for defining the meaning of problems that face us and for judging whether or not our solutions are just."

Thomas Jefferson once spoke of "the brotherly spirit of science which unites into one family all its votaries of whatever grade and however widely dispersed. . . . The basic lesson of the spirit of science is that there may be no barriers to freedom of inquiry, but an ideal of open-mindedness with regard to new knowledge, new experience, and new truth. Science is not based on authority. It owes its acceptance and its universality to an appeal to intelligible, communicable evidence that any interested man can evaluate.

"In science there is no place for dogma. The scientist is free to ask any question, to seek for any evidence, to doubt any assertion, to correct any error. When in the past, science has been used to erect a new dogmatism, that dogmatism has found itself incompatible with the progress of science; in the end the dogma has yielded, or science and freedom have perished together. . . . We know that the only way to avoid error is to detect it and that the only way to detect it is to be free to inquire."

The Application of the Philosophy of Scientific Cooperation

Thus we see that the philosophy fundamental to the advancement of knowledge is based on the following considerations: The entire field of science is devoted to the ultimate welfare and progress of mankind. In pursuing the quest for truth it should be understood that absolute truth is an ideal, a mental conception of perfection, never completely attainable. Therefore, so-called scientific facts, at any given point incomplete and partly fallacious, must be accepted with skepticism, employed only as a working basis for today, to be accepted or rejected tomorrow in the light of tomorrow's discoveries.

If these premises are sound, then no science has a right to be possessive. A struggle for the maintenance of status and privilege is deadly both to that branch of science and to those individuals who devote their energies to maintaining privileged position. Stubborn adherence to status, privilege, tradition, customs, and erroneous facts make scientific advance impossible.

The philosophy of scientific cooperation is one of live and let live. The greatest authorities are sometimes wrong; the most insignificant disciple of science may unearth a significant finding, even though at the time this discovery may seem ludicrous or in conflict with former beliefs. Science can advance only in an atmosphere of experiment, encouragement, friendliness, mutual trust and willingness to help one another. This is especially applicable to the existing situation in regard to psychiatry, psychoanalysis and psychology. All three have much in common; all three have contributed much to the health and welfare of mankind. It is best that each be given a wide latitude in which to experiment; confident in the knowledge that the good will endure, and with time, faulty postulations will be eliminated.

Scientific cooperation is an act of faith and I submit that faith and science are inseparable. It is a mistake to think that scientists in general are men of little faith. Scientists have faith that there are facts far beyond those now known to man; and that as these truths are discovered the universe will progress beyond any concept of present-day thinking. But as they work together they must also have faith in one another and in a common cause; be willing to serve much as one does in a theatrical company. Knowing that he is associated with a group of temperamental individualists, each scientist resolves to subordinate his own interest and desires in an effort to make the play a success and to help every other player perform his part as brilliantly as possible. As he steps into his appointed role on the stage of life he will play the part assigned to him to the best of his ability.

REFERENCES

1. BURNHAM, WILLIAM: The Normal Mind. New York, Appleton Century, 1924.
2. MENNINGER, WILLIAM C.: Psychiatry and psychology. Amer. J. Psychiat., *105*, 389–390, 1948.
3. ——: Relationship of clinical psychology and psychiatry. Amer. Psychologist, *5*, 1950.
4. KUBIE, LAWRENCE S.: Medical responsibility for training in clinical psychology. Jour. of Clin. Psychol. *V*, 1–94, 1949.
5. SHAFFER, LAURANCE F.: Clinical psychology and psychiatry. Jour. of Consulting Psychol. Vol. *11*, 5–11, 1947.
6. RAPAPORT, DAVID: Diagnostic testing in psychiatric practice. Bull. of the N. Y. Acad. of Med., *26*, 1950.
7. SHAKOW, DAVID: Psychology and psychiatry: a dialogue. Amer. Jour. of Orthopsychiatry, *XIX*, 1948.
8. WATSON, ROBERT I.: The professional status of the clinical psychologist. From Readings in the Clinical Method in Psychology, Robert I. Watson, Editor.

Part Four

INFLUENCE OF EXOGENOUS FACTORS ON PSYCHOLOGICAL TEST PROCEDURES

8

THE RELATIONSHIP OF ABSTRACT THINKING TO THE AUTONOMIC NERVOUS SYSTEM IN SCHIZOPHRENIA*

By ARNOLD MEADOW, PH.D. AND DANIEL H. FUNKENSTEIN, M.D.†

THIS PAPER presents the results of an experiment devised to bridge the gap between physiological and psychological areas of study in schizophrenia. The problem investigated was the relationship between the autonomic nervous system and the capacity for abstract thinking.

Funkenstein, Greenblatt and Solomon (9) reported that schizophrenic patients can be divided into several prognostic groups on the basis of their autonomic reaction to adrenergic and cholinergic drugs. Several experimental studies of abstract thinking in schizophrenic patients suggested a similar relationship of a psychological variable to prognosis. Levin (11) formulated the hypothesis that patients who showed signs of loss of abstract power at an early stage of the psychosis were more apt to deteriorate. Bolles, Rosen and Landis (4) using a battery of tests of abstract thinking suggested that the group of patients with the poorest performance on abstraction tests benefited least from insulin shock treatment. Benjamin (2) came to a similar conclusion on the basis of Rorschach tests in 84

* From the Department of Social Relations, Harvard University; the Department of Psychiatry, Harvard Medical School; and the Boston Psychopathic Hospital. The material used in this paper is based on the thesis, "Anxiety, Abstract Thinking and Blood Pressure Reactions," submitted by Arnold Meadow as a partial requirement for Ph.D. Degree, Harvard University, 1950.

We gratefully acknowledge the assistance given us by Harry C. Solomon, M.D., Robert W. White, Ph.D. and Milton Greenblatt, M.D. Lydia Meade, R.N. was technical assistant.

Financial assistance in this investigation was provided by the Committee on Research in Dementia Praecox founded by the Supreme Council, 33rd Degree Scottish Rite, Northern Masonic Jurisdiction, U. S. A.

Mecholyl was furnished by Merck and Company.

† Boston Psychopathic Hospital, Boston, Massachusetts, and Harvard Medical School.

131

schizophrenic patients. Piotrowski (15) concluded that a patient's ability to differentiate genus and species was a good prognostic sign.

The physiological and psychological studies, together with clinical observations, prompted the formulation of the following hypotheses:

1. Schizophrenic patients with a specific type of autonomic reaction would show a poor prognosis.

2. The greater the impairment of abstract thinking in schizophrenic patients, the worse the prognosis.

3. Impairment of abstract thinking in schizophrenic patients would correlate with a specific type of autonomic reaction.

METHOD

1. *Sampling:* Fifty-eight schizophrenic patients admitted to the Boston Psychopathic Hospital were studied. The sample comprised sixteen males and forty-two females. The ages ranged from 17 to 54 years; the average age was 32.9 years. Cases who had received any form of therapy within a period of three months prior to the study were excluded from the sample.

2. *Description of the Physiological Tests:* The test of the autonomic nervous system was administered as follows:

The patient was placed in the supine position and the systolic blood pressure and pulse were taken until the readings became constant for five minutes. On the first day, the patient was given 1 c.c. of normal saline intravenously, on the second day 0.05 mg. of epinephrine chloride in ½ c.c. of water intravenously, and on the third and final day, 10 mg. of mecholyl (acetyl beta-methyl choline) intramuscularly. The systolic blood pressure was followed after normal saline ar.d epinephrine until it returned to its preinjection level; after mecholyl the systolic blood pressure was followed for 25 minutes.

Graphs with the systolic blood pressure as the ordinate and time as the abcissa were constructed for each patient as shown in the figures. The epinephrine and mecholyl curves were superimposed as to time although they were obtained on different days. (The blood pressure responses after saline were not significant in any of these cases.)

Previous work divided the autonomic patterns into seven groups (9). In the present study these groups were simplified as follows:

Type A is identical with the previous Group I (patients with this type of reaction were previously shown to have a poor prognosis).

Type B includes Groups II and III (patients with this type of reaction were previously shown to have a fair prognosis) (8).

Type C includes Groups VI and VII (patients with this type of reaction were previously shown to have an excellent prognosis) (8).

Groups IV and V, which are rare, were excluded from this study.

The criteria for the classification of each autonomic group may be found in the legends illustrating each of the types—Figures 1, 2, and 3.

3. *Description of the Psychological Tests of Abstraction:* Both verbal and motor tests of abstract capacity were given. These included the similarities and block design, subtests of the Wechsler-Bellevue intelligence scale (Form I), the Benjamin proverbs tests and the object sorting "active" and "passive" tests.

The conventional scoring technic prescribed by Wechsler (19) was used for the block design and similarities subtests.

Since there is no equal interval scale available for the object sorting and proverbs tests they were scored by means of categories. The categories used for the object sorting "passive" test were an abbreviated list of those first proposed by Rapaport (16). These are divided as follows:

A. Conceptual level of Verbalization.

   1.Plus   2.Plus minus   3.Minus plus   4.Minus

B. Adequacy of Verbalization.

   1.Plus   2.Plus minus   3.Minus plus   4.Minus

On the object sorting "active" test adequacy of sorting is not always accompanied by adequacy of verbalization. The following additional classification was used in this test alone:

C. Adequacy of Sorting.

   1.Plus   2.Plus minus   3.Minus plus   4.Minus

The rationale of the scoring procedure is discussed in further detail in Rapaport (16).

The proverbs test was scored as either "abstactr," "medium abstract," or "concrete." The patient's total scores in each category were then compared for each autonomic group.

4. *Analysis of the Data:* In order to test hypothesis 3, which deals with the relationship of abstract thinking to autonomic pattern,

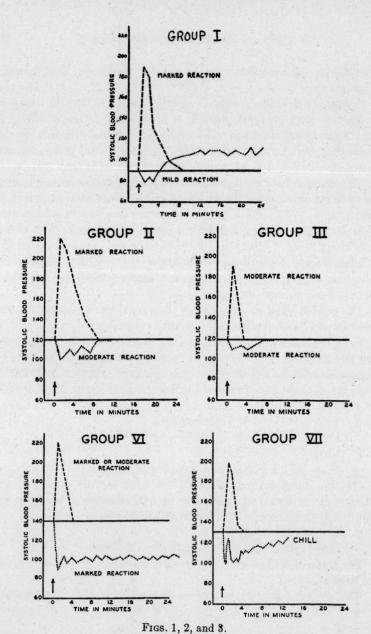

FIGS. 1, 2, and 3.
Type A—Group I. Type B—Groups II and III. Type C—Groups VI and VII.
(See legend on facing page.)

134

the results of abstraction tests of the three groups of schizophrenic patients (autonomic types A, B, C) were compared. These were first equated for age and education.

To test the hypothesis relating capacity for abstract thinking to prognosis, patients were divided into two groups according to the outcome of treatment: (a) "Returned to the community" and (b) "transferred to another mental hospital for further treatment and care." Since schizophrenic patients of the Boston Psychopathic Hospital who do not recover as the result of an intensive therapeutic effort are usually transferred to another mental hospital, it is felt that these two categories satisfactorily separate the cases.

RESULTS

A. Relation of Abstraction Capacity to Autonomic Patterns:

In the analysis of results, a modification of the analysis of variance devised by J. W. Tukey was used (18). Since the measures used in the present investigation did not yield normal distributions they were first transformed into logarithmitic values. On all statistical comparisons, the factor of education has been controlled by the sub-

Fig. 1. (top): This shows the Type A Autonomic Reaction. (Group I.)
Epinephrine: Marked rise in systolic blood pressure with return to pre-injection level within three to seven minutes.
Mecholyl: Slight fall in systolic blood pressure with early rise above the pre-injection level and failure to return to pre-injection level during the 25 minute observation period (failure to establish homeostasis).
Fig. 2. (middle): This shows the Type B Autonomic Reactions. Groups II and III are characterized as follows:
Epinephrine: Marked or moderate rise in systolic blood pressure with return to pre-injection level within three to seven minutes.
Mecholyl: Moderate or slight fall in systolic blood pressure with or without slight rise above pre-injection level but with the establishment of homeostasis within the 25 minute period of observation.
Fig. 3. (bottom): This shows the Type C Autonomic Reactions. (Groups VI and VII.)
Epinephrine: Moderate or marked rise in systolic blood pressure with return to pre-injection level in three to ten minutes.
Mecholyl: Marked fall in systolic blood pressure with failure to reach pre-injection level within the 25 minute observation period (failure to establish homeostasis). Cases in which a chill occurred after mecholyl were classified as Group VII.

traction of the variance attributable to education from the total variance.

The means of the logarithms of the eight measures of abstraction ability (plus the constant one) are presented in Table I. Table I indicates that on six out of eight measures (Similarities, Proverbs

TABLE I

MEANS OF THE LOGARITHMS OF ABSTRACTION MEASURES BY AUTONOMIC TYPE

Abstraction Measures	Cases	Autonomic Types		
		A	B	C
Similarities..............................	51	.86	.99	1.07
Block Design.............................	51	.91	.90	.99
Proverbs Abstract........................	36	.32	.67	.87
Object Sorting Active Abstraction.........	42	.27	.51	.49
Object Sorting Passive Abstraction........	42	.65	.90	.90
Object Sorting Active Sorting Adequacy Plus....................................	42	.20	.38	.44
Object Sorting Active Verbalization Adequacy Plus............................	42	.33	.43	.54
Object Sorting Passive Verbalization Adequacy Plus............................	42	.59	.89	.87

(1) The abstraction measures have been "adjusted" by addition of the constant plus one.

(2) A significant difference between means at the 5% level is indicated by the use of underlining. Three means in a row without underlining indicate no significant difference among the means. A row with one underlined mean indicates that it differs significantly from the other two, which, in turn, are not significantly different from each other. A row of three underlined means indicates that all three means differ significantly from each other.

Abstract, Object Sorting Active Abstract, Object Sorting Passive Abstract, Object Sorting Active Sorting Adequacy Plus, and Object Sorting Passive Verbalization Adequacy Plus) the mean abstraction level of Type A is significantly lower at the 5% level than the mean abstraction levels of Types B and C. On the remaining two measures, the mean of Type A is also lower than the mean of Type C, but the difference does not meet the requisite 5% level. On five out of the

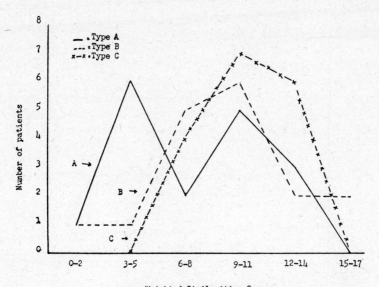

FIG. 4: Number of patients by Scoring Category and Autonomic Type for Similarities Subtest (N-51).

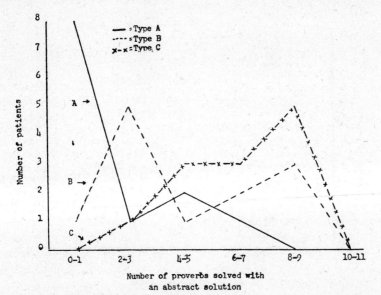

FIG. 5: Number of patients by scoring Category and Autonomic Type for Proverbs "Abstract" Measure (N-36).

137

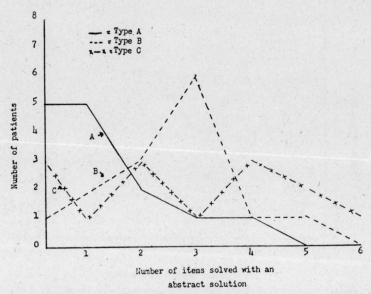

FIG. 6: Number of patients by scoring Category and Autonomic Type for Object Sorting Active Abstract Measure (N-42).

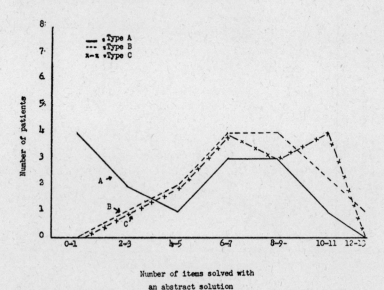

FIG. 7: Number of patients by scoring Category and Autonomic Type for Object Sorting Passive Abstract Measure (N-42).

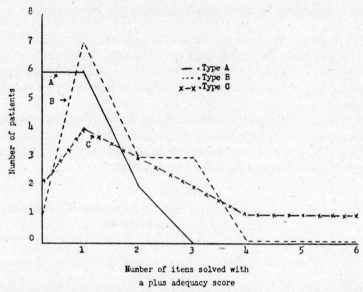

FIG. 8: Number of patients by scoring Category and Autonomic Type for Object Sorting Active Plus Sorting Measure (N-42).

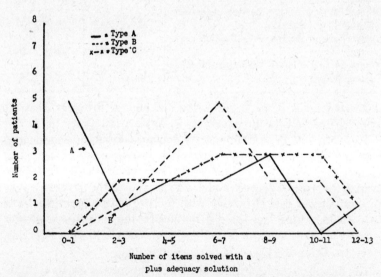

FIG. 9: Number of patients by scoring Category and Autonomic Type for Object Sorting Passive Verbalization Adequacy Plus Measure (N-42).

eight measures, the means of Type C are higher than those of Type
B. Four of these differences are not statistically significant.

The only measure on which the means of Types B and C are separated at the requisite level of significance is that of Proverbs Abstract.

Inspection of the distributions of the measures reveals a consider-
able amount of overlap between the patients of the three autonomic
Types. The one exception is the small amount of overlap between
Types A and C on the Proverbs Abstract Measure.

TABLE II

MEANS OF THE LOGARITHMS OF ADJUSTED CONCRETE CATEGORY
SCORES BY AUTONOMIC TYPES

Concrete Category Scores	Cases	Autonomic Types		
		A	B	C
Proverbs Concrete............................	36	.78	.47	.33
Object Sorting Active Concrete............	42	.63	.51	.36
Object Sorting Passive Concrete...........	42	.76	.59	.52
Object Sorting Active Sorting Adequacy Minus....................................	42	.47	.35	.30
Object Sorting Active Verbalization Adequacy Minus.............................	42	.54	.39	.28
Object Sorting Passive Verbalization Adequacy Minus.............................	42	.71	.53	.49

One patient in Type C falls below the highest Proverbs Abstract
score of Type A and three patients in Type A fall above the lowest
Proverb score in Type C. Frequency polygons of the three autonomic
types on the six significant abstraction measures are presented in
Figures 4–9. Inspection of the distributions reveals that there is least
overlap between Types A and C. Type B has the greatest range
and has a great deal of overlap with the two remaining groups. The
most striking aspect of the distributions is the consistently greater
number of Type A cases in the extreme concrete scoring intervals.

B. Measures of Degree of Concrete Thinking:

The means of the logarithms of the six measures of concrete thinking (plus the constant one) are presented in Table II. The table indicates that the mean concrete thinking score of Type A is significantly

higher than the corresponding means of Types B and C on two measures, the Proverbs Concrete and the Object Sorting Active Verbalization Adequacy Minus categories. The differences are significant at the 5% level. Types B and C are not significantly differentiated on these two measures. The differences between the means on the remaining four measures of concrete thinking are also not statis-

TABLE III

MEANS OF THE LOGARITHMS OF MEDIUM ABSTRACTION CATEGORY
SCORES BY AUTONOMIC TYPES

Medium Abstraction Category Scores	Cases	Autonomic Types		
		A	B	C
Proverbs Medium Abstract................	36	.29	.39	.21
Object Sorting Active Functional..........	42	.32	.25	.36
Object Sorting Passive Functional........	42	.30	.25	.59
Object Sorting Active Sorting Adequacy Plus-Minus.............................	42	.20	.12	.20
Object Sorting Active Verbalization Adequacy Plus-Minus.......................	42	.28	.21	.18
Object Sorting Passive Verbalization Adequacy Plus-Minus......................	42	.26	.22	.20
Object Sorting Active Sorting Adequacy Minus-Plus.............................	42	.43	.51	.36
Object Sorting Active Verbilization Adequacy Minus-Plus.......................	42	.25	.30	.39
Object Sorting Passive Verbalization Adequacy Minus-Plus......................	42	.26	.19	.22

tically significant but they are consistently in the same direction; the means of the concrete thinking scores of Type A are all higher than those of Type B; the means of Type B, in turn, are higher than those of Type C.

C. Intermediate Measures of Abstraction:

The means of the logarithms of the nine intermediate categories of abstraction (plus the constant one) are presented in Table III. None of the differences between these means is significant at the 5% level.

D. Relationship of the Test Variables to Recovery:
(1) Relationship between Autonomic Type and Recovery.
The relationship between autonomic typing prior to treatment and

TABLE IV

CHI SQUARE TESTS BETWEEN AUTONOMIC TYPE AND RECOVERY

	Committed to a Chronic Hospital	Returned to Community	Total
Type A	9	3	12
Type B	1	10	11
Type C	0	13	13
Total	10	26	36

$P(X^2 2df = 20.5) = .01$

TABLE V

CHI SQUARE TEST BETWEEN CONCRETE THINKING INDEX THIRDS
AND RECOVERY

Concrete Thinking Index	Committed to Hospital	Returned to Community	Total
Rank 1–13	4	2	6
Rank 14–26	3	6	9
Rank 27–39	1	10	11
Total	8	18	26

$P(X^2 2df = 6.31) = .04$

(1) Rank 1 is most concrete; rank 39 is least concrete.
(2) A concrete thinking index was computed for 39 patients. At the time of writing information as to ultimate disposition was only available for 26 patients of this type. The concrete thinking index was derived by averaging the rank order of each patient on all concrete thinking test measures.

whether the patient was ultimately hospitalized in another mental hospital or returned to the community is portrayed in Table IV. Table IV indicates that Chi Square is significant at the requisite level; P is less than .01.

No patients in Type C were considered so untreatable as to be committed to another hospital. On the other hand, nine out of twelve patients in Type A were committed. Type B was again an intermediate group, the prognosis of which is closer to that of Type C than to that of Type A.

(2) Relationship between Concrete Thinking and Recovery.

To determine the relationship between initial achievement on abstraction tests and the ultimate disposition of the patient, the rank order distribution of all patients on the Total Concrete Index was first divided into thirds. The cutting points were arbitrary and selected in advance. A Chi Square was then computed between the thirds of the Concrete Thinking Index and the Chronic Hospital-Return to the Community dichotomy. The results appear in Table V.

Table V indicates that there is a significant relationship between the amount of concrete thinking prior to treatment and whether or not the patient ultimately returns to the community (Chi Square = 6.31 P = .04). The ratio between Transfer to another Hospital and Return to the Community is two to one for the most concrete thinking third of the group, one to two for the third of the group with somewhat less concrete thinking, and one to ten for the group with the least amount of concrete thinking.

CLINICAL OBSERVATIONS

In addition to the comparison of the patients on a physiological and psychological basis, their case records were examined and clinical observations were made of their behavior in the testing situation. This data provided information as to diagnostic category and clinical status which can be summarized as follows:

Autonomic Type A: There were eighteen schizophrenic patients in this group diagnosed as follows: paranoid, 10; hebephrenic, 7; and other types, 1. As a group, the patients appeared to be more deteriorated clinically than patients in the other two groups. The ten paranoid patients differed from those with the same diagnosis in the other groups in that their delusional systems were less well organized. In most of the patients of Type A, affect was not appropriate to mental content and the break with reality was more complete.

Autonomic Type B: The twenty-three schizophrenic patients in this group were diagnosed as follows: paranoid, 16; catatonic, 2; hebephrenic, 1; and other types, 4. The paranoid patients of this autonomic type had highly organized delusions. Superficially in the testing situation they did not show the disarray of clothing and general untidness in appearance commonly observed in the paranoid patients classified as Type A. The Type B patients also appeared to have less visible anxiety than was manifested by patients in any other autonomic group.

Autonomic Type C: The seventeen schizophrenic patients in this group were subdivided as follows: paranoid, 7; simplex, 1; and other types, 9. These paranoid patients showed neither the organized systematic delusions of the Type B patients nor the deteriorated characteristics of the Type A patients. When paranoid delusions were found, they did not seem as prominent in the clinical picture as did the accompanying anxiety, depression and turmoil features. The affect of these patients were usually appropriate to the mental content and there was little evidence of personality deterioration.

Although the great majority of the patients in these different groups showed the clinical characteristics discussed, a minority showed clinical features different from the typical cases described for that type. When this occurred, the clinical outcome of such a case usually followed that expected of patients with that type of autonomic reaction rather than that usually expected on the basis of the clinical picture.

DISCUSSION

A study of the relationship of the psychological factors to the physiological factors clearly demonstrates that a *relatively marked impairment in abstract thinking in schizophrenia is paralleled by a specific type of autonomic reaction which has been classified as Type A.*

Levin (11), Bolles, Rosen and Landis (4) and Benjamin (2) have suggested that schizophrenic patients who show a loss in ability for abstract thinking have a poor prognosis. Funkenstein, Greenblatt and Solomon (9) reported that a specific autonomic reaction (Type A) was associated with poor prognosis. This study shows that these psychological and physiological factors which are both related to prognosis are also related to each other. Any theory or explanation of the nature of schizophrenia should explain this interrelationship.

This finding raises several questions. The first is whether or not the relationship of the impairment in the ability for abstract thinking to a Type A autonomic reaction is specific for schizophrenia, or whether or not this relationship may exist in other conditions. It is well-known that an impairment in abstraction is also associated with organic brain disease. Type A autonomic reactions have been found in psychiatric conditions other than dementia praecox, notably in some cases diagnosed as psychopathic personality or obsessive-compulsive neurosis (8). Whether patients with known organic brain disease who show loss of the ability of abstraction would also show a Type A autonomic reaction is not known. Conversely, patients diagnosed psychopathic personality or obsessive-compulsive neurosis, who show on physiological testing a Type A reaction, have not been tested for loss of abstract power. Further experimentation on this problem is indicated.

The similarity of the loss of abstract ability in these patients and and in those with organic brain disease would suggest a defect in the cortex. Many investigators using conventional neuropathological technics have failed to find lesions in the brain in schizophrenia. The implied cortical defect could, however, be on a purely biochemical, physiological or neuropathological basis which has so far defied detection.

The exact neurophysiological basis of the Type A autonomic reaction needs elucidation. Cases which are classified under this heading are characterized by a marked response to epinephrine, a low blood pressure, and a failure of the blood pressure to rise under most stresses (10). This data can be interpreted as representing a "release" of the sympathetic nervous system from higher control in the same sense in which Hughlings Jackson used the concept in relation to the motor system. Cannon (6) and others (13, 21) discussed in detail the extensive evidence for the phenomenon of "release" being applicable not only to the motor system, but to the autonomic and all other nervous tissues as well. An example of this may be in lobotomy where the surgical lesion is a gross one. Rinkel, Greenblatt, Coon and Solomon (17) found autonomic changes after lobotomy which were interpreted as due to release of the autonomic nervous system from higher control.

The combination of loss of abstraction ability and a physiological phenomenon interpreted as representing a "release" of the sympathetic nervous system from higher control makes the following theory tenable: Intact functional capacity of the cerebral cortex is a prerequisite both for abstract thinking and proper "firing" of the autonomic nervous system. When association or reverberation pathways are inadequate, thinking is concrete and the autonomic nervous system is not "fired off"; it is "released" from higher control and acts relatively independently. This interpretation goes back to the work of Bleuler (3) who postulated that the primary defect in schizophrenia was a loosening of the associations which in turn led to a split between affect and mental content. In the great majority of the patients who had a combination of a loss of abstract ability and evidence of "release" of the sympathetic nervous system, clinical studies showed that the affect was not appropriate to the mental content and the break with reality was marked.

No deductions can be made from the present studies as to whether the implied cortical defect is primary, or whether it is secondary to changes elsewhere in the central nervous system, autonomic nervous system, Weiner (20), or adrenal cortex as suggested by Pincus and Hoagland (14).

This investigation is further evidence that schizophrenia is not homogeneous but is made of a conglomeration of syndromes. This follows the line of investigation of Campbell (5), May (12) and more recently Bellak (1). On the basis of the physiological and psychological testing and clinical studies, schizophrenic cases were divided into three types:

Type I (Autonomic Type A, Autonomic Group I) characterized by physiological evidence interpreted as "release" of the autonomic nervous system from higher control, loss of ability for abstract thinking on psychological testing and clinical evidence of an inappropriate affect. These cases have a poor prognosis.

Type II (Autonomic Type C, Autonomic Groups VI and VII) characteristically shows an entirely different autonomic pattern, a relatively intact capacity for abstract thinking and clinical evidence of severe anxiety and/or depression. These cases have an excellent prognosis.

Type III (Autonomic Type B, Autonomic Groups II and III) shows the following characteristics: no disturbance of the autonomic nervous system, relatively little loss of abstract ability, little evidence of anxiety and well organized paranoid delusions. These cases have a prognosis intermediate between Types I and II.

In view of the overlap of measures defining these types, this classification must be considered as a tentative hypothesis.

SUMMARY AND CONCLUSIONS

1. Psychological and physiological tests to determine the relationship of abstract thinking to the status of the autonomic nervous system were applied to fifty-eight schizophrenic patients. The battery of psychological tests consisted of the similarities and block design subtests of the Wechsler-Bellevue intelligence scale, the Benjamin proverbs tests and the object sorting, "active" and "passive" tests. The physiological test was based on the systolic blood pressure reaction to adrenergic stimulation (intravenous epinephrine) and cholinergic stimulation (intramuscular mecholyl). It has been described in detail elsewhere (8).

2. A study of the relationship of the psychological factors to the physiological factors clearly demonstrates that a *relatively marked impairment in abstract thinking in schizophrenia is paralleled by a specific type of autonomic reaction*. This relationship was statistically significant at the 5% level.

3. The psychological findings are interpreted as implying a cortical defect, the nature of which, whether on a pathological, biochemical or physiological basis, has so far defied detection. The physiological data is interpreted as representing a "release" of the sympathetic nervous system from higher control.

4. On the basis of the above data, the theory is advanced that an intact functional capacity of the cerebral cortex is a prerequisite both for abstract thinking and proper "firing" of the autonomic nervous system. When association or reverberation pathways are inadequate, thinking is concrete and the autonomic nervous system is not "fired off"; it is released from higher control.

5. The data of this investigation do not support any conclusion as to whether the implied autonomic defect is primary or secondary to changes elsewhere in the central nervous system or endocrines.

6. On the basis of the physiological and psychological testing and clinical studies, an hypothesis postulating three types of schizophrenia was formulated.

Type I (Autonomic Type A, Autonomic Group I) is characterized by physiological evidence interpreted as "release" of the autonomic nervous system from higher control, loss of ability for abstract thinking on psychological testing and clinical evidence of an inappropriate affect. These cases have a poor prognosis.

Type II (Autonomic Type C, Autonomic Groups VI and VII) characteristically shows an entirely different autonomic pattern, a relatively intact capacity for abstract thinking and clinical evidence of severe anxiety and/or depression. These cases have an excellent prognosis.

Type III (Autonomic Type B, Autonomic Groups II and III) shows the following characteristics: no distrubance of the autonomic nervous system, relatively little loss of abstract ability, little evidence of anxiety and well organized paranoid delusions. These cases have a prognosis intermediate between Types I and II.

REFERENCES

1. BELLAK, L.: Dementia Praecox. The Past Decade's Work and Present Status; a Review and Evaluation. New York, Grune & Stratton, Inc., 1948.
2. BENJAMIN, J. D.: A method for distinguishing and evaluating formal thinking disorders in schizophrenia. In Language and Thought in Schizophrenia. Edited by J. S. Kasanin. Berkeley and Los Angeles, University of California Press, 1946.
3. BLEULER, E.: Textbook of Psychiatry. Translated by A. A. Brill. New York, The MacMillan Company, 1924.
4. BOLLES, M. M., ROSEN, G. P., and LANDIS, C.: Psychological performance tests as prognostic agents for the efficacy of insulin therapy in schizophrenia. Psychiat. Quart., *12*, 733, 1938.
5. CAMPBELL, C. M.: Destiny and Disease in Mental Disorders. New York, W. W. Norton & Co., 1935.
6. CANNON, W. B.: A law of denervation. Amer. J. of Medical Sciences, *148*, 737, 1939.
7. FUNKENSTEIN, D. H., GREENBLATT, M., and SOLOMON, H. C.: Autonomic nervous system changes following electric shock treatment. J. Nerv. and Ment. Dis., *108*, 409, 1948.
8. ——: Psychophysiological study of mentally ill patients. Part I. Amer. J. Psychiat., *106*, 16, 1949.
9. ——: A test which predicts the clinical effects of electric shock treatment in schizophrenia. Amer. J. Psychiat., June 1950.
10. FUNKENSTEIN, D. H.: Unpublished data.
11. LEVIN, M.: The basic symptoms of schizophrenia. Amer. J. Psychiat., *11*, 215, 1931.
12. MAY, J. V.: The dementia praecox-schizophrenia problem. Amer. J. Psychiat., *11*, 401, 1931.

13. MELTZER, S. J.: Studies on the "paradoxical" pupil dilatation caused by adrenalin. 1. The effect of subcutaneous injections and instillations of adrenalin upon the pupils of rabbits. Amer. J. Physiol., *11*, 28, 1904.
14. PINCUS, G. and HOAGLAND, H.: Adrenal cortical responses to stress in normal men and in those with personality disorders. Amer. J. Psychiat., *106*, 641, 1950.
15. PIOTROWSKI, Z. A.: The Rorschach method as a prognostic sign in the insulin shock treatment of schizophrenia. Psychiat. Quart., *15*, 807, 1941.
16. RAPAPORT, D.: Diagnostic psychological testing. The theory, statistical evaluation and diagnostic application of a battery of tests. Chicago, The Year Book Publishers, Inc., 1945.
17. RINKEL, M., GREENBLATT, M., COON, G. P., and SOLOMON, H. C.: Relation of the frontal lobe to the autonomic nervous system in man. Arch. of Neurol. and Psychiat., *58*, 670, 1947.
18. TUKEY, J. W.: Comparing individual means in the analysis of variance. Biometrics, *5*, 99, 1949.
19. WECHSLER, D.: The Measurement of Adult Intelligence. Baltimore, The Williams & Wilkins Company, 1941.
20. WEINER, N.: Personal communication.
21. WHITE, J. C. and SMITHWICK, H. H.: The Autonomic Nervous System. Anatomy, physiology and surgical application. New York, The MacMillan Co., 1947.

9

THE PREDICTION OF SUCCESS IN CLINICAL PSYCHOLOGY

By E. LOWELL KELLY, Ph.D.*

I. INTRODUCTION

D URING the last fifty years, psychologists have administered millions of tests to other people. The results of these tests have been used for diagnosis, evaluation, and prediction in a wide range of situations: military, educational, industrial, medical, and so on. The project about which I am going to report to you at this time is unique in that it has employed psychological tests in the evaluation of psychologists themselves. It represents our profession's first attempt to evaluate the psychological characteristics conducive to success in training and practice in psychology.

Although psychologists have made many notable contributions to the improvement of selection procedures used in industrial, military, and educational situations, their failure to have attacked the problem of selecting future members of their own profession is quite understandable in view of the history of the profession. Previous to World War II, psychologists were trained in relatively small numbers in widely separated graduate schools which had little inclination to coordinate or standardize their practices of student selection or training. Different departments were proud of the differences which characterized the training in their departments and graduates of the several institutions tended to gravitate to the types of specialization for which their particular variety of training best qualified them. As most of you know, this situation no longer characterizes training in any phase of psychology, least of all in clinical psychology. With the increased demands for mental hygiene personnel, and initially— as the result of the large scale employment of clinical psychologists by the Veterans Administration—the demand for clinical training at the doctoral level increased many fold. In 1946, twenty-two uni-

* University of Michigan.

versities undertook a four-year training program in cooperation with the Veterans Administration leading to the Ph.D. degree. During the first year this program enrolled only 200 students but this number has now increased to nearly 700 and available evidence indicates that at least that many more students are in doctoral programs in clinical psychology not associated with the Veterans Administration. In spite of this marked increase in training facilities and in the number of students being trained, the number of applicants requesting such training mounted even more rapidly. Whereas in prewar days, almost any college graduate could obtain admission to a graduate department of psychology and show that he could or could not successfully pursue graduate work, the postwar situation found university departments forced to refuse admission to many more applicants than they could accept.

Thus for the first time, selection of prospective members of the profession became a practical problem. Recognizing this probability the Veterans Administration approached us at the University of Michigan with the proposal that we undertake a program designed to determine the relative validity of several different technics of selecting students for training in clinical psychology. Thanks to the understanding attitudes of persons with whom we had to deal in the Veterans Administration, it was possible to negotiate a research contract which provided for both an intensive and extensive long-term study of this problem to be carried out on a cooperating basis with all institutions participating in the VA training program. Furthermore, the contract provided that none of the findings of the research should be utilized in actual selection by the institution until such time as their use would not invalidate our research findings. Finally, provision was also made that all information obtained concerning prospective students would remain in the confidential files of our project and not be released to the Veterans Administration or to the Civil Service.

II. Relation of Selection to Prognosis

The selection of candidates for any training program is primarily a practical problem. Whenever the number of applicants for a training program exceeds the capacity of the training facilities, some sort of selection is inevitable. The actual basis of the selection may be either logical or illogical. Thus, applicants to be admitted might be picked by assigning each applicant a different number and then making the selection by a roulette wheel or some other game of chance. Another scheme would be to give preference in accordance with date of application, i.e., a policy of first come, first served. And, as we know, still other procedures would give preference to applicants on the basis of sex, religion, ethnic origin, financial status, or some other identifiable characteristic of the individual. Let us note, however, that the moment a decision is made to give preference on the basis of such identifiable characteristics, the assumption is also made that the persons possessing this characteristic are either more likely to succeed in the training program or will constitute better representatives of the group for which the training program is designed. Logical selection, that is, any attempt to select the better qualified applicants for admission to training, presumes individual differences in aptitude which are correlated with later success in training and/or in the application of that training. Confronted with the necessity of some form of selection, logical selection seeks to improve the efficiency of the training program by reducing or eliminating the numer of failures and thus maintaining production of the training unit at its maximum. It should also be noted that even though all applicants possess a minimum of the aptitude necessary to succeed in the program, an effective selection program could still result in a higher average quality of persons completing the program. Although in this situation, the actual numerical efficiency of the training program would not be increased, it is presumed that the higher average caliber of the product trained would represent a contribution to society. In this sense, selection is a practical problem involving the maximization of economic and/or social values.

In another sense, however, the problem of selection is essentially a fascinating problem in pure science. Effective selection, as we have shown above, involves the identification of those variables most closely associated with differential success in training, or differences in the quality of the practice for which students are trained. In either case, it involves the prediction of behavior, behavior-in-training, or behavior-in-practice. And prediction is possible only when relevant variables have been identified and a dependable relationship established between them.

Thus, although we began with the practical problem of evaluating procedures for selection of students in clinical psychology, we have found ourselves increasingly involved with the more general problems of identifying relative variables, devising means of measuring such variables and of determining the degree of relationship between and among them. Methodology has been varied, but in general form it is relatively simple. We have sought to identify the relevant variables of what might be termed to be success in training and competence in clinical psychology and to ascertain the relationship between such measures and a series of measures of the individual students obtained at the beginning of their training.

Actually, because the training program in clinical psychology requires four years and also because we had so little idea of what constituted relevant predictive variables, we began by collecting a very extensive array of measures on each student at the beginning of training, stored these away, and then devoted our attention to the measurement of criterion variables as the students proceeded with their training. Ideally, we should have preferred to have begun by developing the criterion measures but to have done so would have greatly delayed the progress of the research project.

III. The Problem of Criteria

Any attempt to predict human behavior is immediately confronted with the problem of measurement of that behavior. Here I am using measurement in a very general sense to include the mere presence or absence of a behavior which we may point at or identify by some word. Such behavior may be extremely specific, e.g., an eyewink, or it may involve a series of successive behaviors, e.g., a man putting on his coat, or we may elect to group together as a single variable a large number of related behaviors such as would be involved in successfully completing a course of study. In any case, the possibility of lawful prediction of behavior assumes regularity or consistency in the behavior itself. Behavior which is purely random, if there be such, can not be predicted. Our own experience as well as that of many other investigators has led us to conclude that the problem of measuring relevant criterion variables is fully as complex as measuring that of predictor variables.

At first blush, it would appear that the psychologists working in the field of personnel selection would not be plagued by questions of value. Thus the industrial psychologist who sets out to develop approved methods of selecting insurance salesmen would seem to have a ready and defensible criterion, namely, the amount of insurance which the salesman sells in a given period of time. A more careful analysis of the sponsor's interest, however, shows that such is not the case. Two men may sell the same total amount of insurance within the year but since the cost of writing each policy is approximately the same regardless of its face value, the salesman who sells a given amount in the fewest number of policies would be the more profitable salesman to the company. Furthermore, I understand that the company itself does not make much profit on the policy during the first year of the contract. This being the case, the salesman who sells to customers who maintain their insurance policies would be definitely superior to the one who made sales which "did not stick." Thus we see that the question of an appropriate criterion variable is far from simple even here.

As we turn to our own field of investigation, the same type of complex criterion problems confronts us. To be sure, we have a relatively convenient and ostensibly meaningful criterion: that of whether the student succeeds or fails in the training program. Since successful completion of the program is becoming a *sine qua non* of professional status in clinical psychology, it may be argued that failure to complete the program is indeed a valid criterion of success in training.

The use of an administrative criterion such as success or failure in training presupposes the validity of the training program, i.e., that those who succeed in training can do certain things better than those who fail in training. To the degree that this assumption of the validity of the training program is justified, the use of the pass-fail criterion in training is also justified as a means of selecting persons for later performance for which the training is a preparation. There is, however, the possibility that success in training is not related to the demands of the job for which an individual is trained. The experience of psychologists in many World War training programs indicates that such may frequently be true, i.e., success in training may show no relationship to later performance on the job. Even worse, this relationship may actually be a negative one.

In our own project, we are using the administrative criterion of pass-fail as one measure of success but are far from content with it. Because we believe that even among successful graduates of the training program, there will still be considerable differences in professional competences, we are making a determined effort to obtain measures of these presumed competences. These efforts, however, have in turn forced us to ask a great many other questions. Just what is a clinical psychologist supposed to be able to do that someone without training in clinical psychology can not do? How can we identify these competences and how can we secure reliable and valid measures of them?

Because this phase of our study is not completed and because time does not permit, I shall not dwell at length on the problem of measuring criterion variables. I will merely attempt to outline our resolution of the problem and indicate the general directions in which we are working.

Our first approach to this problem is one which grows out of the social characteristics of a profession and its members. To a surprising degree, membership in a profession is a function of the willingness and ability of the candidate to meet certain formal (and sometimes arbitrary) requirements established by that profession as qualifications for admission. Such qualifications include a specified amount and kind of formal training, the passing of specified examinations and the endorsement of more mature members of the profession. Even success in training, evaluated as it is by members of the profession, is to a large extent dependent on subjective evaluation by representatives of the profession. Thus, in large measure, a candidate's chances of becoming a member of the profession are a function of the degree to which he is able to make a favorable impression on his teachers and supervisors. And, in the absence of any more objective criteria of professional competence, his later professional success, including promotion, is similarly dependent on the evaluation of him by professional supervisors.

It is for this reason that we are using professional evaluations as one type of criterion measure. We are obtaining repeated evaluations of students in training by three types of judges: university clinical staff members, field installation supervisors and by other students. Since members of the professional group which we are studying are in themselves more ostensibly efficient than members of many other groups in the evaluation of personal and professional characteristics, it seems only reasonable to include such sociometric ratings among our criterion measures.

Another reason for using ratings by supervisors and peers as criterion measures grows out of the fact that many aspects of professional competence in clinical psychology simply do not seem to be amenable to objective measurement at this time. I have never heard of a clinical psychologist losing his job because of what might be termed technical inadequacies. I have heard of clinical psychologists losing their jobs or failing to be promoted because of what might be termed inadequate inter-professional relations or lack of integrity. Note, however, that such variables reflect solely the evaluation of interpersonal behavior by colleagues or superiors.

We are, however, not at all content with only such subjective evaluations of professional competence. Although convinced that such evaluations are socially important, and although we have evidence to indicate that correlations among the three groups of judges referred to above range between .40 and .50, we are still not satisfied to depend solely on such criteria. We believe, rightly or wrongly, for example, that actual knowledge of content of clinical psychology may be related to professional success. For this reason, we have developed and plan to use objective tests of content knowledge of clinical psychology and of research methodology. Again, because we feel that skill in clinical diagnosis constitutes one of the essential dimensions of clinical competency in our profession, we are attempting to develop objective measures of such diagnostic skills. This in itself has proven to be an ambitious undertaking but results today are sufficiently promising to lead us to believe that such measures can be developed and that they will be more reliable and valid than ratings of diagnostic skill by supervisors, which have been found to vary widely depending on the supervisor doing the rating. Similarly, because we believe that therapeutic skill constitutes another important dimension of clinical competency and again, because we are not satisfied with the interjudge reliability of ratings of therapeutic skill, we are attempting to develop objective indices of the degree to which trainees are able to develop good therapeutic relationships.

It is already fairly obvious that there will not turn out to be any single criterion of what constitutes a good clinical psychologist. Our more modest goal will be: (a) the development of a number of measures of different criteria of the good clinical psychologist, (b) the determination of the interrelationships among these criteria and finally, (c) the evaluation of the various methods for predicting each of them most accurately.

IV. The Predictive Measures Used in the Project

The predictive measures used in our project fall in two broad categories: (a) objective test scores and (b) clinical judgments based on test scores as well as a wide variety of other clinical procedures. Most previous studies of personnel selection have relied heavily on objective test scores in predicting criteria of success. The one notable exception to this statement is the work of the OSS assessment staff reported in "The Assessment of Men." The guiding philosophy of the OSS assessment program as well as the thesis of the book reporting it is that more meaningful evaluations of people as well as more accurate predictions of their future performance in specific job situations can be made by evaluating the person on a global or organismic basis. Unfortunately, the OSS program did not provide the necessary data for a crucial test of this thesis. All persons associated with the assessment program seem to have been impressed with the probable validity of the proposition but actual evidence concerning the superiority of such an organismic evaluation are lacking.

In planning our project, the decision was made to utilize both objective test scores and the more promising of the assessment technics developed in the OSS program. This decision was based not only on the conviction and testimony of OSS staff members but also on the reasonable assumption that success in a profession involving interpersonal relationships, such as psychiatry and clinical psychology, might be assumed to be a function of the more subtle characteristics of personality functioning which might not be tapped by the conventional objective test approach so widely used in industrial selection programs.

The objective measures used in our project included some seventy scores derived from the following battery of tests:

1. The Miller Analogies Test (Form G)
2. The Primary Mental Abilities Tests
3. The Allport-Vernon Scale of Values

4. The Minnesota Multiphasic Inventory
5. The Guilford-Martin Battery of Personality Inventories
6. The Strong Vocational Interest Blank
7. The Kuder Preference Record

The application of more recently developed scoring keys for certain of these instruments will provide us with still more test scores.

The second category of predictive measures are the clinical judgments made by members of our professional assessment staff who spent approximately one week studying the candidates as seen through a wide variety of measures including, (a) the credential file (letters of application, Civil Service Form 57, letters of reference, college transcripts, and so on), (b) a profile based on the objective test scores referred to above, (c) a projective test battery including the Rorschach, Sentence Completion, TAT and Bender-Gestalt, (d) two interviews, the first, a one-hour, and the second a two-hour interview with the candidate at different stages in the assessment program, and (e) several situation tests including an unstructured group discussion, a series of role-playing episodes, an outdoor test involving considerable physical exertion and teamwork as well as situations in which the candidate performed alone in the presence of staff members. In order that these clinical judgments could be subjected to the same type of rigorous analysis as the objective test scores, staff members were required to make them by rating the candidates on a series of 43 variables which preliminary research had suggested as probably relevant to success in clinical training and practice.

These 43 variables fall roughly in three categories. Scale A contains 22 variables, purporting to be essentially *descriptive* or phenotypic in nature, e.g., cooperativeness, gregariousness, cheerfulness, and so on. Scale B contains 11 variables, ostensibly more genotypic or characteristic of deeper and more underlying aspects of the personality. For the most part, these judgments were *evaluative*, e.g., the adequacy of a person's social adjustment, the intensity of his inner emotional life and the strength of his motivation for professional success. Scale C includes 10 variables on which the clinician makes *predictions* as to the future performance of the candidate in the training and clinical work situation. Samples of these variables are academic performance, diagnostic skill, skill in individual psychotherapy and professional integrity. Finally, each clinician makes a summary judgment as to the probable overall success of each candidate as a clinical psychologist.

Because we did not know which of these technics or which combination of them would provide a basis for the most accurate evaluation of the candidate or prediction of future success, our research design provided for a series of sequential judgments to be made by staff members on the basis of increasing amounts of information about the candidate. Whenever possible, we also sought to secure ratings based on individual materials or clinical procedures as a means of estimating the independent validity of each technic as well as the incremental validity when added to other technics. Thus one clinician evaluated the candidate and made predictions about him on the basis of the credential file alone, another on the basis of the Rorschach alone, and still others on the basis of situation tests without any other knowledge of the candidate. Obviously, it was not economically feasible to obtain ratings based on all possible combinations of procedures; when one combination or sequence had to be selected rather than another, we based the decision on the most practical combination from the point of view of future possible use by universities in an actual selection program.

Although time does not allow me to present the details of our research design, I must not neglect to mention that each subject was studied intensively by three clinicians, who, in addition to making their individual judgments about the candidate, later participated in a series of staff conferences and agreed on pooled judgments concerning him. Such ratings were based on all data and impressions gained during a one-week study of the candidate and, in addition to the above, included evaluations of candidates by their teammates, in the form of character sketches, ratings and sociometric choices.

These then were our predictive measures on each candidate: some 70 objective test scores and a sequence of 30 sets of ratings on 43 variables. The next question is how well did these function both individually and in combination as predictors of subsequent success in training.

V. Major Findings to Date

Before presenting any of the actual findings growing out of our study, I should like to emphasize the tentative nature of these findings and hence the limitations of this present report. We began the study in 1946 and only this spring are the first products of the four-year training program completing their training. The group studied most intensively by us, 128 students who began training in 1947, are only now at the end of their third year of training and hence final criterion measures are not yet available for them. Also, because of the tremendous mass of data to be analyzed, it did not seem sound to invest too much time and effort in predicting preliminary criterion measures of the type which could be obtained during the earlier periods of training.

It must also be remembered that the group for whom we were undertaking to make predictions represented an already highly selected sample of human beings. They were all graduates of four-year college programs with records sufficiently impressive to secure their admission to a recognized graduate school. This resulted in a markedly selected group with respect to general intellectual ability. In addition, the group was also selected because of an avowed interest in the profession of clinical psychology which may have resulted in a restriction of the range of personality variables in our sample.

Finally, our analyses to date have dealt entirely with what might be called global criteria, i.e., the overall ratings of the trainee as a clinical psychologist by university staff, field staff and colleagues. Eventually, as I indicated above, we shall analyze the data with respect to the prediction of individual aspects of clinical competence but such detailed analyses against preliminary criteria have not seemed advisable.

With these limitations in mind, let us then look at the major findings thus far growing out of the project. Here are the trends:

1. The absolute validities of all of our predictive measures tend to be low. This statement applies both to objective test scores and to individual clinical procedures and combinations of them.

2. The most valid individual clinical judgments tend to be those made when the staff member had relatively incomplete data regarding the candidate at the time of assessment. Actually, the highest validities are for clinical judgments based on an evaluation of the credential file and the objective test profile. Subsequent predictions based on increasing amounts of data, i.e., the autobiography, the projective tests and the interview, appear to have resulted in suc-

cessive decrement in validity as each additional type of information was made available to the clinician. We regard this finding as all the more significant in view of the fact that the staff had much more confidence in the validity of these latter technics than in the credential file or objective test scores. Evidence for this confidence is based not only on the testimony of staff members but on the operational criterion of increasing spread of ratings as more data became available to them, i.e., ratings made with increasing amounts of data show greater variability.

3. Most of the objective test scores yield low and insignificant validities. There is, however, one notable exception: the Strong Vocational Interest Test when scored with the VA Clinical Psychologist Key developed by this project, consistently predicts rated overall competence in clinical psychology better than any other predictive measure thus far analyzed. Let me emphasize this point; a single objective test score which can be obtained without any contact between the examiner and the candidate at the cost of approximately fifty cents consistently yields validities higher than those for any of the clinical judgments, including the final pooled rating on each subject, which cost approximately $300 per person!

4. The validities of judgments based on individual projective technics tend to be extremely low and some of them are negative. This is also true for judgments based on the clinical integration of the four projective technics used in the study.

5. The pooling of clinical judgments in a staff conference did not increase validities enough to justify the cost of such a pooling. In fact, they were only very slightly higher than those obtained by using a simple mean or median of the individual staff member's judgment. Some evidence strongly suggests that this pooling procedure tended to result in diluted average judgments which were less valid than those of the best clinician participating in the staff conference.

VI. Discussion

Let us examine what appear to be certain implications of these findings:

First of all, I would emphasize the fact that although disturbing, they are not disheartening. In spite of the inherent difficulties of the task we undertook, that of predicting differential success in training of an already highly selected group of students, receiving their training in thirty-five different institutions, each with somewhat different curricular demands and standards of evaluation, we nevertheless are able to make predictions with sufficient accuracy to be of decided use to graduate schools in selecting applicants, especially in view of the high accepted-rejected ratio among applicants. It appears likely that such predictions, with a multiple correlation coefficient of around .50 can be made on the basis of an extremely economical battery of objective tests which may be administered to the candidate without requiring him to visit the institution of his choice.

The disturbing thing about our findings, of course, is that so many of them are not in line with our biases and even convictions concerning the validity of human judgments which supposedly permit the evaluation of psychological variables not amenable to objective measurement and also provide for a more meaningful integration of such impressions than can be obtained with a calculator or set of IBM machines. It is, of course, true that our convictions regarding the validity of such clinical impressions are not substantiated by available evidence. For example, nowhere in the literature have I been able to discover an instance in which a selection interview has resulted in predictions of success in training any more accurate than obtainable from the simplest sort of psychometric device. Likewise, I know of no evidence in the literature or elsewhere, to justify the belief that a clinician basing his judgments on projective devices or autobiographical materials, can arrive at predictions of training success significantly better than chance. Yet it is no accident that these technics were included in our assessment battery. For reasons about which it would be interesting to speculate, most of us clinicians tend to develop a degree of confidence in our favorite tools and in our judgments based on them which are all too frequently not backed up by an actual evidence for our belief.

Our research program undertook the task of evaluating candidates for training in psychology and predicting their success in training for the profession. Because of the nature of the technical problems involved, the emphasis on the project quickly shifted to an evaluation of the tests, technics, and other tools by which we attempt psychological evaluation of human beings. And because most of these tools must be used by a clinician, our interests moved on to an investigation of the validity of the clinician-technic combination. Thus far, our results suggest that the human being is an extremely poor psychological instrument, both as a measuring device and as an integrator of data!

This finding, even though tentative, is of course extremely threatening to the human ego, especially if that ego also happens to have high confidence with respect to the validity of his own functioning in clinical situations. Let me, therefore, immediately warn you against the danger of overgeneralizing from these limited findings. Just because individual clinicians, the clinicians working in staff conferences, were unable to do this particular diagnostic job as well as an objective test using an IBM scoring machine does not mean that the same or other clinicians using the same or other tools could not out-perform any objective test in any situation involving the prediction of human behavior. However, we must not overlook the fact that crucial evidence regarding this point is lacking. Our findings do suggest, it seems to me, the desirability, even the necessity, of determining the validity of a psychological tool for the specific prognostic job at hand before adopting its routine use in the service situation. And, personally, I cannot but be impressed with our findings concerning the inverse relationship between the confidence of the staff members in their judgments at various stages in the assessment program and the actual validities of these judgments as determined by their correlation with later success in training. If it should turn out that this inverse relationship should generally hold, it could lead to extremely dangerous policy decisions regarding procedures to be used in clinical practice, if such decisions are made without previously determining the validity of the technic for the specific job at hand. Face validity, or faith validity, is not enough.

A psychological test is nothing more than an evaluated sample of human behavior. Ordinarily we are not interested in the specific behavior sampled in the test but only in the degree to which the sample behavior enables us to predict the future behavior of the same individual, usually in another domain. For thirty years, it has been the accepted practice in psychology to determine the reliability and validity of psychological tests. Very simply stated the consistency with which test behavior predicts the same behavior at a later date is called reliability. Validity, in the same simple terms, refers to the degree to which the behavior sampled in the tests permits prediction of behavior in another domain. The findings of our project on the assessment of students in clinical psychology forcibly remind us that in the case of most clinical technics, the clinician himself is a part of the psychological test. When viewed in this light, it becomes as pertinent to raise questions about *his* validity as that of any other psychological test which we might use. More specifically, the question must be asked in terms of the validity of the clinician-technic combination for the specific job at hand. In other words, I suggest that the clinician himself or the clinician and his tool must be calibrated, if we are to avoid the possibility of or even the probability of finding ourselves in the unenviable position of using test-clinician combinations with validities so low that we cannot justify their use.

I much appreciate the opportunity to bring you this account of our efforts to predict the training outcomes of students in clinical psychology. Unfortunately, time has not permitted giving you many details of the research design or reporting many other interesting findings which are emerging as the project progresses. Let me again remind you of the tentative nature of these findings. We are not going to obtain our most meaningful criterion measures until next year and the eventual picture of our findings may be quite different than that which I have been able to present to you at this time.

REFERENCES

1. KELLY, E. L. and FISKE, D. W.: The prediction of success in the VA training program in clinical psychology. Amer. Psychol., *5*, 395–406, 1950.
2. O.S.S. Assessment Staff: The Assessment of Men, New York, Rinehart, 1948.
3. RAIMY, V. C., Editor: Training in Clinical Psychology. New York, Prentice Hall, Inc., 1950.

10

THE CONDITIONAL REFLEX FUNCTION AS AN AID IN THE STUDY OF THE PSYCHIATRIC PATIENT*

By W. HORSLEY GANTT, M.D.†

HISTORY

SOON AFTER the establishment of the Pavlovian Laboratory at the Phipps Psychiatric Clinic in 1931, I began to apply the conditional reflex (cr) methodology to the study of the psychiatric patient. The present method, though derived from my experience with the methods of Krasnogorsky and of Ivanov-Smolensky, both of whom I worked with in Russia in 1925–29, is chiefly a new adaptation based on the requirements of the psychiatric clinic.

Krasnogrosky (6) employed the salivary cr mainly in infants and in retarded children. While this is a useful method for the study of infants and very young children, it is of little value in this country with older subjects because of the fact that unless American children are starved they do not show the interest in food that the average Russian child did. In adults, owing to the excessive amount of inhibition of the food reflex in the experimental setting, the salivary method is usually unsatisfactory, even in Russia. The average adult does not give a clear-cut reflex to the experimental amounts of food used to evoke salivation.

Ivanov-Smolensky, whose method was derived mainly from Bekhterev, studied the motor component of the food reflex, or of the orienting reflex (OR) of the child to a picture (17). Neither of these

---

* Based on unpublished reports before the Johns Hopkins Medical Society 1941, the American Psychiatric Association, Washington 1948, the American Psychopathological Association, New York 1950, and the Conference on Research in the Veterans Administration, Houston 1951; and exhibits at the International Pediatric Congress, New York 1947, the American Medical Association, Chicago 1949, Southern Medical Association, Baltimore 1949.

† Associate Professor of Psychiatry; Director, Pavlovian Laboratory, Phipps Psychiatric Clinic, Johns Hopkins University.

methods is applicable to the psychotic patient because of his suppressed interest and reactivity to most stimulations.

Various studies have been made in this country with the cr method in human subjects. Among the early experiments have been those of Watson (24) in 1915 with the motor components, and of Mateer (19) and Lashley (18) with the salivary secretion. Recently, Sutherland and Finesinger (3) investigated the salivary crs in psychotics, and Welch, the psychogalvanic reflex (PGR) in anxiety patients (25). My early work at the Phipps Clinic showed that even though there was a great apparent impairment in some cataleptic patients, a marked difference was seen between the character of the impairment in the psychogenic and in the organic psychoses (8, 9, 10, 11, 12, 21). Thus, I demonstrated that severe catatonics, including cateleptics, could form conditional reflexes, whereas my collaborators and I have demonstrated that many severe organics cannot form conditional reflexes; Gantt and Muncie have demonstrated failure for the Korsakov's (12); Fleck and Gantt (5) found impairment after electroshock; Reese, Doss, and Gantt noted parallel impairment in the psychogalvanic and respiratory components of the cr in organics (21).*

There are, of course, other objective methods for the study of behavior and intelligence. Halstead in his recent book, *Brain and Intelligence*, (16) has stated emphatically both the great need for, as well as the lack of, such objective methods in psychiatry, and he has developed a series of objective tests, the results of which he interprets by a rather complex system of psychological analysis. No attempt is made in the present article, however, to review or evaluate methods other than the one here described.

METHOD

The patient is separated from the experimenter by a partition—a glass window about 30″ x 30″ fitted for one-way vision. On the patient's side is a table on which are two plate electrodes, on a platform suspended by a spring. At a convenient point are placed a series of colored lights (white, green, red, blue). Auditory signals are given from an audiometer. In front of the patient is a rubber bulb for use of the

* During 1950 Reese and Gantt have established a laboratory at the Veterans Hospital at Perry Point, Md. for the study of motor, circulatory, and other autonomic responses in patients (22).

free hand. This bulb is so connected that it serves for short-circuiting the current to the restricted hand and also for recording the movements of the free hand. Movements of the restricted hand are recorded by a pneumograph. A ground glass screen above the table serves for projection of pictures, and written word signals as needed.

For children a food box is provided so adjusted that it can be opened

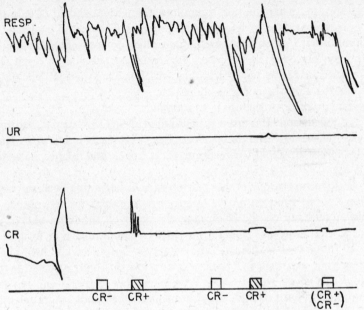

FIG. 1. CR in adolescent (A.G.), age 11. (November 22, 1947.)

by the experimenter at will, but by the child only with the appropriate signal.

On the other side of the partition there is a switchboard controlling (1) the conditional stimulus (cs), visual or auditory; (2) the unconditional stimulus (US), shock, through a time device which is designed to give in regular sequence, usually every two minutes, the cs for 5″, immediately followed by the US. The intensity of the latter is governed through a Variacs producing a voltage of 0–125 AC. A continuous-feed Phipps and Bird kymograph records (1) respiration, (2) conditional signal, (3) movements of the free hand (bulb), (4) movements of the restricted hand (on electrodes). (See fig. 1.)

PREPARATION OF PATIENT

This should be designed to put the patient at his ease, to relieve his apprehension concerning the procedure, avoiding conversation of a suggestive nature. The subject is allowed a few minutes to become quiet in the room; some casual conversation may help to do this. Reliable results cannot be obtained in a patient fearful of the procedure. If any explanation is required, the patient should be told that the examination is to determine his progress or to test his coordination in terms with which he is familiar and which do not excite him unduly. It may, however, be necessary for disturbed patients to come back for a second test; a repeat test is essential on every patient who makes a low score on the initial examination.

The order of procedure is as follows:

1. Perception: Have the patient name all signals—visual, auditory.

2. Sensitivity: Hands on electrodes. Test each hand three times for lower threshold (perception of current) and higher threshold (pain).

3. Five repetitions of one pair of signals, beginning with the negative. No instructions are to be given here except for the patient to place one hand on the electrodes, the other on the bulb, and to observe what happens. Look for evidence of the primitive cr formation.

4. Integrated cr: "Now, from what you have seen and heard here, from your experience, I want you to press this bulb just before you think the shock would come. Press once now so that I can see that you press it hard enough. Hold it a couple of seconds before releasing it. Don't ask questions, but do the best you can from your experience. When you press the bulb at the right time, you won't get the shock. If you get the shock, you are not using the bulb in the right way."

5. After the appearance of the integrated cr with differentiation (failing to press with the unreenforced signal), use auditory signals to see if spontaneous transfer of learning occurs. If it does not, observe in the patient's formulation his subjective feeling about these signals and why he did not react. Grade A— if he fails on transfer.

6. If patient does not learn from the first series of five repetitions or fails to differentiate, repeat training five more times or use electrodes on wrist with constant reenforcement so that he cannot avoid the shock. Grade A—.

Grade as high as B if the patient is capable of reacting correctly by increasing the number of repetitions, however, without the use of pointed directions. Grade B— and not C if integrated crs occur irregularly to signal but do not occur in the intervals between stimuli. If differentiation is poor, grade separately for differentiation.

7. If patient cannot elaborate integrated crs, (a) repeat or, if necessary, (b) have him repeat "shock" and "no shock" with positive and negative lights, and then, if necessary, (c) "white light—no shock," "red light—shock." Grade C after this if he can perform correctly even for three times.

8. Grade D if he fails on above but can execute three times: "Press with red and not with white." D— if irregular or presses to both.

Use kinesthetic reenforcement when necessary and grade as above.

9. Grade E if he fails on D.

With the appearance of the primitive cr, grade the same as for integrated cr except with small letters. Primitive crs occurring with the integrated may be expressed by using, e.g., Aa.

10. Verbal Grading.

Deduct 25 for evidence of failure to note difference between positive and negative signals. If the patient does not mention spontaneously the significance of the two signals, deduct 5 and ask, "Any difference between the meaning of the different lights (or sounds)?"

Failure to *enumerate* negative signals, deduct 5 and ask, "Any difference between meaning of the different lights or sounds?" Failure to note difference between positive and negative signals, deduct 20.

The verbal formulation by the patient is of interest in throwing light on his thinking, or for its contrast with the performance, as seen in many psychogenic patients. Under the conditions of this test, a low verbal grade is not necessarily significant of impairment of cortical function.

Our conventional report sheet of an impairment from a brain tumor appears on pages 170–171.

RESULTS

Normal Variations. All intact healthy subjects from infancy to senescence can form crs, but the pattern of the cr, especially the voluntary, motor component, varies considerably, sometimes in the same individual as a result of disease, but especially from one individual to the other.

Types. The patterns of reactivity show marked variation. An extended study would probably reveal definite functional types related to the personality. Without attempting a complete classification, but

The Johns Hopkins Hospital
Phipps Clinic
*Summary of Conditional Reflex Test
for Cortical Function*

Name_____R. L._____Ward_____Age _37_ Date_____

I. UR: defense to shock

II. Reaction to unconditional stimulus: +++
   (perception)

   a. threshold of sensitivity (rt.hd.): 20-21-20
      (perception) (lt.hd.): 10-11-12
   b. threshold of pain (rt.hd.): 70-65-60
      (lt.hd.): 40-30-30
   c. amplitude of reaction: 1) barely perceptible, 2) diminished, 3) average, 4) increased, 5) greatly exaggerated:
      CR: +   UR: +++

III. CR (motor) function (adaptation):

	Spontaneous (primitive CR)	Integrated CR
Ability to:		
a. form (synthesis):	−	+
b. differentiate (analysis):	−	−
c. extinguish:	−	−
Speed: (no. repetitions necessary):		
a. for elaboration:		>5
b. for differentiation:		
c. for extinction:		
Retention:		
a. motor: +		
b. verbal: +		

$$\frac{\text{Latent period}}{\text{Duration CR}} : \frac{1.5}{2.0}$$

IV. Reaction to conflicting stimuli:

V. Reaction to reality (suggestibility or accuracy of perception determined by estimation of presence and intensity of current):
   a. localized; b. referred; c. *fabrication;*

VI. Emotional reaction: *overt* (muscular); autonomic (*respiratory*)
                                    (speech)   (cardiac)
   a. intensity (1–5 as under IIc.) +
   b. type of response (aggressive, uncooperative, *indifferent, cooperative,* interested, intellectual):

VII. Verbal responses: a. *meager;* b. average; c. profuse; d. spontaneous; e. relevant or *irrelevant.*

VIII. Attention during test (concentration): good, average, *poor*.

IX. Other memory tests:
    a. orientat. t. p. per. x
    b. 100–7:___3 minutes___time (sec.):___errors: 10___
    c. digit frwd___4___bkwd___2___

X. Formulation (verbal) score: 25
    Tell me briefly in your own words the important parts of this examina-
    tion—what you have done and what you have learned from your experi-
    ence here—only the significant items (important things).

Comprehension

Active (spontaneous) = 100
Items: sensitivity (5)
Enumeration of signals (5)
1 2 3 4 5 6
Meaning of signals: positive (45)
                 negative (20)
Use of bulb (15)
Time under 2 min. (10)
    under 3 min. (5)
(allow 5 min.)
Permissible: You needn't give details.
          Don't try to explain it.
Deduct 5 each repetition: "Anything else"?
Score on cr:

Passive = 50
1) How did you know when
    the shock was coming (50)
    If failure ask:
2) What did you see or
    hear? (5)
3) What happened? (5)
4) What did you do? (5)
5) Repeat 1). (25)
    (allow 5 min.)

Key: A = no impairment of formation or differentiation of motor conditional
       reflex (forms in less than 5 trials) formulation, retention, percep-
       tion normal.
    B = slight impairment of 1 or more above elements.
    C = marked impairment of 1 or more above elements; cannot form
       conditional reflexes without help in pointing out signals and in-
       volving speech center.
    D = complete inability to elaborate conditional reflexes; no insight
       into problem, but can execute order, "Press with R, not with W."
    E = same as for D plus inability to carry out orders.
    a, b, c, d, e = used instead of capitals to indicate performance as above
       but in terms of primitive crs.
    If pt. gets above C it means he can elaborate crs without help.

to give a few examples, one may distinguish among normals (1) the
childish type, (2) the artistic type, and (3) the scientific type. The
first type resembles the subhuman (dog) reaction in that the spontaneous crs predominate. (See figs. 1, 2 and 3.)

The second type is characterized by a hyperreactivity with considerable irregularity and disturbance in the respiration. See, for example, the chart of a prominent author (fig. 2).

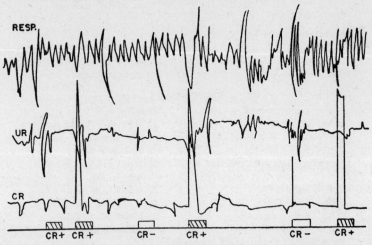

FIG. 2. CR in artistic type (J.D.P.), author. (March 29, 1939.)

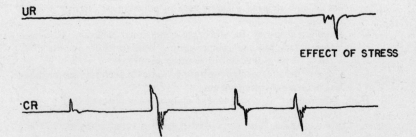

FIG. 3. CR in scientific type (T.P.). (April 16, 1948.)

The third or scientific type is marked by a regularity of response seen in both the respiration and in the movements (fig. 3).

Fluctuations in the Same Hand. The cr is subject to variation not only on the basis of physical and toxic influences, e.g., alcohol, but also it varies with a large number of *conceptual factors.* As an extreme degree of this, let us take the variation that can be brought about in

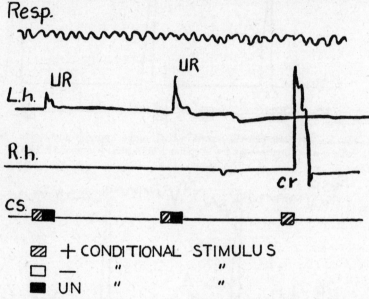

Fig. 4. (Hypnosis I.) Normal CR record, twenty-three-year old soldier (K.H.). (October 11, 1943.)

a susceptible person by *hypnotic* suggestion. The following twenty-three-year old soldier was a patient of Dr. Herbert X. Spiegel. Dr. Spiegel could get this patient to regress to any age level by suggesting under hypnosis that he would act as if he were the suggested age. The mental age measured by the Binet corresponded to the suggested age. The cr record was also comparable to the hypnotic age; the movements were seen to be more intense, as they are in younger children, and to be absent in the baby. (Although babies can form crs they would not be revealed in this type of test used for adults.) (See figs. 4, 5, 6 and 7.)

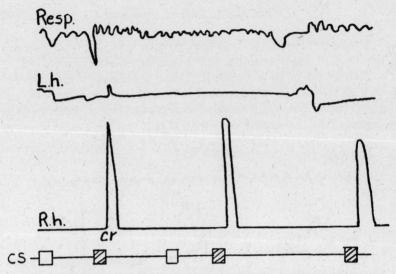

Fig. 5. (Hypnosis II.) CR record in K.H. under hypnotic suggestion "age 11." Same as normal except for irregular respiration. (October 11, 1943.)

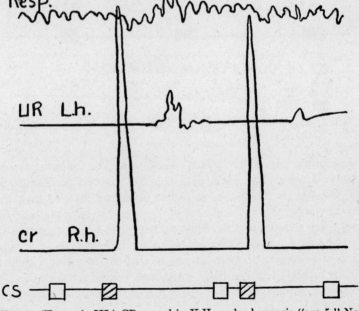

Fig. 6. (Hypnosis III.) CR record in K.H. under hypnosis "age 5." Note increased amplitude CRS, irregular respiration, hyperreactivity L.H. characteristics of five-year old. (October 27, 1943.)

Pathological Disturbances. Deviations from the normal in general can be arranged in a hierarchy from slight to grave. The slightest deviations are marked by an irregularity of latent period—the more intelligent subjects tend to make the latent period nearly equal to the duration of the cs, although this varies with individuals and with

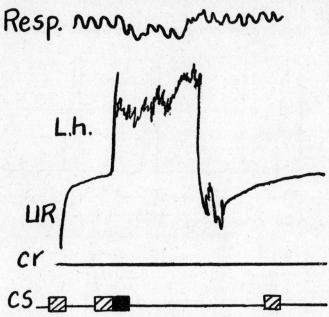

FIG. 7. CR record in K.H. under hypnosis "age 6 months." Note absence CRS, UR activity partly characteristic of baby. (October 11, 1943.) Binet Simon M.A. roughly corresponded to hypnotic ages.

(Experiments of Dr. Herbert Spiegel.)

the apprehension. Next in order come a failure of generalization, a failure of differentiation, a slowness in forming crs, a complete inability to form the specific motor cr but with some emotional components of a general nature (respiratory, circulatory) and finally, in the idiot, intoxicated or poisoned individual there is a suppression of the orienting reflex (OR), as well as of the URs, including the response to pain, etc. (See fig. 10).

Toxic Conditions. Acute intoxications show only a temporary impairment, e.g., acute alcoholic intoxication. Figs. 8 and 9 are records of a normal medical student before and during alcoholic intoxication. Note the appearance of primitive crs in the restricted hand, the irregu-

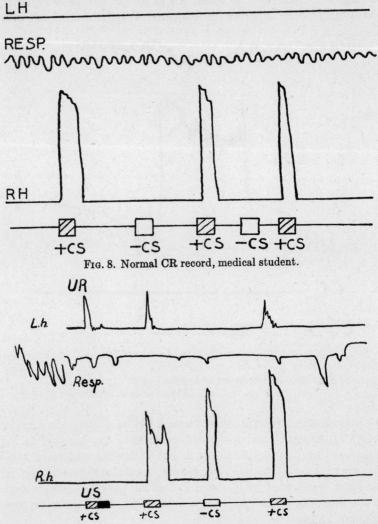

FIG. 8. Normal CR record, medical student.

FIG. 9. Alcohol (2 cc. per kg.) on CR in normal subject (JWTR). (April 29, 1944.)

larity of cr amplitudes, the failure to differentiate between the positive and negative signals. The chronic toxic psychoses, e.g., Korsakov's, alcoholic dementia, post-insulin shock, give the most marked picture— the complete inability to form the motor cr.

Organic conditions, e.g., hydrocephalus, senility, brain tumors, show all grades of impairment according to the damage. In general,

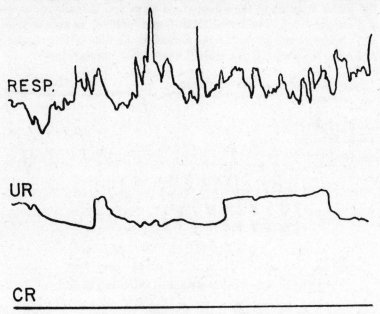

FIG. 10. Imbecile (J.C.), age four.

those which are severe enough to produce psychotic symptoms usually have a loss of ability to form the motor crs.

In acute disorders the impairment of the cr function is more marked than in the chronic. One may see this in the following two patients. The first (10) was a patient with a brain tumor who showed a marked failure to form crs until the operation, but recovery thereafter; the second patient (JDP) who had a congenital absence of one frontal lobe and a cyst of the other, showed only a slight loss of cr function (failure of differentiation). If the injury in this patient had been recently acquired, as in a patient examined with bilateral frontal lobe extirpation, he would have shown a much greater deficit. Evidently the patients with the congenital lesions have a special advantage over the patients with the acquired lesion in the ability to make new adaptations, though perhaps not in the function of retention.

In dogs even with large cortical extirpations, there is relatively good retention of the ability to form new crs. Thus two dogs, "Crazy" and "Checkers," having extirpations of the whole of one cortex and the gyrus cingulus of the other, could form and differentiate motor and cardiac crs to two tones (T256+ and T512−) an octave apart, and also form, though with some difficulty, the time cr to a regularly recurring sequence of two stimuli every two minutes.

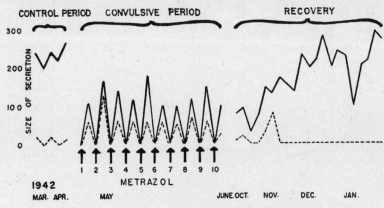

FIG. 11. Effect of convulsions on CRS. (Dog Sechs.)

A variety of procedures in the dog have been shown to impair the cr function—metrazol convulsions (23), exposure to high altitudes (13), alcohol (4, 7), vitamin B group deficiency (14), etc. Judging from those cases where a comparison has been made between human and subhuman species, the equivalent damage will produce a much greater loss of function in the human than in lower animals, and therefore the impairment caused by the same agents (convulsions, anoxia, drugs, vitamin deficiency) would be reflected by a much greater loss of cr function in the human than those we have demonstrated in the dog. (See figs. 11, 12 and 13.)

Fleck and Gantt (5) found in ten patients tested before, during, and after electroshock therapy that there was a decline in performance in six of the ten, lasting from 24 hours to more than 9 weeks. These

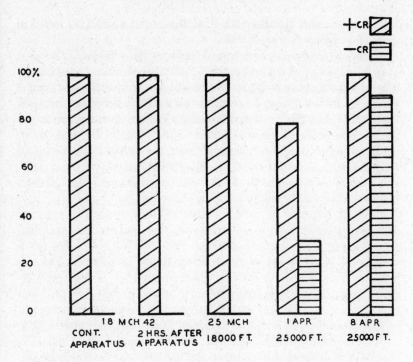

FIG. 12. Effect of anoxia on motor CRS—Pain # 1. (Dog Connie, age four.)

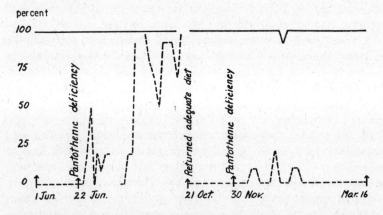

FIG. 13. Vitamin deficiency on CRS. Note impairment of differentiation and return of differentiation with adequate diet. (Dog Neptune II.)

results are roughly parallel with what Rosen and Gantt (23) found in dogs after metrazol convulsions.

Sensory Disturbance (Deafness, Blindness, Anesthesias). This test may be employed to detect hysterical blindness, deafness, anesthesias. The hysterical patient will at first inhibit the cr involving sensations concerned in the illness; however, a distinction can be seen between the organic and the psychogenic sensory disturbance; the latter patient will form the cr but will inhibit the movements, but this movement can be elicited in a variety of ways, the simplest of which is to combine, e.g., an auditory and a visual stimulus (in hysterical deafness); after forming the cr to the compound stimulus the patient will give a reaction to either component used singly.

The test can also be used in those patients, especially children who are unable to talk, to determine whether there is true deafness. I have been using this examination with Dr. W. M. Phelps for a number of years to detect the hearing ability in children. For the last few years, Dr. John Bordley has developed the cr test for deafness using the *psychogalvanic reflex* to shock as the US (2). The psychogalvanic reflex has especial advantages over the motor cr in certain diseases, which will be discussed in a subsequent article (21).

Besides the psychogenic patient, this examination is of value in the study of cerebral palsies, athetoses, and aphasias to determine the ability for making adaptation as well as to compare the right and left sides. So far, there has been no difference discernable in ease of learning between the right and left hands in right and left handed people, nor even in some organic partial hemiplegias, provided the patient can express the learned response. It would also demonstrate the general rather than the specific nature of learning and adaptation (cf. Kellogg).

DISCUSSION

Of the several measurable components of the cr (*general*, e.g., respiratory, cardiac, PGR, and *specific*, e.g., salivation with food or voluntary motor to pain), the respiratory and motor have been used in these tests. The motor more than the others has the advantage of revealing special characteristics of the individual; it has the disadvantage of having manifold nervous connections and of being more subject to conscious inhibition—therefore "voluntary." An ideal study should include both autonomic and motor components; such an investigation is now underway at the Veterans Administration Hospital, Perry Point, Md. (Gantt, Reese, Doss, Harris.) The response in this test is on two levels—first, the spontaneous, primitive, doglike withdrawal response in the restricted hand on the electrodes, and the more complex, integrated response of the free hand on the bulb to avoid the shock by squeezing the bulb. The integrated cr, as we record it, is theoretically more complex than the simple spontaneous one; there are some differences—e.g., in anxious patients, in children, and in some psychotics, the spontaneous cr predominates—but the primitive and the integrated crs are roughly parallel. In most organic patients there is a loss of the ability to form the primitive as well as the integrated cr, with retention of old crs. Retention is a much more stable, less delicate function than is the ability to make new connections.*

Much of the work with patients is in the inductive stage, where we are studying well-defined organic and toxic conditions such as brain tumors, alcoholic and Korsakov psychoses, and contrasting them with the unequivocal psychogenic cases. In spite of the newness of the study and the general lack of laboratories, both theoretical and practical conclusions seem warranted. Although this test has been developed chiefly as an empirical method, it has both a theoretical basis and a relation to previous experimental work.

The function which is tested for is the ability to make adaptations to a new environment. This is a characteristic of every intact living organism, whether simple or complex, high or low. It may be effected through either some sort of conducting system (the nerves) or through chemical substances (endocrines, hormones); frequently, both methods of transmission are present. As we ascend in the evolutionary scale the learned adaptations become more dependent on the most specialized, highest development of the crs, viz., the cortex.

Conditional reflexes may be formed on the basis of simple inborn reflexes, i.e., tendencies to react in the presence of an adequate stimu-

---

* "Learning" would seem the simple word to denote "new connections," but as this word has been used in a broader sense not always equivalent to new cr formation, it is desirable to employ the phrase—in spite of its awkwardness—which best describes the results of the experiments on which my conclusions are based, viz., the "ability to form new crs," or "cr function."

lus—e.g., sex, food, pain. The organism not only combines with the signals for these inborn reflexes, but during its life it must adapt to the signals as they change in value—when the signal no longer signalizes the inborn event, a perfect adaptation requires a newly learned response (differentiation or inhibition). The organism is thus constantly forming combinations and decompositions with its environment.

The inborn reflex used chiefly in this examination is the reaction to the nervous stimulus (pain). Lacking this function (to react to the signals for nocuous stimuli) the individual will rapidly succumb unless he is continually protected.

In the mammals, and especially in the primates, it is known that this cr function—the individually acquired responses—is dependent upon an intact cortex for its existence; a damage to the cortex seriously impairs learning. Although in the rat and in the dog a large part of the cortex can be removed without completely abolishing the cr function, almost any damage to the cortex is reflected by some impairment of the cr function. Pavlov (20) has shown in the dog that although not only the area striata but the whole occipital lobe can be extirpated without eliminating crs to visual signals, nevertheless, the finer discriminations are lost; and I have demonstrated in dogs in whom there has been extirpated the cortex of one side and the gyrus cingulus of the other that both motor and cardiac crs to pain can be formed but that the time cr, as well as the ability for good differentiation, is impaired (15). (Experiments with Dr. Woolsey.)

Furthermore, numerous toxic and circulatory disturbances impair cr functions in dogs, e.g., vitamin deficiency (14), metrazol convulsions (23), certain forms of electroshock (5), alcohol (4, 12), anoxia—four hours exposure at 25,000 feet impaired crs for six months (13), six minute anoxia by pressure of the arteries (Gantt and Kabat unpublished data).

Partly on the basis of the work with dogs and partly on the tests with patients, there appears to be a hierarchy of the aspects of the adaptive cr function. These, when arranged in order from the least to the most serious, are:

(1) Disturbance in the latent period of the cr.
(2) Speed of formation of the cr.
(3) Ability to form differentiated crs, i.e., to positive and negative signals.

(4) Disturbance of the function of generalization.

(5) Ability to form spontaneous but not integrated crs.

(6) Failure to retain previously formed crs.

(7) Inability to form any experimental cr.

(8) Lack of retention of very old crs, including those to word signals and failure of the ability to carry out orders.

(9) Failure of some of the URs, e.g., the OR—seen only in idiots and in severe organic cases.

Retention of old crs is a very stable function and one that is not easily lost. There is a marked difference between the ability to execute an order based on old responses and the ability to make a new connection in the nervous system. Thus, a patient with a hopeless Korsakov's psychosis can readily carry out an order but he cannot form a new cr. There is a tremendous gap between the ability to "press the bulb with the red light but not with the white," and "press the bulb when you expect the shock"; the Korsakov patient can do the first task immediately, but he fails miserably on the second, i.e., to form a *new* nervous connection, even after hours of seeing the red light precede the shock every two minutes. This would mean that a Korsakov patient could never learn to cross the street on the green light and stop on the red, although he could perhaps retain the habit previously formed or cross with the proper light when told each time what to do.

Comparison of this method with our laboratory studies of crs in dogs reveals some important differences. First, language function is ordinarily involved with the patient—although it is possible to arrange the test without the use of language, as we do in children, certain aphasias, etc. In such cases, we look for evidence of learned adaptations in the autonomic responses—respiratory, circulatory, psychogalvanic. Secondly, in the human, we study both the spontaneous, primary, direct cr of the restricted hand as well as the integrated, secondary, indirect, substituted cr of the free hand, while in the animal we ordinarily observe only the equivalent of the primary cr, viz., the withdrawal of the foot.*

There are important differences between the primary, primitive,

---

* Some laboratory methods with animals, such as the opening of problem boxes, as well as animal training, do involve the equivalent of our indirect cr in the human, but the classical Pavlovian methodology employs only the spontaneous, direct cr.

direct cr and the secondary, indirect cr. The former is observed in young children before the integrated can be formed. The primitive cr—viz., the movement of the restricted hand on the electrode, either a sudden, brief jerking or a complete removal—though usually suppressed by intelligent adults and replaced by the secondary cr, may reappear in the normal subject if the US is very intense or in certain types of patients, e.g., in malingerers, hysterics, catatonics, states characterized by anxiety, or even in some hyperreactive normals.

But in spite of the apparent greater complexity of the indirect cr, when the organic patient cannot form this cr, it is found that he has also lost the ability to form the primitive cr; thus, the Korsakov patient finds it just as impossible to withdraw the hand to the cs as he does to perform the more complex movement of an integrated response in the other hand. The great difficulty seems to be in making the nervous connection at the basis of the cr—it is this function that is lost in organic brain disease, although there is usually more or less preservation of the function of retention except in injuries involving a few specific centers, e.g., some of the speech centers where the old crs to word signals are lost.

Although the organic patients usually show a marked difference from the psychogenic in the cr function—in the direction of absolute failure (organic) versus intensity of formation (psychogenic), Leo Alexander has pointed out (1) that the "organic" damage is not always irreversible. Thus, in the impairment of function after electroshock (5), after metrazol convulsions (23), after anoxia (13), and after vitamin deficiency (14), with the removal of the cause there is a gradual return of the cr function. This finds a parallel in the change of cr function postoperatively. Pavlov has shown in dogs (20) and I have shown in patients that even after removal of considerable portions of the cortex, the lost function gradually partly returns.

In the psychogenic psychoses, on the other hand, there is no absolute loss of the function of cr formation, although this function may be suppressed or altered. In some patients, e.g., catatonics and hysterics, due to inhibition the new cr may not be seen, but it can be brought out by using a stronger US. However, the old, deteriorated schizophrenic is difficult to evaluate and I have not determined whether they behave more like the psychogenic or the organic, i.e., they lack absolutely the ability to form new crs.

In brief, the marked organic and toxic psychosis shows an absolute loss of ability to form new crs, while the psychogenic patient with disturbances apparently as severe as the organic, may show an almost normal cr function in this test, or if he has deviations they are aberrations related to the concepts and emotions involved in his psychosis, or they are covered up by a more or less deep inhibition.

COMPARISON WITH OTHER TESTS

In the test for cr function it is possible to study separately the ability to form crs in the present and the preservation of old previously formed crs. Many psychological tests such as the Binet either depend chiefly on the function of retention or else they do not make a clear distinction between retention and new cr formation. Thus, in the Binet, although there are several items requiring present ability as distinct from retention, e.g., the lost ball in a field, the tasks do not usually allow a clear-cut distinction. Also, the question of motivation is not controlled in the usual test; the Rorschach and most I.Q. tests reflect the emotional interest and are therefore often difficult to evaluate in those patients who do not show a spontaneous interest. Emotional interest, though also a considerable factor in the cr test, can be adapted to the threshold of the individual by increasing the faradic shock to the point of obtaining a good unconditional reflex; the unconditional stimulus in this test is not of a standard fixed intensity but it is adapted to the particular person so that he gives an adequate response.

The change in cr function may be parallel with certain metabolic factors (blood cholesterol and M) while the I.Q. does not alter, as seen in the hypothyroid patient after thyroid therapy (fig. 14).

The disadvantage of the cr examination is that it requires more apparatus and a better trained person to administer the test and interpret the results than do some of the simpler psychological tests.

The EEG has the advantage of objectivity, and it is independent of language even more than is the cr test. It also possesses advantages for localization of tumors and in the diagnosis of epilepsy. On the other hand, the EEG depends more upon certain basic metabolic factors and less upon higher nervous activity than does the cr function.

The study of the cr function in the normal human subject, as well as in the patient, should be of even greater importance for psychiatry than is the examination of the tendon and skin reflexes for neurology. Although a well-equipped laboratory for investigation of the autonomic crs (HR, PGR, etc.) would be as costly as the EEG laboratory, simple motor crs can be studied with apparatus costing about $100, as I have described elsewhere (9), and the time involved is about that of an EEG examination or of a Binet.

Unfortunately, the investigation by the method of the cr has be-

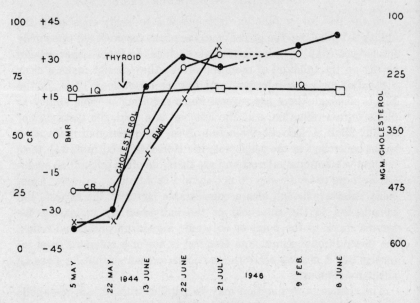

FIG. 14. Effect of thyroid on CR, BMR, cholesterol and I.Q.

come associated in the minds of some people with the restricted views of behaviorism and "reflexology." The conceptual errors of these schools, however, should not blind one to the positive value of the method and the data. One is not committed to any particular theory of electronic constitution of matter when he uses the telephone or even the radio. A lack of complete understanding of the mechanism of the cr should not inhibit our use of the known laws any more than a lack of insight into the nature of gravity should prevent a recognition of Newton's law of falling bodies.

A major deterrent in such a study as this is the lack of instruction in the medical curricula, both of the theoretical and practical aspects of the cr function. In spite of the usefulness in many branches of medicine and psychiatry of the cr methodology, the medical schools where such systematic instruction is given in either theory or methodology can be counted on the fingers of one hand. In turn, the lack of such instruction is partly dependent upon the recognition of the validity and value of the concepts.

SUMMARY

This article describes in detail the method of studying the motor conditional reflexes in normal subjects, in psychogenic and organic psychoses, in children, with both sensory and motor dyscrasias.

(1) The motor conditional reflex is characteristic of the type of individual (e.g., adolescent, artistic, scientific).

(2) Impairment of the conditional reflex function is revealed in latent period, speed of formation, failure to differentiate, failure of retention of previously formed conditional reflexes, absolute failure to form the conditional reflex, dimunition or absence of the unconditional reflex.

(3) Psychogenic and organic psychoses can be distinguished on the basis of the formation of the motor conditional reflex. The former patient may inhibit the expression of the elaborated conditional reflex but the inhibition can be revealed, while the organic psychotic has an absolute failure of the function to form new adaptive responses which function can hardly be improved by practice.

REFERENCES

1. ALEXANDER, LEO: Non-convulsive electric stimulation therapy. Amer. J. Psychiat., 4,. 241-250, 1950.
2. BORDLEY, J. E., HARDY, W. G., and RICHTER, C. P.: Audiometry with the use of galvanic skin resistance response. Bull. Johns Hopkins Hosp., 82, 569, 1948.
3. FINESINGER, J. E., SUTHERLAND, G. F., and McGUIRE, F. F.: The positive conditional salivary reflex in psychoneurotic patients. Amer. J. Psychiat., 99, 1942.
4. FINKELSTEIN, N., ALPERN, E. B. and GANTT, W. H.: Amphetamine (Benzedrine) Sulfate upon higher nervous activity compared with Alcohol. II. Human experiments. Bull. Johns Hopkins Hosp., 2, 61-74, 1945.
5. FLECK, STEPHEN and GANTT, W. H.: Conditional responses in patients receiving electric shock treatment. Amer. J. Psychiat., in press.

6. Gantt, W. H.: Medical Review of Soviet Russia. London, Brit. Med. Assoc., P. 100, 1928.

7. ——: Effect of alcohol on cortical and subcortical activity measured by the conditioned reflex. Bull. Johns Hopkins Hosp., *2*, 1935.

8. ——: Application of Conditioned Reflex Methods to Psychiatry. Contributions Dedicated to Dr. Adolf Meyer, Johns Hopkins Press, 78–80, 1937.

9. ——: A method of testing cortical function and sensitivity of the skin. Arch. Neur. and Psychiat., *40*, 1938.

10. ——: Impairment of the function of adaptability as measured by a simple conditioned reflex test in certain psychogenic contrasted with organic diseases. Sou. Med. J., *12*, 1938.

11. ——, and Fleischmann, Walter: Effect of thyroid therapy on the conditional reflex function in hypothyroidism. Amer. J. Psychiat., *11*, 1948.

12. ——, and Muncie, Wendell: Analysis of the mental defect in chronic Korsakov's psychosis by means of the conditioned reflex method. Bull. Johns Hopkins Hosp., *6*, 1942.

13. ——, Thorn G., and Dorrance, C.: Anoxia on conditional reflexes in dogs. Fed. Proc., *1*, 1949.

14. ——, and Wintrobe, M.: Effect of vitamin B. complex on higher nervous activity. Fed. Proc., *1*, 1945.

15. ——, and Woolsey: Cardiac reactions in partially decorticated dogs. Trans. Amer. Neur. Assoc., 1948.

16. Halstead, W. S.: Brain and Intelligence. Chicago, 1947.

17. Ivanov-Smolensky, A. G.: The Investigation of the Higher Forms of Neurodynamics of the Child. Moscow, 1944. (Russian.)

18. Lashley, K. S.: The human salivary reflex and its use in psychology. Psychol. Rev., *23*, 446–464, 1916.

19. Mateer, F.: Child behavior, a critical and experimental study of young children by the method of conditioned reflexes. Boston, Badger, Vol. 239, 1918.

20. Pavlov, I. P.: Lectures on Conditioned Reflex. (Tr. and Ed. Gantt.) New York, Internat. Publ., 1941.

21. Reese, W. G., Doss, Richard, and Gantt, W. H.: Autonomic Responses in the Differential Diagnosis of Organic and Psychogenic Psychoses. Psychosom. Med., in press.

22. ——, Gantt, W. H., and Strahan, Charles: Technique for study of autonomic (cardiac, respiratory, PGR) and motor adaptive responses (CRS) in the human. Amer. J. Physiol., *3*, 1950.

23. Rosen, Victor H. and Gantt, W. H.: Effect of metrazol convulsions on conditioned reflexes in dogs. Arch. Neur. and Psychiat. *50*, 1943.

24. Watson, John B.: The place of the conditioned reflex in psychology. Psychol. Rev., *23*, 1916.

25. Welch, Livingston: See Chapter 15 of this book.

11

SOME THEORETICAL AND PRACTICAL ASPECTS OF THE DIAGNOSIS OF EARLY AND LATENT SCHIZOPHRENIA BY MEANS OF PSYCHOLOGICAL TESTING

By MILTON S. GURVITZ, Ph.D.* AND JOSEPH S. A. MILLER, M.D.†

ONE OF THE most crucial, unsolved diagnostic problems in psychiatry is the detection of early and latent schizophrenia. It is the contention of this paper that psychological tests, for both theoretical and practical reasons, deserve an equal place with clinical means for this type of diagnosis, and in very early cases psychological tests often offer a unique method.

Clinically, the classical hallmarks of schizophrenia have been delusions, hallucinations and extreme withdrawal. Unfortunately, as has been universally recognized, these are restitutional symptoms (ways in which the individual compensates for the actual disease process) and not primary manifestations of the disorder.

The primary manifestations of schizophrenia which can be subsumed under the headings of primitivization and severe regression include:

1. Fantasies of world destruction.
2. Hypochondriasis and depersonalization.
3. Feelings of grandeur.
4. Archaic ways of thinking and speaking.
5. Hebephrenic regression and early catatonic manifestations.

Obviously, however, most of these are not common to a large majority of cases of early and latent schizophrenia. A common thread that does seem to run through the very large majority of cases is the primary disturbance of thinking, and a feeling of inner disintegration

---

* Chief Psychologist, Hillside Hospital; Assistant Clinical Professor of Psychology, Adelphi College; Consultant Psychologist, Connecticut Commission on Alcoholism.

† Medical Director, Hillside Hospital; Professor of Psychiatry, Adelphi College.

which is projected onto the world. When these are frank, there is little or no problem in making a diagnosis, but, only too often the patient hides his disordered thinking behind a facade of adjustment. The words are the same, but the meanings are different, the fantasies are common but the symbolization is archaic and personal. Another complication is the presence of neurotic defenses against a break with reality which act as lighting rods to divert attention from the more subtle, underlying symptoms. In individuals of good intelligence, an adjustment can frequently be made and frank symptoms forestalled by intellectualization and use of creative capacities for the simplest problems of adjustment.

The task, then, is to use more sensitive instruments than those of the clinical interview for the detection of the early manifestations of thinking disorders and inner sense of disorganization. Psychological tests appear to provide such instruments.

In the experience of the authors, a minimal battery of such tests should include the Rorschach, the Wechsler-Bellevue and drawings of the human figure with associations. Frequently, it is desirable and necessary to add other tests such as the TAT, the MAPS and others. Administration and interpretation constitute a full day's work for a clinical psychologist and often longer periods of time are necessary. This, however, is still an economical procedure since it can often obviate long analyses or psychotherapy before recognition of the underlying schizophrenia.

The question might naturally arise as to why psychological tests provide data in cases which are so ambiguous clinically. Indeed it is a not too uncommon experience to find doubtful cases revealing themselves so strongly on the tests that formal interpretation for diagnostic purposes is unnecessary and the clinician is readily convinced.

One such outstanding case was a young boy of seventeen who came to the hospital with the chief complaint of anxiety and other vague neurotic symptoms. He worked well in therapy, related to his therapist and showed no blunting of affect or inappropriate behavior. His therapist did become suspicious when he began to have incestuous dreams and fantasies, and so referred him for psychological testing. The following response to card VIII of the Rorschach is illustrative of his general protocol:

"There is a man in the center. He's a son of a bitch. He's my father. The animals on top are torturing him by pulling his hair out. As each hair is pulled out he loses a drop of blood and when they are finished he will bleed to death. The two animals on the side are waiting for him to die so they can eat him up; no, he is holding them apart so they can't get together, they want to suck each other off. And the two at the bottom are fucking like hell or jerking off, I don't know which."

With material such as this, the diagnosis becomes obvious. Another recent case was that of a man whose analyst, after three years, decided he was a well-intellectualized schizophrenic. He showed only a brief period of paranoid behavior in a stress situation at the hospital, aside from severe anxiety hysteria and compulsive behavior, and gave the following responses to card X of the Rorschach:

"These are a lot of dirty and filthy shapes and colors. Somehow they make me uncomfortable. It's as if someone were messing the place up. Blood and guts and vomit and things like that. As if someone had spilled his guts, just like I do with my doctor."

There are several cogent reasons, both theoretical and practical, for the ability of tests to reveal the presence of early schizophrenic regression:

1. The tests are designed to examine in many ways the defenses of the patient; and to mobilize anxiety through a variety of stress situations and, in effect, to measure, to some objective degree, magnified samples of behavior. Tests, in effect, present the patient with crucial, fairly isolated segments of life behavior, the reactions to which can be observed in relative isolation. A number of striking examples come readily to mind. The most outstanding is the impact of color upon the patient in the Rorschach cards. Color and affect have long been equated in Rorschach interpretation and this has been brilliantly explored in a paper by Schachtel. When the patient is suddenly confronted by the red in cards II and III, or the bright color in the last three cards, the resulting emotional response often releases enough of the controls to allow underlying mechanisms to appear.

On the Wechsler-Bellevue, a frequently revealing test is the Picture Arrangement where the subject is required to recreate a social situation represented in sequence by cards. It is often surprising how a schizophrenic will reveal himself, despite apparent social adjustment, either by an inability to make an acceptable sequence, or, in subtler ways, by his misinterpretation of the sequence which he has constructed and the *non-sequitur* he used to arrive at his intellectualized conclusions.

2. Tests present two generalized type of stimuli which place the patient in situations which it would be impossible or inadvisable to duplicate in an interview without great trauma to the patient:

(a) In the first of these alternatives, the patient is placed in an unstructured situation by tests such as the Rorschach in which the patient cannot depend on previous learning for behavioral clues but must respond in new and untried ways.

(b) Other tests, such as the Wechsler-Bellevue, on the contrary, place him in over-structured situations in which samples of behavior can be constantly matched against very objective right and wrong, and, furthermore, where the patient is aware of this evaluation of his performance.

Caught on the one hand between the Scylla of an unexplored, unstructured experience and the Charybdis of being forced to walk the tightrope of an overstructured experience, it is a rare patient who does not reveal himself in many significant ways. Practically, however, positive signs are always relatively more reliable than negative ones.

Furthermore, since these are after all tests, and not reality, even though hidden emotions and fantasies are stirred and defenses lowered, the patient is not disturbed to the same degree were these phenomena to appear clinically. There is still a vast difference between killing off a hated father figure on the Rorschach, as seen in the first example, and expressing the same feeling toward the actual figure in an interview. One can reveal in the Rorschach the crumbling of an inner world especially in small or inanimate movement responses, without being able to broach or be aware of feelings of world destruction in actuality.

3. Finally, interpretation of psychological tests is, or should be, in the hands of personnel whose main training and work has been in the field of diagnosis, who usually have had extensive experience with

the testing of normal as well as neurotic and psychotic patients and, most importantly, who do not have a transference relationship with the patient, nor do they have an administrative responsibility. In this connection, it is important that the psychologist work without knowledge of the clinical examination or the case history. Not only does this tend to build up confidence in the psychologist's independent diagnostic role but it makes of each case an experimental situation.

Some of the ways in which early and latent schizophrenia reveals itself on tests are surprisingly often quite open and frank, and it offers a real diagnostic problem less frequently than it does clinically, despite the absence of delusions and hallucinations. Other ways, however, are quite subtle and require not only a careful study of the formal features of the tests but a searching examination of the exact verbalization of the patient. In this connection, it cannot be too strongly emphasized that psychological tests and procedures are clinical and *not* laboratory methods; it is the psychologist who makes the diagnosis and not the tests. The various procedures which are dealt with below are analogous to the use of a stethescope in the examination of the heart and *not* analogous to the EKG. They are means for quantification and amplification of data, not unique methods of evaluation. Nevertheless, they are objective because they enable us to assess the patient's responses in ways which reduce to a minimum his conscious and unconscious defenses and previous modes of functioning. They are also objective in that they tend to reduce to a minimum counter-transference attitudes on the part of the diagnostician. In short, the use of psychological tests tends to minimize those emotional attitudes and understandings which are so important in normal intercourse between individuals, and which are also the greatest barriers to an early realization that the words and symbols of the schizophrenic have special and pre-logical meanings; that only the husks of words and ideas remain, and that their inner, true meanings have become peculiar and deviant.

The diagnosis of schizophrenia is not comparable to the diagnosis of the neuroses when using psychological procedures. In the neuroses, we look for the methods of defense, the way in which the individual adjusts to his problems, in short the personality structure. In schizophrenia, on the other hand, we look for the breakdown of these defenses. It is for this reason that Beck calls such Rorschach's "schizophrenic solutions," and Skalweit's careful, repeated examinations showed "personality disintegration."

How, then, do we see personality disintegration in our tests? The Wechsler-Bellevue intelligence scale helps because its subtests have been so treated statistically that the average person makes about the same weighted score on each subtest. One way in which a schizophrenic can reveal himself is by great drops in performance on some subtests, while functioning adequately in others. These are frequently, but not invariably, concentrated in the areas of judgment, concentration and conceptualization. Even more important than intertest scatter, is intratest scatter, the inability to do and solve easy problems and yet to successfully complete much harder ones. Not only is failure important but even more so is the reason for failure, or, for that matter, for success. Two recent patients with the diagnosis of early schizophrenia had opposite reactions to the repetition of digits. One could only repeat four numbers because he was convinced that to remember them you had to add them up; the other was able to repeat nine digits because his inner spirit wrote it down and repeated it to him. An analysis of the verbalization is probably the most critical tool. One extremely well-preserved schizophrenic gave, as his only revealing sign on the Wechsler-Bellevue, the definition of the word "gamble": "To gamble is life; some people think I've lost, but when all those people know what I know, then I'll win!"

Grossly, we can often see the deficiencies in intellectual functioning in a tremendous lowering of the actual performance level, well below the previous functioning capacity as revealed by school performance or the subtests resistive to deficit, such as vocabulary and information.

Of the tests in our battery, it is the Rorschach which consistently comes up with the most reliable diagnostic data.

The most important clue to early schizophrenia on the Rorschach is usually found in an analysis of the movement responses, particularly when these concern human movement and inanimate movement, since these are direct clues to the fantasy and ideational life of the subject. Peculiar and deviant human movement responses, or peculiar or poor form responses in animal movement, are direct evidence of autistic fantasy and schizophrenic thinking. Frequently this is buried behind casual and usual responses and only alluded to indirectly, or by a nuance of inflection or mannerism, but is revealed in full flower by indirect questioning in the inquiry. The poor form level of the responses points to the lack of ego control, but the quality reveals the dynamic significance. It is here that we get the first clues to the feeling of inner deterioration. This can be extremely subtle, as in an allusion that the two men in card III were casting "particularly dirty looks at one another" which was amplified by the patient, after prodding, to mean that each felt "that he was 'shot' and so he was taking it out on the other guy and the rest of the world." Or, it can be unmistakable, as a direct statement that an obscure smudge buried within card I was "a battle between two armies with the dead and dying strewn over the battlefield." Both responses are from patients with equally well-concealed symptoms.

An even more direct clue to the feeling of inner disintegration is found in the inanimate movement response, particularly when this is combined with human movement, or most particularly when the form element is poor or secondary. A flying missile or a hurtling plane would not be positive; but volcanoes erupting, rocks or houses breaking or falling, and human beings exploding or bursting are direct evidence of inner feelings of unrest being projected as world destruction. Sometimes this is done entirely abstractly as forces tending to pull apart, or projected onto human beings in the sadistic manner described in the first example. A classic response of this kind was given by a patient to card X, which was described first as simply a mess of animals trying to eat each other up. When this was explored on the inquiry, the patient added, "This is the dog eat dog life we live in. The people in the center are blowing, like I said, they are creating something. Maybe they are having intercourse, creating the new life which will take the place of the old when it dies." Here we have not only the full blown world destruction fantasy, but also the beginning of the delusional defense.

The form level of the responses, as we have said, is a clue to the quality of ego control. This is the ability of the subject to approximate the objective values in the ink blots. Here, again, we have to know why the form level is borderline. Is it due to a preoccupation with the small detail of the obsessive; is it due to the intense anxiety of the hysteric; or is it due to actual breaks in the thinking process? Naive inquiry into this by the examiner often reveals the basic thinking. It is precisely in this area that sophistication is fatal. An examiner can never take for granted that gaps in the patient's thought process will be filled in logically. Often what seems to be a logical or "brilliant," response turns out to be the product of confabulation, contamination or other forms of autistic logic, or, very simply, queer content. These are to be noted particularly when they occur in a record which is otherwise of high quality. Here again, as on the Wechsler-Bellevue, the sudden and unexpected variability is suspect.

Affective symptoms in the schizophrenic are indicated by rather characteristic responses to color. In some cases this is simply an increase of peculiar and deviant responses when bright color is encountered. When, however, blunting or inappropriateness of affect is a beginning symptom, the color responses become either arbitrary (green sheep, pink man) or assume pathological or deteriorated aspects. Thus, to the brown in card X one associated simply, "shit"; while to another the red and orange in card VIII becomes "an accessory organ like the appendix, only diseased and rotten." In a well-intellectualized schizophrenic who has never had more than momentary breaks with reality, the response was, "feces smeared all over the place."

Here again we must use qualitative differentiators. It is not so much the use of pure color or the dominance of color over form, but rather the use of color, as of movement, to convey the inner sense of destruction and deterioration.

Figure drawings do not as yet present the same possibilities for diagnosis since they have not been studied as thoroughly as the technics described above, but their primary value is to give a direct opportunity for the patient to display his body image. Here, again, we look for the signs of inner disintegration, and in a surprising number of cases the figure is bizarre enough in itself, or is so obviously a deteriorating individual in clothing, outline or facial features, that it affords additional evidence for the diagnosis.

In the beginning paranoid we frequently see an accentuation of the organs of reception either by shading, increase of size, or unusual elaboration. The projection of sexual organs onto other parts of the body is also often noted, for example, a nose shaped like a phallus.

The accompanying drawings represent typical figure drawings of early schizophrenics. The first was done by a young medical student who broke down in his second year. Particularly to be noticed are the

FIG. 1.

FIG. 2.

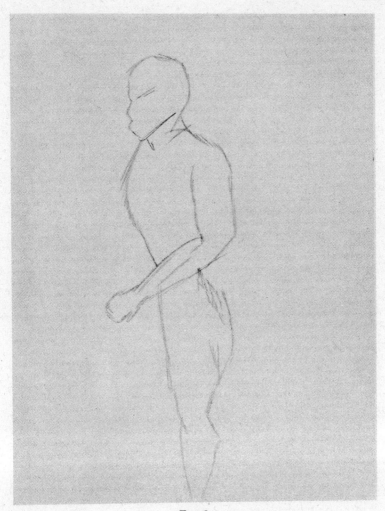

Fig. 3.

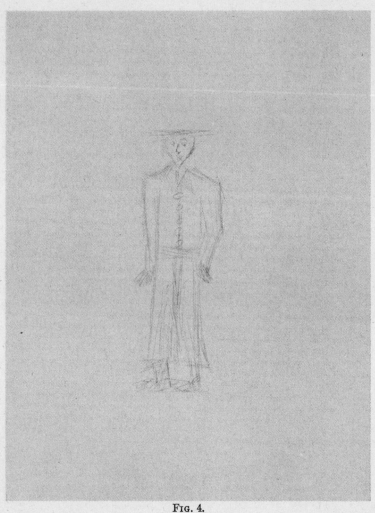

FIG. 4.

Fig. 5.

absence of arms, emphasis on breasts and navel, and the trumpet-shaped ear.

The second example was drawn by a sixteen-year old. The bizarre-ness is self-evident, particularly the size of the head in relation to the body, attachment of arms to the neck, infantile hands, and emphasis on eyes and mouth. Despite the mustache, his comment was, "Could be either male or female—male is as good as female."

This third example was drawn by a patient who had extensive training in art; nevertheless it reveals the patient's sense of emptiness and inability to make contact with the environment, as witness the absence of facial features and the closed or narrowed eyes.

The next (4) is the product of a twenty-three-year old chemist. Here we see in the waviness and irregularity of the lines, and the constant breaks in the body outline, the sense of inner deterioration.

The last (5) although the most obvious on the drawing, is the least obvious of the patients, clinically. It represents a real perversion of the body image, bisexuality in structure, and emphasis on oral re-gression in mouth and breasts. The short heavy strokes are a direct representation of his sadism.

There are other tests which may prove helpful, such as the TAT and the MAPS test, but it is seldom that they provide more than con-firmatory evidence although they may be important in etching the dynamics and determining the direction which the symptoms will take.

It is probably easiest to see the interplay of these factors in a single case. This case has been chosen because it emphasizes the dif-ference between the clinical and the test pictures.

The patient is a twenty-nine-year old graduate of the University of Pennsylvania. He obtained his degree Cum Laude. Aside from what seems to be a paranoid break in his freshmen year in college, from which he made a spontaneous recovery, he had no outward symptoms of schizophrenia. He is, however, a severe obsessive-compulsive who all of his life has been a champion of unpopular causes, has never held a job for any length of time, constantly seeks out the dirtiest and most undesirable of jobs, and in general has done nothing with his high potentialities. In his sexual life, he ends up by either present-ing his girl to another, or by taking the cast-off girl friends of his acquaintances.

This man has been seen by psychiatrists for some ten years and has also had three previous psychological tests. In each instance the clinical diagnosis was mixed psychoneurosis, the psychological diagnosis, early or incipient schizophrenia.

Let us now look at the test results. That this man still retains his

SUMMARY OF PSYCHOLOGICAL TEST RESULTS

RORSCHACH

Location	Determinants	plus	minus	total	
DW 1					F%—46
					FK+F+Fc—53%
W 8	M	4	14	18	
D 43	FM	7	9	16	F+%—59
d 10	m	3	1	4	
S 4	K	1		1	
de 8	FK	1	2	3	sum C—8½
di 7	F	27	19	46	M:sum C—19:8½
dr 9	Fc	2	2	4	8, 9, 10%—28
dd 10	c	2	1	3	W:M—9:18
	FC'	3		3	
R — 100	FC	1			sequence—irregular
	CF	5	3	8	shading shock

WECHSLER-BELLEVUE

Vocabulary	16	Full Scale I.Q.	134
		Verbal I.Q.	133
Information	15	Performance I.Q.	129
Comprehension	13		
Digit Span	13		
Arithmetic	16		
Similarities	14		
Pict. Arrangement	11		
Pict. Completion	13		
Block Design	16		
Object Assembly	14		
Digit Symbol	16		

high intellectual functioning is obvious, but even more interesting are the breaks in functioning on the W-B subtests. The first break is in comprehension. While there is nothing peculiar in the definitions themselves, we can still posit a deficit in judgment. The lowered digit span obviously reflects the impaired attention. The lowest of all the subtests, however, is picture arrangement, the ability to function in social situations.

FIG. 6.

While these deficits in judgment and social adaptation are suspicious of schizophrenia, it is important to get confirmation from the qualitative aspects of performance. On the information test, the capital of Italy is said by the patient to be Vienna, while the Vatican is defined as "the omnipresent reality of the spiritual forces of the prince of peace."

On picture arrangement, the low score is accounted for by the last sequence of cards where the actual fishing sequence is correct, but where the diver is seen as Neptune upbraiding the man for fishing out of season, and the little King is shouting defiance.

Turning now to the Rorschach, it would be immediately apparent to psychologists that the large number of minus M's and FM's, and the presence of four small m's, together with a borderline reality testing as revealed by the low F+ per cent and a large number of CF− responses, add up to a diagnosis of schizophrenia. What do these terms mean clinically? As we have said, the movement responses are indices to the fantasy and ideational life of the individual. Let us examine some of these movement responses and see why M− and m in profusion means schizophrenia.

On card IV, for example, responding to inquiry about a slight protuberance, the patient said, "On what is the rump of the dog, there is a man looking belligerently at a woman. She's cringing. Someone in a Mexican hat is sneaking up behind the woman." Here we can see the autistic fantasy and the paranoid undertones. Then he continues, after another response, with "Further down on the dog's rump there is a lever. I have a feeling that if you would pull the lever it all would explode into action and start moving." Here again we have the feeling of manipulation by outside forces.

A direct representation of inner disintegration is seen in the response to card IV, "This is a speeding asteroid about to explode into a million pieces."

With these responses in mind, it is not difficult to see the peculiar fantasy life and perverted ideation.

The borderline level of reality testing is evidenced by the fact that only 59 per cent of the form responses are on an acceptable form level, that is, bear a reasonable relationship to the blot as it is usually seen by healthy individuals.

Pathological affect is seen in the predominance of responses in which color is dominant over form; or clinically, affect over ego. What makes this schizophrenic are responses with deteriorated content, such as to the brown areas of card X, "The brown parts are ... are smudges of feces made on the wall by a child."

Having established the diagnosis, we can go to the other Rorschach factors to find the defenses and note from the predominance of small and unusual detail, and the fact that M responses are more numerous than color, that the subject is libidinizing thought and using intellectualization and obsessive-compulsive mechanisms to maintain reality contact. This then is a man who is using his very superior intellectual abilities to maintain himself on a precarious level.

The figure drawing (6) shows the emphasis on oral sadism and illustrates beautifully the mechanistic concept of himself which we were able to infer from the Rorschach.

Although we have made a diagnosis, there is much left unsaid about both the dynamics and the personality structure. This is the problem of a full psychological report of which the diagnosis is only a part.

From a practical point of view, the next question is, of course, prognosis, of which we know a good deal less than diagnosis. There are actually two aspects. One is the short-term prognosis in which we can at times make a fair estimate; the other is the long-term prognosis, dependent, in part, we may be sure, on environmental factors impossible to take into account when making the prognosis. This is a problem which cannot be settled by even the most rigorous, intensive investigations. This is a five- to ten-year project involving interdisciplinary cooperation which would richly reward some research group.

Since psychological testing is usually the province of the clinical psychologist, a number of practical problems arise in the relationship of psychologist to therapist or psychiatrist, especially in an institutional setting. Probably the biggest problem is time. It is a rare psychologist who has time enough to spend a minimum of a day with a patient. More mistakes in psychological testing are made because the psychologist has too little time to give a full battery of tests, and still less time to interpret and report them, than for any other reason except, of course, poor training. To make matters worse, it is the inexperienced psychologist who is more often than not overwhelmed with a case load to which few senior psychologists would submit. One extremely unfortunate result of this lack of time is that the psychologists cannot sit down with their psychiatric colleagues and painstakingly go over the test results to show exactly how they made their diagnoses and how they arrived at their evaluations of personality and character.

CONCLUSION

At the present state of psychological knowledge, psychological tests can certainly offer invaluable aid to the diagnosis of early and latent schizophrenia, although prognosis is not as reliable. The procedure is based on a qualitative examination of the responses to reveal evidence of disturbances of thinking and inner deterioration of the personality structure. Psychological tests are able to do this because psychologists can then examine samples of human behavior in both unstructured and over-structured situations and compare them with the functioning of normal and other pathological groups.

On a practical level, this means that the psychologist must gain the confidence of the psychiatrist and interpret to him the need for a battery of tests, and the means by which his conclusions are made. On the part of institutions and physicians, it means a recognition that it is the psychologist who makes the tests valuable, and that time to think over a case is time as well spent as actually testing or writing the report.

Part Four: Discussson I

By LEWIS R. WOLBERG, M.D.*

D R. KELLY's interesting paper highlights a number of studies made in recent years on methods of predicting, through the use of psychological tests, the quality of success in the training of professionals. The use of test materials for purposes of predicting the outcome of training has been motivated by the fact that trial and error methods of choosing candidates is fraught with a great deal of hazard, often eventuating in disaster for both the candidate and the clients he treats. Were it possible to perfect a means of predicting in advance the outcome of training, many existing difficulties would be resolved. Unfortunately, little material is available which we may use as predictive criteria of professional competency.

In the past a chief method of selection consisted of studying the applicant's credentials, as well as of assaying through interview the applicant's suitability for the studies he wished to pursue and the professional role he was expected to play. Great variability was to be expected in the results of such predictions. These were dependent largely on the evaluative skills of the person studying the student's credentials, and on the intuitiveness and clinical judgment of the interviewer. Indeed, the variability proved itself to be so great as to inspire the search for more objective measurements.

In the study reported by Dr. Kelly, the research methods employed were most extensive. One would hope that in the vast array of materials some instruments would be found which might give us a clue as to the future performance of the candidate. Surprisingly, as Dr. Kelly reports, the validities of the predictive measures were extremely low. More astonishingly, the old methods of prediction, namely the study of the candidate's credentials, and a determination of the strength of his incentives, yielded higher validities than the elaborate tests to which he had been exposed. As a matter of fact, the study would seem to indicate that not even a personal interview is required, and that a vocational interest test given at the cost of approximately fifty cents is better than a battery of tests and interviews which costs over three hundred dollars per person.

* New York Medical College.

How do we explain such findings? It seems to me that the answer is largely that traditional tests and interviews cannot predict what the individual's specific reactions will be in the learning situation. All learning involves a substitution of new patterns for old. This is bound to evoke some anxiety. The sources of anxiety are associated with the fear of change as well as with the desire to cling to familiar patterns. Resistances to learning develop in response to anxiety, the specific kind and degree varying with the individual. It is manifestly impossible to predict in advance, by any known test or interview, the intensity of anxiety that will be evoked in the process of training; nor is it possible to anticipate the specific character of resistance and manner of its resolution.

One fact is well recognized in all learning—that adequate motivation is the greatest help in resolving anxiety and resistance. If we are able, from interview or vocational interest tests, to detect strong motivation, we may speculate on greater possibilities of success. Similarly a review of the candidate's credential file which indicates satisfactory learning and performance experiences may be significant. In short, if we have an idea that the candidate has, in past learning situations, been able to endure the vicissitudes involved in learning, and if we insure ourselves that he has sufficient incentive to handle the anxieties associated with his present learning situation, it is possible—provided the individual has the accepted qualifications and intelligence—to predict that he will be successful in his new learning experience.

Considerable narcissistic damage will accrue to those who believe their test materials to be so infallible as to anticipate almost any contingency. One of the great evils that befalls any science is to credit it with omnipotent virtues it does not possess. It is tragic to observe how psychological tests, particularly projective tests, are being tortured in an effort to fit them into a scheme of things for which they never were originally intended. When such tests are employed to predict the eventual success of a clinical psychologist or psychiatrist, errors are bound to occur. Indeed, we find this now so often to be the case as to be tempted to discard all psychological test materials.

In my opinion, this would be sheer folly, since the test materials do yield important data. I have a feeling that in the not too distant future a series of tests will be elaborated that will overcome many of the shortcomings of the present materials, and will yield validities in predictive measures infinitely higher than those Dr. Kelly reports. The fact that current psychological tests are of no great help in anticipating the performance of professionals does not invalidate the tentative use of tests for purposes of appraising future skills, provided that we retain a good measure of scientific skepticism. For no test or group of tests can cover completely the prediction of the varied functions involved in psychological or psychotherapeutic work.

As an aid in diagnosis, psychological tests can render an invaluable service to the clinician. I have developed a profound respect for psychological diagnostic testing done by a competent and experienced clinical psychologist. It has been my impression that projective tests, particularly the Rorschach, and certain aspects of the more structured tests like the Wechsler-Bellevue, can reveal potential schizophrenia better than a clinical examination made by the great majority of psychiatrists. This is the thesis of the paper presented by Gurvitz and Miller. I should, however, like to inject one word of caution. In my opinion, a psychological diagnosis of schizophrenia is an extremely dangerous entity. There are many individuals who have a disintegrative potential, yet who maintain themselves adequately in a life situation which they control through various characterologic and neurotic defenses. Psychological tests may reveal tendencies toward schizophrenia, but this does not at all indicate that the individual will inevitably develop schizophrenia. We would be forewarned of this possibility, of course, and this warning would be extremely valuable in arranging a vocational or a therapeutic plan; but it should not prejudice us toward thinking that under any circumstance the end result will be a schizophrenic disorganization.

I should now like to comment on the paper by Meadow and Funkenstein. The significance of their findings, to the effect that an impairment in abstract thinking in schizophrenia is positively correlated with a specific type of autonomic reaction, is difficult to evaluate. It does accent the hypothesis that man is not composed of isolated functions, but rather is an integrate of many. Whether the reported intellectual and somatic defects in schizophrenia imply an involvement of a specific area in the cortex is a matter that can merely be postulated at our present state of knowledge. Of extreme interest is the data reported in the paper to the effect that three types of schizophrenia seem to exist: the first, which has a poor prognosis, is associated with a disturbance in abstract thinking, "release" of the autonomic nervous system from higher control, and inappropriate effect; the second, with an excellent prognosis, is associated with a relatively intact capacity for abstract thinking, a different kind of autonomic responsiveness, and evidences of anxiety and depression; the third, with a fair prognosis, is associated with no disturbance of the autonomic nervous system, little loss in the ability to abstract, little evidence of anxiety, and with a paranoidal type of symptomatology. I presume that lack of time made it impossible for the authors to describe their criteria of prognosis of which I should have liked to have heard more. There is so often the tendency to look upon recovery or remission in schizophrenia as an automatic phenomenon associated with vague internal reactions in the individual. It seems to me that we have also to take into account the specific kind of environment in which the patient is living, the pressures to which he is being subjected, the type of therapy to which he is being exposed, and, most important, the kind of therapist to whom he is relating.

My final brief comment is on Horsley Gantt's paper. In recent years our profound interest in the psychogenic aspects of psychiatric problems has tended to divert us from research of a non-psychogenic nature, including biochemical and neurological. The work of Gantt is a healthy counterbalance to this emphasis. His present paper provides us with a wealth of material that may help out in the study of diagnosis as well as in the understanding of certain psychopathologic constellations.

Part Four: Discussion II

By PAUL H. HOCH, M.D.*

D R. MEADOW AND DR. FUNKENSTEIN have tried to solve the important problem of prognostication in cases of schizophrenia. They believe the impairment of abstract thinking linked with an impairment of the autonomic regulation indicates poor prognosis. Until now not one of these attempts at prognostication has been conspicuously successful, and I hope that in the long run this prognostic test will be more effective than many of the others which have been tried on a physiological or psychological level. The great difficulty with these tests is in determining how reliable the actual responses are. For instance, the tests of abstract thinking showed very little alteration in patients who underwent frontal lobotomy whereas the clinical impression was that some impairment, even though temporary, was present in these patients. The questions then arise—are tests concerning abstract thinking reliable enough? Do they merely show up those patients in whom a rather marked schizophrenic disorganization is present, while others slip through as normal? If only markedly disorganized patients show an impairment of abstract thinking, this does not add much to our prognostic knowledge because it is obvious that those patients who show such an impairment are less apt to recover than others.

Tests concerning the autonomic functions in schizophrenic individuals were studied by many investigators and again the difficulty was that only some schizophrenic patients showed such impairments and others did not. In addition, it was found that the same patient did not always respond in the same way to autonomic drugs which made the evaluation of such experiments quite complicated. We feel that a certain doubt is expressed in the observations of the authors in the second group of their cases. Seemingly these do not show such clear-cut responses as the first and third groups. We believe that only an extended follow-up study obtained on a varied schizophrenic case material will be able to substantiate the validity of such tests. The greatest difficulty at present is the inability to differentiate

* Columbia University.

clinically or with different tests between schizophrenic patients who are regressed and regardless of the seriousness of the clinical picture often show a good remission, and those patients who are deteriorated and show little capacity for recovery.

It is important that such a study be undertaken regardless of the outcome of the author's observations. After many trials and errors a method will emerge which will give us a better appraisal of the schizophrenic patient and will give us more reliable prognostic hints than we have today.

Dr. Kelly's very interesting paper statistically confirms observations which many of us have made who have dealt with the selection of candidates for training. We have always felt that the present criteria of selection are very unreliable and depend upon many factors which are not yet fully scientifically appraised. There are those working in this field who are convinced of their great clinical ability and skill to pick candidates. Others who work with tests are equally convinced that a few tests, and especially the projective technics, are precision instruments appraising the personalities of the candidates and foreseeing for decades what these candidates will and will not do. I am always impressed how often mistakes are made with the clinical or test evaluations, and how very often opinions on candidates are reversed after a few months based on their actual performance in training. I believe that, even though not foolproof, a probationary period of work in a certain setting would disclose much more about the person's ability and interpersonal behavior patterns than all the tests and interviews combined.

Dr. Kelly made the interesting observation that if the candidate were judged on incomplete data, the appraisal of him was more correct than when all data were available to formulate a judgment. All the data, of course, does not mean only the credential file of the person, but all the impressions gained and the testing results. The latter two are much less reliable than the first. Even in clinical diagnosis it is not uncommon that if too many data are available on a patient, it somehow obscures some of the basic issues present.

Dr. Gantt's conditioned reflex investigations on psychiatric patients showed a certain regularity in response which in the future will probably have a diagnostic significance. Of course, a large number of patients must be tested to determine whether individual variations in these test responses are sufficiently small and that all the alterations seen in such test responses can be imputed to the pathology which is present. It would be interesting to know how far affective changes in the patient could influence the outcome of such conditioned reflex experiments, and how far the recovery of the patient would reflect in these experiments. I believe that such conditioned reflex studies would be of special value in the study of psychosomatic patients because in many of them there is a conditioning of the vegetative innervation.

Dr. Gurvitz and Dr. Miller are discussing a very timely topic in their paper, namely, the diagnosis of "latent and early" schizophrenia. They maintain that the psychological tests are more sensitive instruments than the clinical interviews and in doubtful cases the schizophrenic structure of these patients reveals itself strongly in these tests but not clinically. It is undoubtedly true that many clinicians do not diagnose schizophrenia as often as the clinical structure of the patient would indicate. Most likely the diagnostic criteria for schizophrenia will have to be investigated further and made more clear. In our work on the pseudoneurotic form of schizophrenia we have attempted to outline some of the diagnostic features and we hope that in future studies the diagnostic criteria of this group of schizophrenics will be even further advanced. Our considerable experience with this type of patient does not confirm the statement of many psychologists that psychological tests, and especially the Rorschach test, are superior to the clinical appraisal of the patient. We saw quite a number of schizophrenic patients belonging in the above-mentioned group where the psychological tests failed to reveal schizophrenic manifestations but the patient had to be adjudged clinically as such. The follow-up study confirmed the correctness of the clinical opinion. We also saw the reverse. In some instances the psychological tests indicated schizophrenia, but clinically the examining psychiatrists did not find schizophrenic manifestations. This is very often the case if the psychiatrist is not acquainted with this particular type of patient or is unwilling to accept the existence of schizophrenia in the absence of gross symptoms such as delusions, hallucinations, regression phenomena, etc.

Another difficulty is that some psychologists increasingly make the diagnosis of every patient they see as schizophrenia. They do this even where there is really no clinical evidence of such a disorder. In doubtful cases the clinical and the test approach should be used, but we feel, as many others, that the clinical evaluation of the patient is still of paramount importance and if it is done by experienced clinicians it is superior to any test which is used today in diagnosing schizophrenia. We will have to object to statements made that these tests which are used today to diagnose schizophrenia are precision instruments and are objective, whereas the clinical examination of the patient is subjective, thus implying that the first is more scientific than the latter. We will have to call attention to the fact that the tests use clinical categories and all the fallacies of the clinic are also automatically incorporated into the test evaluations. The tests follow the clinic like a shadow and the evaluation of these tests is very often as subjective as the clinical evaluation of the patient. The tests used today are not independent evaluating methods, but are strongly bound with the nosological uncertainties of the clinic.

We are not opposed to the use of psychological tests because they do illuminate some of the mental functioning of patients, but we do not believe the claims made are justified and that these tests are superior instruments giving us the diagnosis, prognosis, and therapeutic possibilities in a given case of schizophrenia. We believe that joint investigations of a large number of patients supplemented with careful follow-up studies would reveal clearly in what aspect of the schizophrenic disorders tests are of value to support the clinical evaluation.

In order not to be misunderstood, we would again like to emphasize that we think the tests as research tools are of great importance and they can help in evaluating dubious cases. However, we object to their use when it is implied that they have the certainties and diagnostic security of an X-ray or a Wasserman. The investigation of those patients would be of special value where no concordance, but a discordance is present between the clinical opinion and psychological test results. To our knowledge such discordant material has not yet been carefully scrutinized and scientifically evaluated.

Dr. Gurvitz and Dr. Miller's paper showed clearly some of the fundamental mental disturbances these patients suffer from and we are in agreement with many of their clinical formulations. There is a question in my mind, however, if these patients can be called "early or latent" schizophrenics. Many of these patients have shown this symptomatology for many years and therefore the designation of "early" schizophrenia is often incorrect. We rather believe this to be a special subform of schizophrenia, but in some instances we see the symptomatology of these patients being quickly followed by the appearance of massive psychotic signs. Usually such a development is very slow and in some patients these gross psychotic manifestations never occur.

"Latent" is not a very good term because these individuals, in our opinion, are schizophrenics even though they do not show gross psychotic manifestations; rather, their manifestations are similar to those seen in simple schizophrenia where we are able to recognize them as schizophrenics even though delusions and hallucinations are absent. Latent would indicate that the schizophrenia is not visible, whereas actually with the use of finer clinical examination and with test methods we have tried to show they are. This would be a contradiction if we demonstrate schizophrenia in a patient and then call it latent. To call cases borderline is also open to criticism. It was for this reason that we thought to call them pseudoneurotic because these patients usually have symptoms which appear to be neurotic, but where a schizophrenic structure can be detected. There are those that will object to this designation, and probably an entirely new clinical term will have to be introduced for these patients whom we believe are a special group of schizophrenics similar to the hebephrenic, catatonic, and other types.

Part Five

INFLUENCE OF THE PSYCHE ON PSYCHO-LOGICAL TEST PERFORMANCE

12

RORSCHACH STUDIES IN COMBAT FLYING PERSONNEL*

By LEO ALEXANDER, M.D.† AND ALBERT F. AX, PH.D.‡

I. INTRODUCTION

THE ROLE AND IMPORTANCE of the Rorschach test in psychiatric diagnosis has recently been challenged on a number of pragmatic grounds, not all of them validly applying to its basic principles and purpose. To us it seems that the value of the Rorschach test is mainly two-fold: (1) To highlight important features in the functioning and structure of the personality by exposing the individual to a standardized test situation; (2) To supply quantitative and thereby comparable data for large-scale surveys of specific groups. To be sure, such findings must always be viewed in the context of the total clinical picture; in this respect the Rorschach findings are no different from those obtained by any other clinical test.

An understanding of the dynamics of the situation in which the subject finds himself is, of course, a prerequisite. Early in the war we were impressed with the number of violent, gory, and explosive responses—responses which in a peacetime setting are seen in hardly any but psychotics but which were rather common in the Rorschachs of anxious patients who had been through combat and even in some of those who showed no overt anxiety. We also found in testing normal-performing combat personnel that a restriction and impoverishment of normal fantasy life, which again in the civilian setting might have sinister diagnostic connotations, became rather characteristic of any group of men who had been in combat for a significant

* From the Neurobiologic Unit and Research Clinic, Division of Psychiatric Research, Boston State Hospital.

† Director, Neurobiologic Unit and Research Clinic, Division of Psychiatric Research, Boston State Hospital. Instructor in Psychiatry, Tufts College Medical School, Boston, Mass.

‡ Instructor in Psychology, University of Washington School of Medicine, Seattle, Washington.

length of time without, however, showing any lowering of their efficiency from either the administrative or medical point of view.

In considering these findings it would have been incorrect to conclude that all these people were sick and should be hospitalized, for they were not necessarily sick in the setting in which they were functioning; sending them to a hospital would have deprived the Army of valuable and competent warriors. The conclusion to be drawn from these findings concerned rather the dynamics of the combat situation, what combat meant and did to these men. We ascertained this fact fairly early in the war while studying normal-performing combat personnel who had flown 18 or more missions without becoming medical or administrative problems. As we soon found out, in healthy personalities changes were only temporary; the normal richness and fullness of the personality began to re-assert itself almost immediately once the stress was relieved and the combat tour completed.

It is therefore of greatest importance to interpret the Rorschach as part of the clinical and environmental picture as a whole—that does not mean that the findings should be disregarded if there is contradiction but that they should be interpreted with understanding and caution. While it would have been wrong to relieve men of combat duty because their Rorschach showed constriction, it was very important to be aware of this personality constriction in evaluating their needs and their reactions to social situations, military and otherwise. This knowledge was used in giving expert testimony to military courts and in interpreting to Red Cross personnel the, to them, astonishing and alarming "abnormal" reactions of combat personnel to certain types of recreation which were considered wholesome, and to calm the alarm about the lowering of personal tastes and the recrudescence of animalistic and primitive urges. On the basis of our personality studies and Rorschach findings they were reassured that a reexpansion of these restricted personalities might be hoped for and that the dreaded permanent change—a fear at that time prevalent at the home front as well—would not materialize, except possibly in the few really sick persons. There is no doubt that our Rorschach studies gave weight and quantitative validity to our clinical observations.

Against the background of the usefulness and validity of the

Rorschach test we should like to present the findings of our wartime study.

II. Case Material and Method

This study is based on correlated personality studies and Rorschach tests carried out in a group of 276 patients suffering from neurotic or psychopathic reactions during air-combat duty and in a group of 106 normal control subjects on active air-combat duty, chosen at random from combat aviators who had flown 18 or more missions without becoming medical or administrative problems. Fourteen men (12 patients and 2 normal-performing men) were retested after changes in the stress situation, including completion of the tour of combat.*

The tests were administered in the usual manner except for the fact that no inquiry was held in order to avoid giving clues to the patients and other groups tested as to what responses we may have been particularly interested in. Instead, we encouraged our patients to point to the location of what they saw as they went along in order to facilitate recording.

III. Description of the Clinical Groups from Which the Operational-Fatigue Group was Selected for Comparison with the Normal-Performing Group

Before discussing statistical findings, we should like to characterize the clinical groups from which the operational-fatigue category was selected for the purpose of this study. In the urgency of the wartime setting, the most important decision upon seeing a patient was to determine how sick he was. Diagnosis led to treatment and disposition. Patients regarded as sick were treated; those regarded as essentially

---

* One of us (L. A.), aided by his war-time assistants, Captain Nicolas Camara-Peon, Lieutenant David Vinson and Sergeant Taul B. White, carried out the clinical studies in the field and administered the Rorschach tests; he also subjected the tests to preliminary evaluation according to a simplified scoring method. The other (A. F. A.) re-scored the tests according to the standard methods and subjected them to statistical evaluation by means of criteria specially adapted to this material in addition to the standard ones. This evaluation constitutes the subject matter of a thesis entitled "The Effect of Combat Fatigue on Imaginal Processes," in Widener Library, Harvard University.

unadaptable were reassigned. On the basis of type of treatment or immediate disposition, they fell into the following groups:

1. *Psychotherapy:* The mildest forms of psychologic disturbances were treated solely by psychotherapy. If it were possible to give a patient sufficient understanding or encouragement to enable him to return to duty with a reasonable expectation that he would continue to perform efficiently, he fell in this category. Needless to say, psychotherapy in a combat setting sometimes consisted merely of saying the right word or showing the right attitude that would make it possible for the patient to go on.

2. *Deep Narcotherapy of Three Days' Duration Followed by Insulin Subshock Treatment:* Severe states of stress-conditioned neurosis were included in this group. It was found that states of excitation responded most favorably, irrespective of other diagnostic categories (anxiety, depression, hysteria, and so on).

3. *Abreaction:* States of recent stress-conditioned neurosis in which profound inhibition was the prevailing phenomenon were subjected to abreactive treatment procedures, which were repeated as often as appeared necessary.

4. *Insulin Subshock Treatment:* Patients essentially in the phase of secondary symptom formation—i.e., where complaints were projected to their organ systems (stomach, heart, head) or to certain functions like sleep or coordination, without profound emotional participation—were given this treatment, usually over a two-week period.

All these physical methods of treatment (2, 3, 4) were of course accompanied as well as followed by psychotherapy.

5. *Transfer to Ground or Administrative Duties:* This group consisted of men essentially not severely sick but psychobiologically unable to cope with the stresses involved in their combat assignments. This group was reclassified on the spot and sent back to the air base as soon as possible. (Patients who were reclassified to ground duty after psychiatric treatment are not included in this group.)

6. *Zone of the Interior:* Men regarded as entirely inadaptable and nonrehabilitable for overseas service were returned to the Zone of the Interior. (Patients returned to the Zone of the Interior after psychiatric treatment are not included in this group.)

7. *Psychosis:* Most psychotic patients were referred to a central

hospital for treatment before return to the Zone of the Interior. However, a few cases of severe reactive depression who were in states of excited agitation were treated in our hospital unit since it was found that they responded to three-day deep narcotherapy.

8. *Organic Disorders:* This group consists of men referred for neuropsychiatric consultation whose disorders turned out to be primarily organic.

9. *Refusal of Duty:* A few cases are included in this study in which refusal of duty was the only overt manifestation of neurotic or psychopathic reaction. All these cases were sent back to duty after some psychotherapeutic orientation and with the aid of some manipulation of the environment which made it possible for them to resume functioning. Cases of self-mutilation were handled in a similar manner.

While these groupings have reasonable bases for clinical categories, there was little reason to believe that such cleavage lines would impress themselves upon the Rorschach performance. A grouping that did seem plausible as possibly evidencing the greatest contrast to the normal-performing group consisted of those receiving substantial hospital treatment, such as insulin subshock treatment, abreaction, and deep narcotherapy. These men were all sick from the medical point of view, in need of immediate treatment. Thus the three drug treatment groups (2, 3, 4) were designated the *Treatment Group* and used as the *Operational-Fatigue Group* (F, 83 cases) for statistical comparison with the *Normal-Performing Group* (N, 84 cases).

IV. CHANGES OF THE RORSCHACH RESPONSE UNDER CHANGING STRESS

It soon became apparent that the Rorschach picture reflected the existing amount of stress, both internal and external, and changed as the degree of stress varied. This was demonstrated in fliers who were tested at various phases of their combat tour and after completion of their missions.

Combat stress influences personality organization in two profound ways: The first is an internal reorganization permitting adequate performance as exemplified by the normal-performing group; the second is a more drastic change constituting a disorganization leading to inadequate performance and to symptoms. The first type of adjustment can be seen from a comparison of Air Cadet precombat Rorschach norms with those of our normal-performing combat group. According to the Rorschach findings, the influence of combat on the cases who did not break down seems to be (a) a reduction of fantasy without loss of productivity or creativity; (b) a general decrease in responsiveness to subtle nuances of feeling but with maintenance of emotional rapport; and (c) a shift in orientation from the global to the specific. This distortion of the Rorschach profile may represent the strain on the personality produced by the stress of combat and may be described as a healthy adaptation to severe environmental stress.

When the strain on personality exceeds the adaptive limits, as revealed by operational-fatigue symptoms, further distortions in Rorschach profiles appear. Those distortions represent a lowered productivity, a further decrease in fantasy life including now a decrease in creative imagination, a preoccupation with personal safety, a reduced rapport with people, further constriction of interests and spontaneity, and finally, reduced power of organization.

The changes in Rorschach responses brought about either by removal from stress as in completion of a combat tour or by subjection to new and greater stress were striking and illustrate the degree of responsiveness and rich variability of the Rorschach pattern in the same individual under different conditions of stress.

The following case is an illustration of improving personality organization being reflected in the Rorschach.

Case 1. (Subject 117) A twenty-one-year old navigator of a B-17 developed acute anxiety-tension symptoms with some depression after he was discharged from the hospital where he had been treated for flak wounds received on his seventh combat mission. While in the hospital he had felt fine emotionally, but as soon as he was discharged he found himself unusually apprehensive about bombing while on leave in London, sudden noises startled him, his sleep was poor, and he felt ill at ease with other flying men.

This patient had enlisted in the Air Cadets after finishing high school. After he washed out of pilot training, he did well at navigation school. Of his seven missions, he rated only the last as rough. Returning home from this mission the crew had to fly through overcast and became uncertain of their position; then whether due to his miscalculation or because of the enemy radio—the patient did not know which—he signaled the pilot to descend, thinking that they were over England; instead they were over "the heaviest concentration of flak in the world" at the Pas de Calais. The plane was immediately riddled and severely damaged; that they escaped at all was a minor miracle. Patient received flak wounds in the face, hand and knee, and was hospitalized for three weeks.

This seventh mission had entailed sudden severe stress and great danger to the patient and the rest of his crew—possibly because of a mistake of the patient's. This man thus had to deal with two things: first, a strong conditioning against flying and second, guilt feelings arising from the blame he put on himself (an accusation of himself which he also projected to other flying personnel, their supposed unspoken criticism making him feel uncomfortable in their presence). While in the hospital he was removed from the immediate threat of combat flying and in the logic of the unconscious was atoning for his guilt by his suffering. Once recovered from his wounds and discharged, however, he was confronted face on with both conflicts. Anxiety arising from these conflicts was welded to that arising from objective sources, i.e., imminent return to combat with its now very real threats. He developed acute anxiety-tension symptoms and the concomitant reactive hostility and aggression apparently joined with punishing superego urges to turn inward in the form of depression.

The first Rorschach test, administered at this time, showed marked constriction and depression. It was depleted of movement and completely devoid of color, except for one ineffectual attempt to deal with emotion ("I see the red but can't fit it in").

The protocol* follows:

Figure I

1. W F Y Art   Like the product of some surrealist.
   W fG+y Art— 1.0 D
2. W F+ A P   A bat.
   W FG+ A—P 1.0 1
3. D F+ Ad   Mandibles of a beetle.
   D FG+ Ad— 2
4. d F— Ad   Protruding eyes of a frog.
   d fB—Ad— 1

* In this and the other Rorschach protocols the upper line of the score of each response represents the standard score, following Beck; the lower, the score specially devised for our statistical evaluation (see Table I).

Figure II

5. D s F A   This looks like a manta ray (white space).
   S FG A— 2

Figure III

6. D M Y H P   Two niggers jitterbugging.
   D MFG+Cl H P 4.0 org.2   Don't see anything else—I see the red but
                               can't fit it in.

Figure IV

7. W F— A   They all look reminiscent of a sea animal.
   W FB— A— 2.0 1   This looks kind of like a ray.
8. D F+ A   Some insect with the antennae sticking out.
   D FG+ A— 2

Figure V

9. W F + A P   A butterfly. (W)
   W FG+ A—P 1.0 1
10. W F A   Flying fox. (W)
   W F G+Q A— 1.0 2

Figure VI

11. W Y F A P   I can't see anything except a bearskin rug.
   W TGFt A+P 2.5 2   (W)

Figure VII

12. Ws F Y Ls   A Japanese coral atoll, a lagoon inside. (W,
   Ws fG+V Ls+ 4.0 1   white space)

Figure VIII

13. D F+ A P   Some animal, some canine. (P, F)
   D₁FG+ A P 2
14. D F+ An   Skeleton of a fish.
   D3 FG+ An 2 p

Figure IX

I can't get anything out of that.

Figure X

Like two creatures out of Mars.

15. D F A
   D? F A 1
16. DF+ Ad P   Rabbit's face.
   D₈ FG+ Ad— P 2

Under neuropsychiatric treatment this patient improved greatly.
He regained his normal feelings of vigorous health and well-being on
a regime of deep narcotherapy of three days' duration, followed by
insulin subshock—feelings that were important not only in providing

additional vigor but also in giving him a sense of power and ability. Meeting infantrymen on the neuropsychiatric ward convinced him that the air war was not the worst. He gained insight into his reactions during psychotherapy, particularly during group psychotherapy, and became convinced that they were not abnormal or bad. He was thus able to allay his guilt to a great extent and to accept a new picture of himself. He still could not quite overcome his reaction against flying heavy bombers but returned to combat duty when allowed to make his own choice and he successfully completed a full tour of 35 missions—that is, an additional 28 after discharge from the neuropsychiatric service.

This officer's subsequent excellent performance in combat is interesting to analyze. It meant a great deal to this man to feel he had some hand in directing his own fate, that he was not powerless—that, for instance, was one of the most important meanings to him of his regained physical vigor. He was motivated to continue flying; his father, who had been wounded in the first World War but had continued fighting, had endowed him with a strong masculine ego ideal. He was allowed, moreover, to ease back into flying pretty much at his own discretion—the patient chose first whether he would fly, then when and how he would fly, how many missions would comprise his tour, until finally he regained full confidence in himself and his ability. This apparently suited well the directive, executive drives of his ego. Still strongly conditioned against flak, he would control the uneasiness it created in him by various unconscious and conscious devices. When the device of producing psychological distance by drowsiness on missions, after the 20th, was routed by medication (benzedrine), he undertook a course of self-medication with alcohol which helped him relax. He blew off his accumulating anxiety and tension by high jinks at the club.

That these were strictly utilitarian devices is shown by his abruptly discarding them, feeling no more need for them, after completing his tour. These emotional vents headed off the formation of more disturbing anxiety symptoms, except for loss of appetite after his 25th mission (when he decided to extend his tour from 25 to 35 missions). He received emotional support through companionship and identification with a bombardier whose experiences closely paralleled his own. With these bulwarks, the patient's already strong **ego was able** to handle effectively the temporal increment in anxiety. His sleep was good until he reached the climax of his last two missions. After completion of his tour he felt tremendous relief and release, followed by rapid return to his usual cheerful, vigorous personality pattern. It was then, three days after having completed his tour, that he returned and took the second Rorschach test—six months after the first. This time his responses showed greatly increased productivity, creativeness, warmth, better social reactivity, including good color, form and movement responses. Statistically his Rorschach pattern now fell within the normal group. The protocol follows:

Figure I

1. W F + A P
    WF G+ A−P 1.0 1   Bat.
2. W F+ A   Crustacean also. (W)
    W FG+ A− 1.0

Figure II

3. W M A P   Bears playing patty-cake, (usual).
    W MFG+ A+P 4.5 org 3
4. D F+ Ad   Some kind of insect head with antennae.
    D₃ FG+ Ad− 2
5. D F+ Ad   Or crayfish.
    D₃ FG+ Ad− 2

Figure III

6. D M Y H P   Two Negroes jitterbugging.
    D₁ MFG+ H P 4.0 org 3
7. D M H   Two figures, like the Follies, kicking up
    DMFG+ H 4.0 org 3   their legs.

Figure IV

8. W Y F A P   A bearskin rug, at sort of an oblique angle.
    W TFG+ A+ P 2.0 1   (W)
9. DF+ Ad   Some sort of insect head, with pincers and
    D FG+ Ad− 2   antennae.

Figure V

10. W F+ A P   A bat.
     W FG+ A−P 1.0 1
11. W F A   A flying fox with big ears.
     W FG+Q A− 1.0 2
12. D F+ A   A bird, looks like it has a large mouth
     D FG+ A− 2   (side view).

Figure VI

13. W F Y A   Some sort of rug. (W)
    W TF+G A P 2.5 1

Figure VII

14. W F− A   An animal, perhaps an ant-eater. (W)
    W FB− A− 2.5 2
15. D F+ H P   Some sort of savages, sunken foreheads
    D FG+ H P 2   with fancy hair-do's (right and left top,
                     usual).

Figure VIII

16. D F Y A   An x-ray of some kind of crab (green top
    Dy f B−Y A−xray 1   section).
17. D F+ A P   Red, both sides, a hyena, or dog.
    D_1 FG+ A P 2
18. D C F Na   A technicolor picture of stalactites, or
    D CfB− Na 2   limestone cave formations (red and
                     orange).

Figure IX

19. D F+ H P   (rust detail) A court jester with dunce cap
    D_3 FG+ H P 2   on.
20. D F+ HdP   A face with a beard (red, usual).
    D_1 FG+ Hd P 2
21. D F+ A   A camel's face (usual reindeer).
    D_2 FG+ A+ 2

Figure X

22. D F+ H   Blue just looks like what they are, ink
    D FG+ H 2   spots. Looks like some advertising figures,
                     vegetables, like carrots with legs (top
                     gray).
23. D F− A   Like a sea horse (gray detail, right side,
    D_8 FB− A− 2   central).
24. D M H − Ls   Two guys on each side of a chasm, shaking
    D MFG+V H.Ls± 4.5 org 3   hands.
25. D F+ A   Two more sea horses (green top center).
    D_4 FG+ A− 2

This has been a description of a basically sound ego structure in
an emotionally secure man which staggered under its first severe
blow but which regained and kept its footing once emotional security and self-confidence were restored and it was allowed to follow
its own pattern of self-direction—changes which were clearly reflected
in the two Rorschachs.

That the Rorschach may likewise reflect changes in the direction of personality disorganization under increased stress is shown by the following case:

Case 2. (Subject 216) After completing eight combat missions involving moderate stress, this twenty-six-year old navigator had a mild anxiety attack which expressed itself in acute gastrointestinal upset and subjective uneasiness about flying. His Rorschach responses at this time indicated rigid reality-oriented control, and constriction, with depressive features. The protocol follows:

Figure I

1. W F+ A P   A bat. (W)
   W FG+ A−P 1.0 1

Figure II

2. D F− Ad   A head of something, kind of animal (midline
   D₄ fB− Ad 1   black).

Figure III

3. D F+ H P   Two people (black).
   D₁ FG+ H P 1

Figure IV

4. W Fy A P   A bear skin. (W)
   W FG+ T A+ P 2.0 1
5. D Fy A   A beaver skin (part, plate reversed).
   D? FB T A− 2

Figure V

6. W F+ A P   A bat or butterfly.
   W FG+ A−P 1.0 1
7. D F+ Hd   A leg of a person (black lateral).
   D₁ FG+ Hd P 1

Figure VI

8. D F+ Ad   The head of a reptile.
   D₂ FG+ Ad− 1
9. W Fy A   Part of a bear with its head off.
   W FG+T A+ (mut) 2.5 1

Figure VII

10. D F− Ad   An arm and leg of something (black-viewed
    D? fB− Adx (mut) 1 from bottom).

Figure VIII

11. D F+ A   A mole.
    D₁ FG+ A− 2
12. D F+ An P   A backbone.
    D₂ FG+ At P 1

Figure IX

13. D F− A   A clam shell open (orange).
    D3 FB− A− 2.5 O− 2

Figure X

14. D F− Ad   Pincers of a clam (gray).
    D? FB− Ad− O− 1

He responded rather promptly to psychotherapy that was brief indeed (one session) and returned to combat flying and performed efficiently on three more missions, the last of which, however, (the 11th) was an especially harrowing one. While over enemy territory his plane sustained severe battle damage and the bombardier while beside the patient was hit by flak which tore away the lower part of his face. The patient held the wounded and severely mutilated man in his arms for more than an hour, administering oxygen to him and taking care of him till he died. In the meantime, in spite of the fact that they were out of formation and without fighter escort, the patient plotted an excellent course through flak areas to the home base. After this mission, anxiety erupted in full-blown form although still without a thorough-going break in his overt self-control or efficiency.

A second Rorschach test taken one month after the first and four days after the traumatic 11th mission revealed marked reduction in intellectual control with the eruption of many fantasies of mutilation, seven of them involving crude color, indicating a severe full-blown break-through of anxiety. The repression behind the previous constriction was now released into emotional outbursts and frank acute anxiety, the test seeming to act as a stimulus to abreaction (e.g., card II, "a man's leg partly blown off," on III the center red interpreted as "my bombardier's face," VIII and X "a bloody mess," IX "blood all over"). The complete protocol follows:

Figure I

1. W Y Fk   Flak.
   W YfB− Flk. C.T.C. War 1.0 1
2. W F+ A P   A bat.
   W FG+ A P 1.0 1
3. D F A   Body of a reptile (center).
   D_1 FB a 1
4. D F+ Ad   Head and claws of something.
   D_1 fG+ Ad 0

Figure II

5. D C Bl   Red stuff, looks like blood.
   D_2 C Bl, (mut) 0
6. D Y Fk   Flak look of black stuff.
   D KC^1 FK, CTC War 0
7. D F+ Ad   An animal without a head (lateral half).
   D_1 FG+ Adx (mut) 1
8. d Cm An   A man's leg, partly blown off (half of
   d CmFG Hn mut 1   red and black, lower right).

Figure III

9. D C F Hd. Bl   My bombardier's face (red center).
   D_3 CFB− Hd. Bl (mut) 3
10. d F− An   Backbone of animal (midline center).
   d FB− An 1

Figure IV

11. W Y Fk   Flak look.
   W KY FK war CTC 0
12. W F Y A P   Bear skin.
   W FG+ T A P 2.5 1
13. D Y F Ad   Tail end of some kind of skin (center
   D_3 TfB− Ad 1   top).

Figure V

14. W Y Fk   Flak.
   W YfB FK 1.0 0
15. W F Y A   Animal skin.
   W fB+T A 1.0
16. D F+ An   Bone in man's leg (left projection).
   D_1 FB+ Hn 2
17. D F+ Ad   Tentacles of some kind of spider (top
   D_8 FG+ Ad 2   center).

Figure VI

18. D F Ad   Head of a water spider (projection).
   D_6 FG Ad 2
19. D F Ad   Part of a bat flying through air (part
   D FBQ Adx 1   of projection and wing formation).

20. W F Y A P

    W FG+T A P (mut) 2.5 2

Part of a bear skin without head on it

21. d F H

    d? F H 2

Two people (detail center top).

Figure VII

22. D F Yn An

    D FBTm An (mut) 1

Animal leg and arm pulled apart (lower right). (Inq:) Split in two, a bad job of skinning.

23. D F— A

    D_4 FB— A 1

Bat (top construction).

Figure VIII

24. D C Bl

    D2 C Bl mut 0

Bloody mess (top center).

25. D F+ A P

    D_1 FG+ A P 2

A wolf (red).

26. D F+ An P

    D_3 FG+ An P 2

A backbone of a fish (center).

Figure IX

27. D C Bl

    D C Blood mut 0

Blood all over (red and rust). Just looks like a mess.

28. D F— A

    D_{s3} FB— A 2

A clam with tentacles (white space).

Figure X

29. W C Bl

    W C Bl mut 0

Another bloody mess.

30. D F Ad

    D_8 FB Ad 2

An owl face (gray, top right).

31. D F+ Ad

    D_5 FG+ Ad 1

Head of an animal (rabbit head).

32. D F+ A

    D_3 FG+ A 2

Dog (yellow, usual).

33. D C Bl

    D_9 C Bl mut 0

Blood (red, right side).

In spite of this acute reaction, his orientation to reality, his ability to organize and to perceive according to group standards remained at an adequate level and there was evidence of intrapsychic attempts to deal with these disrupting tensions.

V. A Simplified Scoring Method Adapted to Performance Problems

When the tests were interpreted by a simplified method which appeared adapted to such performance problems, comparison of the normal-performing group with all groups who reacted with neurotic or psychopathic-evasive symptoms showed in general the following differences:

Number of Responses: The total number of responses was greater in the normal-performing group than in the operational-fatigue group, and in the latter group was greater in those cases who recovered sufficiently to return to full duty than in those who had to be removed from combat status.

Proportion of Good-Form Responses: A high percentage of good-form responses—Klopfer and Kelly's intellectual control rating—was likewise a favorable prognostic sign, while decline of good form responses was a sign of poor prognosis. In a way, the ability to interpret the blots in terms of good-form responses appeared related to the ability to cope with the environment and to discriminatory capacity; impairment of good-form responses denoted diminished ability to handle environment objectively and to keep up combat performance.

Proportion of Good Small-Detail Responses: The third favorable prognostic sign was the number of good small-part responses, which were particularly prominent in those breakdown cases who ultimately recovered sufficiently to return to full duty. A high number of small-detail responses appeared to be clinically related to obsessive personality traits acting as an inner compulsive to the patient to prove himself by returning to full-duty status. It was generally found that all other factors being equal, the obsessive personality had a better chance of continuing to perform in spite of anxiety and symptom formation than did an unobsessive person with the same degree of anxiety or symptom formation.

Crushing-Threatening Content Responses: The prevalence of responses which we should like to designate as characterized by "crushing-threatening content"—that is, the verbalization or description of the blots in terms of crushing-threatening images of warfare (CTC) or of mutilation (Mut)—was found to be indicative of poor prognosis.

Some more obvious examples of such responses are: "a bomb bursting" (card 2), "a man coming down in a flaming parachute" (card 10), "a torn organ of some kind" (card 3, red center), "the appearance of the after-effects of severe burns on a person's face" (card 2), "a bomb burst on an oil refinery" (card 2), "bursts of flak" (card 2 or almost any other card), "a plane blowing up" (card 3), "a guy's chest here with a hole in it—bullet wound no doubt" (card 3, lower center), "a mangled body with his mouth open" (card 3, lateral red), "the backbone and a guy's head all smashed up" (card 9), "smoke towering up" (card 6), "one person torn in half, opened up that way, split from the head down; the red would figure in that, being the inner organs, possibly the heart" (card 3), "Magdeburg right over again, the sky over Magdeburg—here, two B-24s burning (red), like the two wingmen who exploded on us—the rest is confusion and flak" (card 10), "some meat sliced, opened, blood coming out" (card 9), "something with a hole blown out of the middle of it" (card 7), "a B-17 split in two" (card 1), "if that were red (the blue) it would remind me of the way blood looks in an airplane when a man gets shot, the way it spat-splatters. Usually when a 20-millimeter hits the head, it tears out big chunks of blood and throws them all over the cockpit" (card 10).

Two cases will illustrate the significance of such responses.

Case 3. (*Subject No. 338*) A former instructor pilot who had been sent to the ETO as a squadron commander with the rank of major, when faced with actual combat, had developed several minor illnesses which delayed his first combat mission. After completing his first mission, a deep but relatively easy penetration, he developed ear trouble and was temporarily grounded. When he was referred for neuropsychiatric check-up of his fitness for combat, his Rorschach responses revealed very marked anxiety with 9 responses out of 33 being in terms of fantasies of mutilation, annihilation, and crushing threat—four of them associated with crude color, four with white space, and one with marked shading shock. He saw: a foot cut off with the bloody stump showing in red (card 2); a pelvis with the bowels in the white space (card 7); the flesh around the ribs with the space for heart and lungs in white (card 9); a burst of flak (card 5). He interpreted the red in Card 8 as "a deep penetration into the body, sensitive to the touch" (note the use of the phrase "deep penetration" commonly used in referring to combat missions deep into enemy territory). One white-space response (out of the total of four) referred to "a channel in the female sex organs, stopped up by some sort of affliction" (card 9). (He had previously expressed his worry that his wife might be physically unable to have children.) He twice referred to red areas as blood (cards 3, 9), once as inflamed tissue (card 9), (in addition to the reference to deep penetration in card 8). He interpreted card 10 as "the disintegrated burned body of a boy who did what I did (buzzed) ... infested with germs."

This patient's condition was diagnosed as a severe anxiety reaction following mild stress. He was considered psychobiologically substandard for aerial combat and for all positions involving administration and planning of air combat units. He did, however, fly nine more missions and was drowned on his eleventh when his plane, the group lead-aircraft, ditched in the Channel shortly after taking off from England. His group-mates expressed the opinion that he could have crashlanded the aircraft, a safer procedure than ditching, had it not been for his phobia against crashlanding on solid ground.

Case 4. (*Subject 53*) is that of a tail-gunner who developed disabling neurotic symptoms during convalescence from flak wounds received on a harrowing first mission which he had flown as tail-gunner in the last ship of the lower formation, popularly known as the "Purple Heart Corner." He was subsequently awarded the Purple Heart and the Silver Star for continuing to fire after being wounded— he received 13 wounds in all—and for shooting down an enemy fighter, thereby saving his ship and the formation. He was a genuine hero, but he developed a strongly conditioned horror of the flaming, searing, tearing death he feared might be his in combat.

The Rorschach test revealed numerous anxious fantasies of being crushed, smashed, cut off, broken, split: "a broken seashell cut in two and folded out, the actual inside of the oyster in red" (card 2), "a pear, or any fruit, that is crushed or smashed" (card 5), "an animal skin with the head cut off and the tail split" (card 6), "two prehistoric animals climbing out of a swamp; they seem to dwarf anything else" (card 8), "vapor coming out of pots with flame under them" (card 9). Although this patient's physical and emotional exhaustion and his jangled nerves were greatly benefited by deep-sleep and insulin subshock treatment, his neurotic reaction became more deeply entrenched with the passage of time. He was judged unrehabilitable for service in the ETO and was returned to the Zone of the Interior.

Content of White-Space Responses: Another set of observations, not necessarily related to prognosis, concerned the fact that intense conflict was frequently projected into the white spaces. Scrutiny of the white-space responses, if present, frequently supplied useful clues for interpretive psychotherapy. A highranking officer, commanding officer-of a heavy bombardment group (*Case 5, Subject 232*), who had been (in his opinion) unduly humiliated publicly by his general for substituting an easier secondary target for a difficult primary target became aphonic after this incident. His conflict was indicated in a remarkably revealing way by two white-space responses in the Rorschach test, one being aviator's wings (card I), the other a silhouette of George Washington (card 7).

In order to put these clinical correlations to test, the material was completely reviewed in terms of standard Rorschach scoring and interpretation and was statistically analyzed. The procedure of this analysis is described below.

VI. Statistical Analysis of the Rorschach Protocols

The original Rorschach protocols were copied by an assistant on standard forms and randomly mixed. They were scored in order of their random numbers without knowledge of their diagnostic category. The scoring system was based on both Beck and Klopfer with some additions. For example, the organization score differs from Beck's Z score in that it is not influenced by the "whole" response, but only by the organization of parts into an integrated percept. Three types of form were scored: (1) an accuracy rating which indicates how well the percept fits the ink blot; (2) a definiteness-vagueness rating which rates the degree of specificity with which the blot is perceived; and finally, (3) Beck's form level. Another innovation in scoring was to generalize to all determinants the importance of form in relation to the accompanying determinants as is done routinely with color. These importance ratings were suggested by Zubin's scheme, but considerably simplified.*

On clinical evidence only, independent of the Rorschach data, a selection was made including the eighty-four fliers of the normal group who had no clinical signs of fatigue and the eighty-three of the fatigue group given medical treatment. Each of these two groups was randomly divided into three sections. Section 1 (consisting of twenty-eight normal-performing and twenty-eight operational-fatigue cases)

---

* Zubin, J.; Chule, E.; and Veniar, S.: A psychometric approach to the evaluation of the Rorschach test. Psychiat., *4:* 547–566, 1941.

was inspected for score values which occurred with sufficiently unequal frequencies in the two groups to provide some discriminative
value. These score values were designated as preliminary signs and
polarized as indicative of belonging to the normal or fatigue groups.
A discriminatory sign is a score value, or combination of scores,
which has the most significant difference in frequency of occurrence
in the two groups. For example, more than three human responses
occurred in 22 of the Rorschach records of the normal group, but
in only 3 of the operational-fatigue records. Thus, having more than
3 responses of human content is a highly favorable sign.

Another feature of this analysis was the card by card sign selection.
It was discovered that the total popular score for a record had little
discriminatory power, but that certain popular responses such as the
two men on card 3 was much more frequent among the normal-
performing fliers, while the animal skin of card 6 was more frequent
among the fatigue cases. All of the determinants and the content
were analyzed by this card by card method, the scores being algebraically added to produce the discriminatory signs. Section 2 (also
consisting of 28 normal and 28 fatigue cases) was likewise inspected
for preliminary discriminative signs. Of the 160 signs thus denoted,
107 were not reversed on either of Sections 1 or 2 and were thus
designated as discriminative signs.

Each normal subject was given a plus check mark for each "normal"
sign he possessed and a minus check mark for each "fatigue" sign,
with the reverse arrangement for the fatigue subjects. The plus and
minus checks for each subject were algebraically added to produce
the *discriminative score*. Next, the subjects of Sections 1 and 2 were
classified as "certainly" or "doubtfully" diagnosed in terms of their
discriminative scores. The purpose of the "doubtful" designation was
to provide a sample of cases on which discriminative signs could be
evaluated as to whether they contributed more minus than positive
signs to the doubtful cases. By eliminating such signs, the discriminative power of the total battery should be increased. In effect, one
starts out with an elaborate sign matrix which "over-weights" all
characteristics, then chisels off the excess until the shape of the group
psychogram truly represents the distinguishing characteristics of the
group. This principle of sign selection is not unlike the natural selection as practiced by Nature—try out everything, but retain only

TABLE I

THE RORSCHACH SIGNS OF SIGNIFICANT DISCRIMINATION*

Sign No.	Sign Symbol	Frequencies		Description
		Normal-Perform-ing Group	Opera-tional-Fatigue Group	
1.	$(R_2 \text{ gr } 3)$	18	5	The number of responses on card 2 is greater than 3.
2.*	$R_2 \text{ gr } 4$	12	0	No. resp. on card 2 is greater than 4.
3.*	$(R_5 \text{ gr } 2)$	21	6	No. resp. on card 5 is greater than 2.
4.*	$R_5 \text{ gr } 1$	35	17	No. resp. on card 5 is greater than 1.
5.	$(R_9 \text{ gr } 3)$	20	7	No. resp. on card 9 is greater than 3.
6.*	$(R \text{ gr } 22)$	32	15	No. resp. on all 10 cards is greater than 22.
7.	$W\% \text{ ls } 14$	16	6	No. whole resp. is less than 14% of total.
8.*	$(D \text{ gr } 17)$	25	8	No. prominent detail resp. is greater than 17.
9.*	$D \text{ gr } 19$	22	6	No. prom. detail resp. is greater than 19.
10.	$F(D\% \text{ ls } 40)$	14	28	No. D resp. is less than 40% of total.
11.	$F_0 \text{ gr } 19$	17	5	No. of pure, clear form resp. is greater than 19.
12.	$(G_0 \text{ gr } 11)$	31	16	No. of pure accurate form is greater than 11.
13.	$-1 \text{ gr } 1$	10	2	No. of Beck's minus primary form responses is greater than one.
14.*	$smFr \text{ gr } 19$	26	6	All form responses algebraically summed per card is greater than 19.
15.	$(M \text{ gr } 2)$	19	7	No. human movement responses is greater than 2.

* Signs starred have a chi-square rating greater than 6.6; all others greater than 3.8. The "F" indicates this sign is characteristic of the Fatigue Group. All others are characteristic of the Normal-Performing Group. The discrimination frequencies of the score taken per card for section 1 are algebraically summated so as to maximize the discrimination. When preceding a sign symbol, "sm" always means this kind of summation score.

TABLE I—*Continued*

Sign No.	Sign Symbol	Frequencies		Discripition
		Normal-Performing Group	Opera-tional-Fatigue Group	
16.*	M_2 gr 0	24	8	Secondary human movements are present.
17.	($MQ_•$ gr 0)	33	17	Extensor movement is present.
18.	Y gr 1	25	13	Undifferentiated shading is greater than 1.
19.	O6— gr 0	8	0	Predominately bad form organization responses on the sixth card are present.
20.*	sm O gr 1	35	17	Summation organization per card is greater than one.
21.*	smZ gr 11.0	21	7	Summation per card of Z is greater than 11.0.
22.	A gr 13	12	2	Animal responses are greater than 13.
23.	Ad gr 2	33	19	Animal detail greater than 2.
24.	Ad_1 gr 0	18	6	Special animal detail is present. (Wolf head, wings, fish parts, lobster parts).
25.*	H gr 3	22	3	Human content responses number greater than 3.
26.*	H_2 gr 1	27	10	Responses containing two or more humans are greater than one.
27.	(Hd gr 2)	20	7	Human detail is greater than 2.
28.	Ar gr 0	13	3	Architectural responses are present.
29.*	Cg gr 0	31	13	Clothing responses are present.
30.*	Im_1 gr 0	22	4	Special implement responses are present. (Musical instruments or mechanical gadgets).
31.*	Ob gr 2	23	3	Responses of unusual content number more than 2.
32.	Pl_1 gr 0	30	17	Special content of leaf or named plant is present.
33.*	Cnt— gr 12	20	5	Content objects smaller than human number more than 12.
34.	F sm4 gr 1	14	27	Sum of the four content categories of War, CTC (crushing-threatening content), Abd (abdominal anatomical references), Mut (mutilation responses) is greater than 1.

TABLE I—*Continued*

Sign No.	Sign Symbol	Frequencies		Description
		Normal-Performing Group	Operational-Fatigue Group	
35.*	Sp gr 1.7	38	20	Specificity rating is greater than 1.70.
36.	Sp₂ gr 21	14	4	More than 21 responses have a specificity rating of 2.
37.	(Sp₂ gr 12)	35	19	More than 12 responses have a specificity rating of 2.
38.	(Sp₃ gr 3)	18	7	More than 3 responses have a specificity rating of 3.
39.*	smP gr 1	42	20	Summation per card of discriminative popular responses is greater than 1.

those characteristics which contribute to survival (in this case, discrimination). Inspection revealed that 31 signs were contributing an excess of minus checks to the fifty-four doubtful cases and were eliminated. The plus and minus checks of the remaining 76 signs were again summated for each subject to produce his *balanced discrimination score*. The cutting point for maximum discrimination was set empirically for Sections 1 and 2 combined.

The balanced sign check list of 76 signs was finally applied to Section 3 designated as the *test* or *prediction* sample. The number of subjects of Section 3 correctly designated by being below or above the predetermined cut-off point is the measure of the discriminative power of the sign check list on a *new random sample* from the same population. Of the fifty-five cases in Section 3, 38 (69%) were correctly classified which has a null probability of less than one per cent. Thus it is demonstrated that when such signs are determined, the Rorschach test has a moderate validity for discriminating between normal-performing and operational-fatigue combat fliers.

The Rorschach differences between normal-performing and operational-fatigue listed below are based on those 39 signs (see Table I) which had consistent discrimination on all three sections and which had a chi-square greater than 3.8; i.e., a null probability of .05 or less. Thus we feel confident that these conclusions are valid for the populations tested. However, without the refined analysis and the balanced-sign check list of discriminatory signs, such high validity coefficients could not have been found. We wish to emphasize that the total discrimination between the normal-performing and fatigue groups which had a null probability of less than one per cent was based on Section 3, the *prediction section* which was an entirely new sample, and thus free from the contamination so often encountered in this kind of work where validities reported are based on the discrimination frequencies of the same groups on which the signs were set up. Our groups would have had almost perfect discrimination if we had followed that more customary error.

The following findings based on the 39 significant signs show how the Rorschach results agree with the Combat Fatigue Theory.

VII. EVALUATION OF THE EFFECT OF COMBAT FATIGUE ON IMAGINAL PROCESSES

1. The number of responses, as a measure of productivity, is lowered in fatigue. Fatigue theory would postulate lowered productivity because of exhaustion, anxiety, lowered drive, and less ego strength. Depression is an additional important feature.

2. The *detail-to-whole* ratio and *specificity* score as measures of relative concern with the concrete details of the immediate environment versus the holistic, over-all concern about the total situation, is reduced in the operational-fatigue group as would be expected when anxiety about personal safety has overcome the problem-solving attitude dealing with concrete realities. The increase in war-mutilation responses further supports this finding.

3. Form-dominated human movement responses as a measure of controlled, creative imagination are reduced by fatigue. Anxiety, depressive constriction, loss of spontaneity, and tendency to suppress frightening fantasies, would all tend to reduce controlled imagination according to fatigue theory.

4. Rare content categories of the Rorschach productions were much less frequent among the fatigue cases. This loss may be evidence of decreased imagination, more constriction, narrowed range of interests, loss of self-confidence and lowered productivity.

5. The reduction of human, clothing, and popular responses for the

fatigue group may represent the reduction of rapport with their fellows so critical for high morale according to war-neurosis theory.

6. The organization score, as a measure of personality integration through the ability to see relationships both in the environment and of the self to the environment, is reduced in fatigue as fatigue theory would predict.

No significant discriminative frequencies appear which contradict the concepts of operational fatigue or are in opposition to general Rorschach theory. The lack of discrimination by form level, color, and shading responses was unexpected, but may be a function of the prevalence of depression among the fatigue cases (which often raises form level) and the profound constriction among many of the normal-performing men.

Several general conclusions from this study appear plausible:

1. The Rorschach test when quantified by a *balanced-sign list* can describe with a modest but significant validity some of the characteristic differences in personality between normal-performing and operational-fatigue combat fliers.

2. The Rorschach profiles are sensitive to covert personality strains produced by environmental stress.

3. Validity of the Rorschach test can be enhanced by constructing profiles of weighted signs for specific populations.

4. Confidence in both Rorschach and traumatic-neurosis theories is increased by the finding of considerable agreement in Rorschach profile changes which articulate with those predicted by traumatic-neurosis theory.

5. Clinical and Rorschach evidence is presented suggesting that a large proportion of traumatic neuroses of the type seen in combat personnel are psychopathologically and psychodynamically depressions rather than neuroses in the general clinical and genetic sense of the word.

13

THE USE OF SERIAL TESTING IN
REGRESSIVE ELECTROSHOCK TREATMENT

By BERNARD C. GLUECK, JR., M.D., JACK D. KRASNER, M.A. AND
RAMON PARRES, M.D.*

THE PURPOSE of this paper is to demonstrate the multiple utility of psychological testing in the handling of the more seriously disturbed psychiatric patients of the type commonly seen in in-patient hospital practice. It has been our experience that psychological testing, especially of the repetitive or serial type, has tremendous value both as a research tool and as a laboratory technic in conjunction with therapy. We will try to demonstrate this dual function in our study of regressive electroshock therapy by presenting a detailed individual case report, which is, however, a prototype of the majority of cases receiving this type of therapy.

The following description of regressive electroshock therapy will help to orient you in our use of this term. We have been employing a modification of the technic first described by Milligan (1). Three grand mal seizures a day are given, on consecutive days, until an adequate state of regression is achieved. We feel that we have arrived at this point when the patient loses control of the ordinary cortical functions; becoming dysarthric, incontinent of both urine and feces, showing motor incoordination to the point of being unable to walk unassisted, and having to be spoon-fed. Patients at this stage usually lie quietly in bed, frequently assuming the fetal position, and at times have shown pathological reflexes, e.g., grasp reflex, sucking reflex, beginning Babinski, and extrapyramidal postural reflexes. In addition, they show occasional psychological changes similar to those seen in frontal lobe pathology. At this time, and usually for some 48 to 96 hours before this level is reached, these patients show a marked change in the psychiatric picture, losing all of their tension and anxiety, becoming very placid, childish, and frequently showing a warmth and intensity of affective response that was absent in the

* Stony Lodge, Ossining, New York.

original clinical picture. Recovery following cessation of the electro-shock treatments proceeds in a fairly characteristic manner; the recovery of motor function occurs within 48 to 72 hours, but tne passive immature emotionality persists for a longer time, usually for 7 to 10 days. At this point, recovery of memory begins and may proceed very rapidly. These patients are avid for details of their past and develop an intense dependency on the people in the immediate environment—preferably the individual psychotherapist—who are able to supply them with the missing memory details. We feel that this particular phase of the reaction is extremely important from the standpoint of future psychotherapeutic success. Many of these patients at about the 10th to 14th day, show a period of intense psychomotor excitement, usually coinciding with the recall of traumatic memories. We have been able to control this response successfully by coma insulin, beginning these treatments at about the 7th or 8th day of the recovery period and continuing for approximately two weeks. By the end of the third week of the recovery phase, much of the memory has returned and psychotherapy, including an analytic type of therapy, becomes possible at this point.

The initial psychological tests are usually given during the first week of hospitalization, at a time when many of these patients are severely disturbed. This means that they are disorganized in one way or another, and are not reliable informants. The psychiatrist secures a history from the patient and the family in order to make a formulation of the case. This procedure, however, often offers a serious problem, in that the patient is frequently too disorganized and confused to offer information which is not distorted. The reliability of the information received from the family may also be of doubtful value. It is quite logical for the family, consciously or unconsciously, to taint the early history of the patient to look "good" or "bad," depending upon the individual informant's particular attitude. This diagnostic handicap can be alleviated by the psychological tests. The psychological test results, and their interpretation, give a dynamic picture of the patient which acts as an objective check to the psychiatric interview and formulation.

The psychologist does not see or communicate with the patient again until the patient has fully recovered from the "regression." The second test is done during the third or fourth week of the recovery phase. The patient's reaction to the administration of the same tests is notable. Most patients have some awareness of having had the tests before, but are not able to recall the tests or their previous responses to the various tests. Others deny ever having taken the test. It is also significant that some of these patients do not even recall speaking with the examiner before the second testing session. The second administration is to determine the effects of the treatment on the patient. The results again act as an objective evaluation which is compared with the psychiatric clinical evaluation.

The psychologist's participation in the life of the patient does not end with the termination of the "regressive electroshock treatment." The patient, after recovering from the regression, continues to receive psychotherapy. During this time there are usually changes going on within the patient which may be manifested in specific behavior patterns, the dynamics of which are not always clear. Periodic psychological examinations help to obtain a more objective evaluation of the patient's progress.

The individual tests which comprise the psychological battery include the following:

1. *C.A.S.* (2): This test is a modification of the verbal part of the "Wechsler-Bellevue Intelligence Scale for Adolescents and Adults." It includes three subtests: (1) Comprehension, (2) Arithmetic, and (3) Similarities. The evaluated and prorated subtests give an indication of the patient's verbal intellectual functioning. This modification is time-saving.

The Comprehension subtest measures the individual's "common sense" or his ability to profit by past experience, and his practical or social judgment in everyday situations. The Arithmetic subtest measures numerical reasoning which includes the speed of numerical manipulation, concentration and the capacity for sustained effort. The Similarities subtest indicates the individual's ability at verbal concept formation (abstraction), and also indicates this way of thinking (rigid-flexible, or abstract-concrete).

2. *Rorschach Ink Blot Test:* This test is a projective technic and is used in evaluating the personality structure of the individual. The technic of the Rorschach is familiar to most people in the psychological professions and need not be elaborated here.

3. *Bender Visual-Motor Gestalt Test* (3): The nine gestalt designs

selected by Bender were at first used as a guide in determining cerebral organic diseases. After much experimentation, it was learned that the test might also be used as a projective technic (6). As such, it is very helpful in determining the presence of various drives and their intensity, behavior in interpersonal relationships, and the consistency of behavior patterns.

4. *Figure Drawings* (4): This test is used both as a measure of intelligence, actual functioning and potential, and as a projective technic (5).

5. *Controlled Word-Association Test:* This test and its numerous modifications have been used for many years by both psychiatrists and psychologists. This testing technic is familiar to most people and needs no clarification.

The battery of tests is administered to each patient. The results of the different tests and their interpretation are not used individually, but are combined to give a well-rounded description of the individual. The use of a number of tests in the battery also offers the opportunity of comparing several objective evaluations.

The patient to be discussed is a twenty-eight-year old white female, C. G., who holds a master's degree with a major in Greek and Latin. She was admitted to the hospital on August 6, 1949 in an acute psychotic state, having been mute and regressed for a period of 8 months prior to admission. The onset of overt psychotic symptoms 4 years ago was followed by a series of hospitalizations at various institutions, during the course of which she received insulin, electroshock and psychotherapy with, at best, temporary periods of improvement never lasting more than a few weeks. She had been totally incapable of maintaining herself outside of an institution during the major portion of the 4 years. During the course of this admission she was seen by the psychologist on four different occasions over a period of 8 months. The progressive changes in her overt behavior reflect the basic personality changes that took place within C. G., and are paralleled by her performance on the different psychological examinations.

C. G. received the first psychological examination on August 26, 1949 (fig. 1). When the examiner entered the room and asked her how she felt, she replied that she did not know for she was hearing voices of people making derogatory remarks about her religion and her racial origin. Contact with her was difficult to attain and impossible to maintain for more than a few minutes at a time. Her speech was very low and often incoherent, and she had to be asked to repeat her remarks several times before being understood. She drifted into hallucinatory states throughout the entire session, returning to the testing situation only upon the insistence of the examiner. When this was done, she became irritated and indicated an annoyance at having her attention disturbed.

The psychological tests revealed that C. G. was a person who once functioned on a high intellectual level, but at the time of examination was functioning in a rigidly constricted and regressed manner. Her contact with reality was extremely poor, and her thinking was contaminated with transductive reasoning and autistic logic. She scored a verbal I.Q. of 100 (C.A.S.) which could not be accepted as a true evaluation of her intellectual endowment. Her Rorschach consisted of 27 responses and included a form level per cent (F%) of 89/96 (rigidity), 4 popular responses (minimum for conventional thinking), no movement responses (inhibited fantasy), arbitrary use of color (limited understanding of affective situations), a positional response (autistic logic), a confabulatory response (irrealistic thinking), and an oligophrenic response (fragmentary inhibition).

The figure drawings indicated severe anxiety and insecurity, and a triple withdrawal—(1) into deep fantasy, (2) a negativistic turning away from the environment, and (3) an insulation of herself from the environment. The figures and their dress are characteristic of the 16th–17th century. The eyes are absent in an attempt to shut out the environment, but this is not enough for she encases herself in an additional frame. The fantasy may be related to narcissistic concern over her physical appearance and strong exhibitionistic drives as expressed in the pronounced waistline and the low-cut gown on the female. The hallucinatory trends are suggested by the emphasis of the ears on both figures.

A period of 3 months passed, during which time she received regressive electroshock therapy, following which the patient was seen again on November 18, 1949. Contact at this time was better than before, and she participated in the testing in a very passive and compliant manner. She spoke in a low voice, sometimes trailing off to a whisper, and frequently had to be asked to speak louder in order to be heard. On several occasions she became very anxious because a voice kept telling her what to say, "Not you and not someone outside. Just a woman's voice, so I hesitate."

C. G.'s reactions on the psychological tests at this time showed positive progress, but there were indications that she had not fully recovered from the regressive treatment and was still unable to take

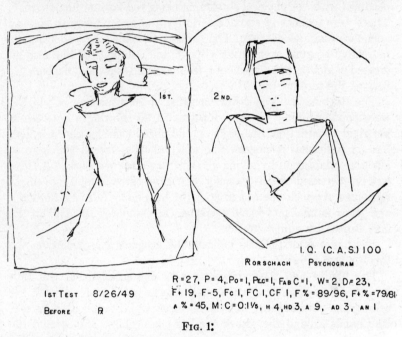

1st.   2 nd.

I. Q. (C. A. S.) 100
RORSCHACH   PSYCHOGRAM

R = 27, P = 4, Po = 1, Pec = 1, Fab C = 1, W = 2, D = 23,
1st Test   8/26/49   F+ 19, F-5, Fc 1, FC 1, CF 1, F % = 89/96, F+ % = 79/81
Before   R   A % = 45, M : C = 0:1½, H 4, HD 3, A 9, AD 3, AN 1

FIG. 1:

advantage of her intellectual potentialities. Her verbal I.Q. score rose to 119, but the improvement was most notable in her dealings with abstract, non-personal material (Similarities). The projective technics, especially her performance on the *Bender Visual-Motor Gestalt* test, indicated that she was able to make contact with others, but only with much caution and deliberation. She attempted to react with some emotional feeling, but usually her interpersonal relationships were affectively flat. She desperately tried to project herself into the environment, but her uncertainty was too severe. She tended to withdraw in an attempt to be safe and unthreatened. There were also indications of aggressive drives which she tried to inhibit. The inhibition, however, was at the expense of intense anxiety which resulted in regressed behavior. This testing session also brought out significant material relating to her sexual conflicts. Sex appeared to be a very disturbing thing for her, and she indicated great concern and anxiety over relatively strong homosexual drives. She was preoccupied with her physical stature, of being too fat and unattractive. There were feelings of sexual inferiority and an inability to play an adequate feminine sex role. The feelings of inadequacy appeared to be related to guilt over earlier orgastic self-stimulation. She also indicated evidences of ambivalence, feelings of hostility and dependence toward the mother (fig. 2).

The Rorschach psychogram consisted of 26 responses, of which 6 were popular. The F% went down to 54/93 showing a decrease in her rigid constriction. She gave one fabulized combination response, but no positional responses. She still indicated forced attempts at affective adaptation by giving an arbitrary color response, but there was an increased use of the color. She gave three human movement responses of which one was of poor $(M-)$ quality (autistic fantasy), and three animal movement responses as compared to none on the first Rorschach administration.

The figure drawings also indicate the progress she made over the three-month interval.

The figures and their dress are now characteristic of the 19th century. The position of the female's arms and hands indicate her attempt at outgoingness, but the necessity of keeping within herself. The bands around the top of the low-cut neckline and around the arms indicate that the exhibitionistic drives still exist, but there is a strong effort exerted to inhibit its expression. The flowering gown shows an attempt at concealment, and a high degree of fantasizing in relation to her body problems. The fist on the male and the fingers of the female indicate muted aggression and impulsive outbursts usually turned against the self. The coy expressions on the figures suggest that she is still absorbed in fantasy, and that her contact may be greater with her fantasy world than with reality. The emphasized ear on the male suggests the continuation of auditory hallucinations.

After a two-month interval, during which C. G. received psychotherapy, another examination was done on January 27, 1950. There was a notable change in her overt behavior, and she displayed an amiable and cordial attitude. She remembered having worked with the examiner in the past, but did not recall what was done or what tests were administered. She continued to be compliant, but seemed to have gained some self-confidence and was able to speak without

1ST. 2ND

HAIR AND FEATURES
DRAWN LAST

2ND TEST 11/18/49 I.Q. (C. A. S.) 119
1MO. POST REGRESSIVE

RORSCHACH PSYCHOGRAM

R = 26, P = 6, F$_{ab}$C = 1, W = 6, D = 16, d = 2, D$_d$ = 2
M 1, M-1, FM 3, F+11, F-3, Fc 2, c F 1, FC 3, CF 2
H 7, HD 3, A 9, NA 2, O 2, F% = 54/93, F·% = 79/84
A % = 35, M:C = 3:3½, FM + M · Fc + = 3:3

FIG. 2.

hesitating over each word. There were also no complaints of voices telling her what to say.

The test results (fig. 3) indicated great progress in her ability to make contact with others, but there was still a definite difficulty in establishing heterosexual relationships. Her contact with reality improved, and she was able to project herself into the environment. This, however, was not accomplished without great effort on her part. She showed caution and hesitancy in structured situations. When on her own, she tended to regress and her reactions appeared to be determined by her anxiety and her need to be dependent rather than by the objectivity of the situation. She began to exhibit a great desire and need for emotional satisfaction from interpersonal relationships. There were indications of the capacity to form affective contacts, but her comprehension of emotional situations remained too limited for successful adaptation. Strong emotional stimulation tended to aggravate her already intense anxiety and resulted in a tendency to seek relief in fantasy. There was, however, increasing effort to make overt reactions to stimulation rather than resort to fantasy.

Her ambivalence toward her mother and the anxiety related to her sexual conflicts persisted. There were indications that she was slowly becoming aware of the feelings involved, but had difficulty in accepting them. She tried to rationalize and intellectualize, but was still unable to cope adequately with her feelings. There was evidence of an increased sensitivity to stimulation and tendencies toward intermittent depressed moods accompanied by suicidal ideas. At this time it became evident that the rate of progress was decreasing and the acceptance and working through of her conflicts would be a very slow process. Any attempt to force her suddenly into reality would cause anxiety too intense for her to handle and result in regression and withdrawal. These findings confirmed the therapist's clinical impression of some regression, a reaction to the recovery of extremely traumatic sexual memories antedating the onset of the psychosis.

The Rorschach psychogram at this time consisted of 31 responses, including 7 popular and 1 fabulized combination. The F% decreased to 36/90 showing the absence of rigidity. She gave 2 human movement responses, of which one was minus, and 4 animal movement responses, of which one was minus. There was, however, a definite shift of the experience balance to the color side, resulting in an $M:C$ ration of 2:4 which indicated a greater attempt at outgoingness. Tension and anxiety were expressed in 1 inanimate movement response and 8 shading responses, and the attempt at intellectualized control in an "X-ray" response.

The figure drawings are of the present century in person and dress. The stance of the figures indicates the persistence of tension. The woman's dress suggests that she has thrown off a great deal of fantasy, but still fantasizes dominance in social situations. The arm lines showing through the dress sleeve indicate the continued occasional breaks in judgment. The male's ears now suggest apprehension and sensitivity to criticism, but the eyes are now open. The arms and hands of the figures show that she is reaching toward the environment for social relationships. She is, however, still feeling her way (shown by the hand of the male) and still needs support which is both helpful and friendly (demonstrated by the female holding on to the dog). The neckline also indicates that the exhibitionism is more reasonable and better controlled.

The patient was seen for the fourth time on April 4, 1950. At this time C. G. was attractively dressed, cosmetics and all, in anticipation of going to New York City for the weekend. She remembered

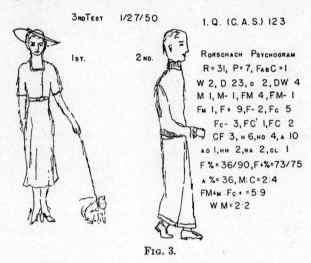

3ʀᴅTᴇsᴛ 1/27/50   I. Q. (C. A. S.) 123

Isᴛ.   2ɴᴅ.   RORSCHACH PSYCHOGRAM
R = 31, P= 7, FᴀʙC =1
W 2, D 23, ᴅ 2, DW 4
M 1, M- 1, FM 4, FM- 1
Fᴍ 1, F+ 9, F- 2, Fᴄ 5
Fᴄ- 3, FC' 1, FC 2
CF 3, ʜ 6, ʜᴅ 4, ᴀ 10
ᴀᴅ 1, ʜʜ 2, ɴᴀ 2, ᴄʟ 1
F % = 36/90, F+%=73/75
ᴀ %= 36, M:C= 2:4
FM+ᴍ Fᴄ + = 5:9
W M = 2:2

FIG. 3.

and greeted the examiner in a very cordial manner, as any polite hostess might receive a visitor. She appeared to be relaxed and started a conversation with little apparent difficulty. She showed no hesitancy in taking the tests, but welcomed them as a task to be accomplished within the context of an interpersonal relationship.

The psychological tests showed no pathology of the psychotic type so in evidence in the past. The performance on the intelligence tests indicated that she was beginning to take advantage of her potentialities and utilize her great wealth of knowledge. She scored a verbal I.Q. of 137 (C.A.S.) and a top performance of 140 (H.T.P.). Her judgment was very good, but doubts of herself persisted in most situations, and an attempt to conform to moralistic ideals inhibited spontaneity and resulted in action and thought patterns which had a compulsive tint. The past cloak of rigid constriction vanished, but she still approached situations in a rather rigid manner and coped with them on a high intellectual level. She was able to make contact with others, but could not gain the emotional satisfaction she desired and needed. She continued to be sensitive to the feelings of others, and her feelings of sexual inadequacy continued to prevent any continuous or long-lasting interpersonal relationships. There were, however, occasions on which she was able to gain some enjoyment, and

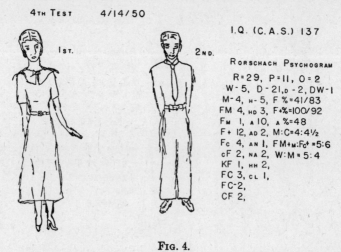

4TH TEST   4/14/50

1ST.   2ND.

I.Q. (C.A.S.) 137

RORSCHACH PSYCHOGRAM

R=29, P=11, O=2
W-5, D-21,D-2, DW-1
M-4, H-5, F%=41/83
FM 4, HD 3, F+%=100/92
FM 1, A 10, A%=48
F+ 12, AD 2, M:C=4:4½
FC 4, AN 1, FM+m:Fc+ =5:6
cF 2, NA 2, W:M = 5:4
KF 1, HH 2,
FC 3, CL 1,
FC-2,
CF 2,

FIG. 4.

the frequency and intensity of depressed moods decreased. Her ideas of suicide became highly intellectualized and there was great doubt that any actual attempt would be made. There were also indications of strong orality which suggested the use of infantile oral drives as a means of compensating for the emotional satisfaction she was, as yet, unable to experience on a mature level. The test results indicated that she had reached a level where she was able to function fairly well in society.

The last Rorschach psychogram (fig. 4) appeared to be as close to a theoretical normal as one could expect. She gave 29 responses which included 11 popular and several good original responses. The F% was 41/83 and the form quality per cent (F+%) was 100/92.

She gave 28% human and only 48% animal responses. The experience balance was dilated, having an M:C ratio of 4:4½, and the form-color to color-form to pure color ratio (FC:CF:C) was 5:2:0.

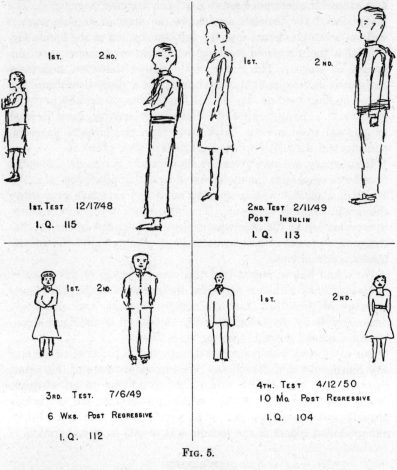

FIG. 5.

She also gave 6 shading responses (4Fc and 2 cF), and one cloud response (KF).

The figure drawings characterize her progress up to the time of examination. Both figures are facing forward showing her facing the problems that exist. Her level of emotional maturity is indicated by her reference to the female as being a "mannequin" which is usually drawn by adolescent girls. The shaded emphasis of the male's hips is indicative of her continued anxiety over her femininity, and the ears suggest the continued sensitivity to environmental criticism. The placement of the female's arm shows the attempt at outgoingness without seeking external support, but the shading of the hands suggests that the unassisted reaching out to the environment is accompanied by anxiety. The stance of the figures, however, suggests a movement in the direction of environmental and social relationships. These findings confirm the clinical impressions of marked improvement, with a disappearance of hallucinatory activity, great increase in personal freedom—e.g., trips away from the hospital unaccompanied—and a much improved grasp of reality problems.

In summary, we have given the above report in considerable detail in order to emphasize the usefulness of repeating psychological evaluations of a patient who is showing rapid and extensive personality changes in response to therapy. The importance of this sort of objective evaluation of the otherwise subjective judgment of the psychotherapist, in terms of an adequate clinical evaluation of therapeutic results, seems obvious.

We would like to repeat that this case is typical of the majority of cases studied with this particular therapeutic technic. The results in many of the other cases are equally dramatic and objectively demonstrable by psychological study—as shown in the figure drawings of a second patient. (See fig. 5, p. 255.)

Our experience with regressive therapy is still too brief to warrant any conclusions as to its efficacy. We can simply state at this point, that it shows considerable promise as an adjunct to an adequate program of psychiatric therapy which includes the use of various physiological procedures, as well as psychotherapeutic measures. A more detailed report of the technic and results is in preparation.

REFERENCES

1. MILLIGAN, W. L.: Psychoneurosis treated with E.C.T. The intensive method. Lancet, *II*, 516–20,. 1946.
2. RABIN, A. I.: A short form of the Wechsler-Bellevue test. J. Applied Psychol., *27*, 320–24, 1943.

3. BENDER, L.: A visual-motor Gestalt test and its clinical use. New York, Amer. Orthopsychiatric Assn., 1938.
4. BUCK, J. N.: The H.T.P. technique, a qualitative and quantitative scoring manual. J. Clinical Psychol., Monthly sup., #5, 1948.
5. MACHOVER, K.: Personality projection in the drawing of the human figure. Springfield, C. C. Thomas, 1949.
6. BROWN, F. and KRASNER, J.: Unpublished data collected on 500 cases.

14

ILLNESS: THE REALIZATION OF AN INFANT'S FANTASY WITH SPECIAL REFERENCE TO TESTING METHODS

By FLANDERS DUNBAR, M.D.*

INTRODUCTION

DEPRIVED CHILDREN have little *recourse* and few *resources*. Having experimented somewhat futilely with the world around them, they resort to fantasy and the range of fantasy like their environment is somewhat limited.

Fantasy one: They can "kill" mother, father, nurse, but then what would happen—no one to give them dinner and a nice warm bed (food, shelter, and clothing). They would also suffer loss of love so this fantasy is rejected for survival rather than for moral reasons. To an infant or young child, killing means little more than getting rid of something that is frustrating. Another way of coping with the situation is to run away; but where then get food, shelter or love?

Fantasy two: "I'll kill myself and you'll be sorry when I'm dead," but an infant or young child has to be very sick in order to do more than *dramatize* this fantasy.

Fantasy three: The last resort for the deprived child is to be *very sick* without dying—so sick that he gets attention from his parents, his siblings and perhaps the community, trying to get enough to make up for all the love and attention he has missed.

Adults, thinking they may be mentally or physically ill, in consulting a physician are likely to act out one or all of these fantasies. If it happens to be fantasy number one, they are usually making a superhuman effort to control their vindictive and murderous tendencies. They are likely, therefore, to be very polite. If it happens to be fantasy number two, they have usually waited a long time to consult a physician. In one way or another they hope that the physician will

* New York City.

save them from their psychic or somatic suicidal impulse or tell them that they *have to die*. Fantasy three is the most frequent because the physician and community are readily exploited. To become a chronic invalid for the rest of one's life is a very comforting idea to a neglected human being.

The practicing physician should never laugh at the infants, chronologically adult, entering his office who are governed by these fantasies. Of course, one never says "snap out of it" because the illness tendency was established at a preverbal level and no words—kind or unkind—will cure the patient unless he is helped to understand his fantasy.

A brief illustration may serve to clarify this statement:

Case of Jenny

Jenny, aged 30, was tired to death and came home on Christmas eve to an annoying husband and children. No one wanted to help her decorate the tree and so she had to do it all by herself. She broke some of the glass balls but did not bother to pick them up. She was crawling around the floor and got glass splinters in her knees. Her knees became swollen and feverish but she refused to call a doctor. Finally some friend dragged in a doctor and it was found that she had septicemia.

While Jenny was getting better she told a friend who visited her at the hospital that she was sorry she was getting well because having taken care of so many sick people in her life, she wanted to be taken care of by someone else. Jenny didn't want to die but wanted to be sick because it was her turn to be taken care of.

Perhaps further discussion of illness should be preceded by a definition of the term "deprived children." Of course it is not a synonym for underprivileged children because we have our poor little rich girls and boys; our little Lord Fauntleroys. *One might say that a deprived child is a child whose parental and social environment is generally against his growing up.* Ego development is taboo and the family or community hearthstone is cold. Under these circumstances there is not much difference between a child kicked out in a blizzard to sell newspapers and a child showered with presents from the uncles and the cousins and the aunts.

Some physicians use finger painting occasionally as a supplement to the other projective technics. The finger painting (see fig. 1) presented in this connection is of considerable interest. Since it is impossible to ask for a reader's vote as to whether it was done by a man or a woman or the age, it may be of interest to note that most people who have seen this painting guess that it was done by a young man or middle aged woman. Actually, it was done by a man of twenty-two but his personality, because of identification with his mother and younger brother, is really a mixture of the two. When asked to describe this picture, he said that it was the picture of a sea monster: "I guess Mother."

His physician said, "What is that over to the right?"

He said, "It is a scared rabbit about to be flipped into nowhere by mamma's tail."

"What's that at the left?" he was asked.

"Oh, that's a sea wall. I put that in at the last moment. I thought she should be walled in on one side because you know she's very dangerous."

This painting was put away and shown again to the patient one year later.

The patient said, "You know that scared rabbit was really the ghost of an ego."

The Rorschach report taken at the time of the painting read as follows:

The Rorschach reactions indicate an intelligent, sensitive personality with marked neurotic difficulties which hamper his relationship with other people, strongly affect his self-confidence, and interfere with the development of objective interests and the free use of his good mental potentialities.

His insecurity concerns his own status as a person as well as his capacity to form opinions, make judgments and decisions, have definite feelings. He does not at all believe in himself as a person in his own right, with his own wishes, opinions. He tends to feel inadequate, inferior to others, incapable of doing the things he feels he ought to do. His deeply rooted sense of weakness and of helplessness takes a characteristic form: It is as though it were *not* really he who lived, acted, felt, were related to the world outside him. He does not seem to have real confidence in anybody and unconsciously his feeling is that people are apart, distant from each other, and potentially hostile, hence untrustworthy.

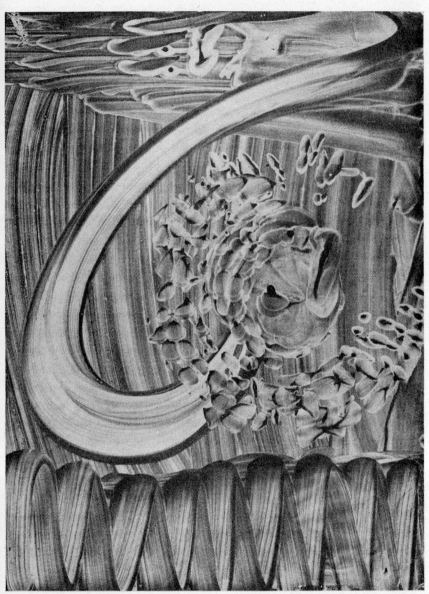

FIG. 1.

On the other hand, he lives under considerable pressure. He tends to feel all the time that he ought to *do* something, ought to do it better than he does, ought to live up to certain standards which he does not feel capable of reaching and cannot quite accept. But this pressure, too, is indefinite. Among his Rorschach responses there is a recurrent percept which expresses the fear that somebody gets hold of somebody else (himself) and "makes them do things." But these percepts are strangely impersonal. They suggest that he lives under the pressure of a powerful parental authority, but that this pressure is veiled, elusive, difficult to put one's finger on. It seems to be experienced by him as the hold of an invisible force and as the unspoken reproach that he is not worthy, not strong, not good enough. He cannot battle it, nor even resent it, because there does not seem to be anything concrete to battle or resent.

He is unconsciously so convinced of his inadequacy that he does not feel any real wish to try. If he does not really enter a situation, if all his life remains on a tentative basis, then nothing very dreadful can happen to him. Then he has not really committed himself to anything definite, and also the vaguely feared authoritative power cannot really get hold of him.

The "unreality" of his life, its tentative, slight character, are compensated for by vague fantasies and daydreams into which more of his positive feelings seem to go than into his actual relations to people or into his work.

It is obvious that this patient in his few comments on his finger painting had given the essence of his own Rorschach report in fewer words than are contained in the foregoing excerpt from the report. He really felt that nothing he said came from *him*. If his physician indicated assent to a given statement, there was immediate panic. Then "you agree with mamma" or "you disagree with mamma." The suggestion that one might agree or disagree with the patient himself was completely rejected because *whatever he thought* came from the guidance of mamma or from the hypnotic effect of the doctor. Nothing he possessed, from his clothes to his ideas, could be his own.

This patient having suggested, a year later, that the scared rabbit was the ghost of an ego said, "I showed Mummy Steig's *Agony in the Kindergarten* and mamma said that it was all distorted—it was all wrong inside." He continued, "But Mary (his girl friend) and

I were talking about it last night and we thought we knew exactly what it meant."

His mother said, "Perhaps it's all right for your generation but not for mine."

There was a considerable pause and he ventured, "Mother has been partially pyschoanalyzed and she taught in a school and she knows all about children—I don't understand."

After a long pause, during which there was no comment from the doctor, he said, "Mummy did say that she did not have much imagination. You talked about empathy and Einfuhlung. Do you think she really can't know what somebody else feels? Maybe she does feel but she doesn't know what to do about it which is the saddest and most sadistic thing of all."

There was another long pause then: "Well you know Mummy is very interested in Child Guidance and she spends an hour every day getting Guidance. Do you suppose she wouldn't need to spend so much time getting Guidance if she could feel what other people feel?"

Children economically and educationally deprived have difficulties. Children emotionally deprived have greater difficulties. In order to get a true evaluation of a person, the I.Q. must be looked at side by side with the E.Q. (the emotional or personality quotient). The balance determines the effectiveness and social relationships of the person.* An individual with a very high I.Q. may rate as a moron from the point of view of the E.Q. and conversely. The term E.Q. is a relatively new term in projective technics. A high E.Q. and low I.Q. can indicate a constructive person and a high I.Q. and a low E.Q. can indicate a destructive person.

Increasingly during the last ten years the Rorschach test has been found to be a valuable aid to the consultant in parent-child relationships. Usually a child is brought to the office as a "problem child." If time does not permit a thorough clinical investigation, or if it appears advisable to send the child to another physician for treatment, the recommendation for treatment and the choice of a physician well-equipped to carry out the treatment is facilitated by a Rorschach evaluation.

* The E. Q. used in this sense should not be confused with the Educational Quotient. It would be convenient were we to substitute some such term as Personality Quotient or Adjustment Quotient.

There are two other ways in which the Rorschach test is useful, which may be of even greater importance: First, since the problem with most "problem children" lies primarily in one or both parents rather than in the child, wherever possible one or both parents should be persuaded to take the test along with the child in order to see in what way the child may resemble the parents or what factor in the parent-child relationship the parents may be overlooking. Most parents are willing to cooperate if asked in some such words as these. The information thus gained is useful, but as a second point it should be known that it has a value in developing insight in the parents.

After going over the reports of the child and one or both parents, it is useful to pick out the points which the parent will understand most readily in relation to the child's difficulties and to his own difficulties with the child. The fact that it is possible to state that the clinician's evaluation is supported by the Rorschach test usually increases the parents' interest and makes them more cooperative. Hence the test serves a useful purpose even though it may tell the physician nothing he had not guessed before. In the majority of cases the parents, becoming more objective, then shift at least a part of their anxious interest from the child *they wanted* to what they can do for the child *that is*. In nine cases out of ten, if the parents' cooperation is gained in this way, treatment of the child becomes unnecessary.

A case in point is that of a married woman, forty years old, small, blond, attractive, aggressive, whose special interest is allergy. She brought in her nine-year-old asthmatic daughter for treatment. While taking a brief history, she wept and expressed feelings of inadequacy as a parent, and doubts about all of medicine, because none of the doctors whom she had consulted had been able to help the girl. A Rorschach test was recommended for both of them. After a brief explanation, she concurred. The Rorschach tests (which included other projective material, such as analysis of drawings and handwriting) were reported to the mother in a considerably modified form. The brief abstracts which follow give the essential points but it should be noted that the full material was not presented to her all at once.

Female, Age 9.

This is a gifted, creative girl of superior intelligence. She is very disturbed at present, and although she shows a fundamentally sound personality structure she is tending too much toward introversion and is probably quite a behavior problem.

She is ambitious and conscientious but so reactive, impulsive and absorbed in fantasies that she cannot concentrate well on any project she has not herself initiated. She has quite a variety of interests in the world outside her personal affairs. She can think and observe accurately and logically, has good common sense and is normal, not eccentric, in her points of view. Her factual knowledge is somewhat limited in favor of her story-telling and other artistic abilities.

Emotionally she is highly reactive but she is withdrawing more and more into herself as a retreat from a disturbing environment. Marked ambivalence and vacillation in attitude toward her parents is indicated. She wants to love and be loved but her love objects constantly frustrate her. She is friendly and adaptive but always distrustful and quick to retreat from contact. She is aggressive but more through stubborn independence, indifference, and intellectual self assertion than through any direct behavior.

Instincts are too repressed for a normal girl; she is too mature, too intellectual. Adult problems and responsibilities have probably been forced upon her attention and she has not been allowed to be childish long enough in a stable family milieu.

A dominant and disturbing mother image is conspicuous—a sexless, masculine, dangerous mother. Parental conflict is also suggested by the repeated theme of conflict between her human figures. The girl has introjected this conflict and feels torn apart probably both by divergent parental standards and by conflicting attitudes toward a given parent. She also feels victimized by the external conflicts and tries to defend herself from further hurt.

Her fantasy contains both projections of her inner disturbance and self-expressive creative themes. She would like friendly, cooperative relationships but she always expects the worst of people. She tends to belittle and to take a satirical attitude—there is always something ugly about everything beautiful.

Female, Age 40.

The subject has superior intellectual abilities which are very inefficiently applied. She is so absorbed in her personal life problems that she cannot pay attention to objective matters or the practical details of daily life. She can be efficient and get satisfaction from such activity but insecurity quickly distracts her from it, leaving her unsure of the value of anything. Just beneath the surface of consciousness are feelings of discouragement, emptiness, inadequacy, and guilt. She has little capacity for critical introspection, however, and would probably admit only that she is distressed and distrait.

The contents of her associations, together with her handwriting and her drawings, suggest an ambivalent attitude toward men and the masculine life role—admiration, jealousy, ridicule. Yet with this role she associates beauty and pleasure. She can accept neither one role nor the other, cannot reconcile the two, and is pulled in both directions. A background of severe parental conflict is indicated with an especially inadequate mother relationship.

After a little objection she agreed to further interviews in which she wanted to be told just what to do for her child. After the first interview with the mother, the daughter was more or less forgotten. Her own problems and those of her husband, and the effect of their relationship on the child, were discussed.

After twelve sessions with the mother over a period of three months, the girl, after seeing the psychiatrist only once, discontinued her treatments with the allergist, as well as with her nose and throat specialist. She remained well for several months and when the season of the year arrived in which she had for the preceding seven years experienced her most acute asthmatic attacks, she said to her mother: "How does it happen that I have not been seeing my doctors and I am not having my Fall asthma?" The mother's treatment was continued, with interruptions, for another year, but there has been no return of illness in the daughter.

Space does not permit a full report of the mother's psychodynamic development, but the following points may be of interest:

(1) The daughter resembles and was named for her father. There was a history of allergy in the father's family; none in the mother's. The mother, herself, suffered from a marked variety of syndromes, including migraine, dysmenorrhea, dysuria for which no adequate reason was ever found, periods of extreme (alternating) depression and elation, along with great fatigability. The latter is partially explained by the fact that she worked hard and she was under constant strain in attempting to protect her children from her alcoholic husband who spent a great deal of time at home while she was working.

(2) It appeared that the mother felt extremely guilty about her antagonism toward her asthmatic daughter and blamed the daughter's disability on the father, whom she hated cordially. With her other

children she was able to be more patient and somewhat objective. With this child she was very strict, even to the point of slapping, beating, and locking her in a dark closet, all of which were "against her principles."

After the patient had related this material while walking up and down the room, clenching her hands, shrieking, and wanting to smash things, she had an asthmatic attack, the first in her life. Her behavior was discussed against the background of fuller clinical material than can be given here, but she left very angry, saying, "I came to have my child cured of asthma; instead, you have given me asthma." However, it was during the following week that the daughter recovered from her asthma, and the patient has had no further attacks in a period of over three years.

(3) In the next appointment following this episode the patient was able to talk more freely about her guilt—guilt related to her child, husband, father, and mother, and to say that the reason she was so mad with her physician was that she with her profession, should never behave like that in a doctor's office. But, she said she had never been able to talk with anyone before "without all the brakes on." At this time she reported a greater ability to be objective in her human relationships, and an improvement in dealing with her professional obligations.

(4) Her conflict related to male and female roles was discussed with her in further detail, including the fact that, although her father was master of the house, he was alcoholic like her husband, and the mother "took the brunt of things," compensating for this necessity by representing herself as a martyr. The patient rebelled against being a martyr like her mother, and her major goals in life were to be a good mother and a good worker.

The obsessive-compulsive elements in this parent-child problem have not been stressed, but from the point of view of day-to-day experience each was wondering whether or not one or the other had "done right," and both were greatly confused about what might or might not be "right." Neither one really wanted to live with the other, and it was only when this situation became clear to the mother and, indirectly through her to the child, that their relationship improved. Then, first the child, and later the mother, began to lose their respective illness syndromes.

By way of indicating the intensity of the emotional contagion in this family atmosphere it may be added that the child stuttered periodically when under emotional stress. The mother reproduced this symptom also, under treatment, but both recovered. It is interesting that the mother had been previously diagnosed as potentially schizophrenic with a manic-depressive pattern, or psychopathic, by other psychiatrists whom she had consulted.

This mother had given during her first two interviews the essence of her own and her child's Rorschach reports. Nevertheless, she derived great satisfaction from a discussion of the reports because she felt that two completely different approaches to her problem resulted in the same diagnosis and suggested the same therapy. Whether or not the clinician learns from the projective tests, they may help him, as they do his patient, to a greater security in diagnosis and therapeutic management.

Projective tests made it easier for this mother to understand the conditioned reflex elements in her own behavior and in her child's illness. Here it is not necessary to explain the term *conditioned reflex* because the work of Pavlov, Liddell, Gantt and others has become an integral part of the training of all specialists in psychosomatic medicine.

It is much easier and more economical of time and money to pasteurize milk, clean up wells and eliminate typhoid carriers than it is to cope with parents who are foci of emotional infection in the family. Shortly after World War I, Frankwood Williams wrote that the home is "a place of conflict, openly acknowledged or bravely denied. Into this children are born, and the place becomes one of infection, an infection more pestilential, perhaps, than the bacterial diseases usually so classified."*

The observation that certain types of illness appear to run in families is centuries old, and for a long time it was believed by physicians and parents alike that the reason lay in the physical heredity of each new born child. We spoke of familial disease, but now we recognize that although many diseases are familial, the term should be understood in more than one sense. Freud and Williams were among the first to call attention to the immediate family into which the child is born as a focus of contagion probably more determinative of behavior and susceptibility to illness than the child's inherited con-

* Frankwood E. Williams, Adolescence. New York, Farrar & Rinehart, 1921.

stitution. The family is the matrix within which develop health or disease in parents or children or both, but familial disease is determined less by heredity than by exposure.

There have been comments in medical literature about parents who, without actually providing the bacillus, play a large role in determining the susceptibility of their children to tuberculosis, an illness in which the concrete causative agent is, of course, the tubercal bacillus. Present studies indicate that in illnesses for which no infectious agent is determinable, home and social influences play the determining role. Even if further bacteriological and chemical research should isolate some virus now unknown, present indications are that successful interruption of the causative sequences which produce illness will involve not only bacterio- and chemo-therapy, but also careful attention to factors which may increase or decrease susceptibility. Some when they become ill, seem likely to develop cardiac dysfunction, asthma, hay fever, skin eruptions, accident habit, spontaneous abortion habit, cold habit—just to mention a few.

An even more recent advance has been the realization that some family patterns tend to the development of specific illness patterns. It used to be said by John, age 13, the third child in his family, "I don't see why I'm so different. We have the same heredity and the same parents and they treated us all alike, but I'm sick and the others aren't. Maybe something is wrong with the genes."

Whether there are two or six children in a family, the stresses and strains to which each is subjected have little to do with cultural background. Those who say we have the same background and the same parents and so why shouldn't we all be sick in the same way, might be told that the first child, second child, last child, first girl, first boy in any family have something in common whether the parents are English, German, Greek, Italian, Jewish, Puritan, or almost any other racial or cultural group on the map. What they have in common is more determinant of illness than their heredity and culture. Of course, this means that the psychodynamic relationships in any family are more determinant of health or illness in children than race, heredity or culture.

The loved or unloved child is supposed to take after the loved or unloved parent as the case may be but it is interesting that with adopted children one hears that "she takes after my husband's family," "he takes after my side of the family," and vice versa. It has been found with adopted children that the illness pattern of the adopted child follows that of one or another side of the adopting family. Such observations have led to the delineation of a family profile which is more or less likely to be pathogenic. We need now to add to the concept of individual personality profiles the concept of a family personality profile.

Probably there will never be enough psychiatrists to pick up all the pieces once the damage has been done but such resources as we have will go much further if all those in the practice of medicine think in terms of the family and its setting. Such thinking, whether or not other members of the family are treated or referred for treatment, will lead to the integration of therapeutic and research goals, but most important of all will increase the effectiveness of any medical program directed toward the preservation of health.

Conclusion

1. The importance of understanding the type of infant fantasy which underlines any patient's, "chief complaint" has been indicated briefly. A case history has been given to illustrate three major fantasy types.

2. The child-parent relationship should be carefully checked in all patients, whether or not chronologically adult. This is often aided by projective technics among which intelligent use of finger painting might be included. Such technics may help both patient and physician to understand the fantasy.

3. The conditioned reflex component which becomes part of the acting out of the fantasy associated with any mental or physical illness is so great that it should be given particular attention in any approach to therapy.

4. The strength of nations lies in the soundness of their children. The creative trend today is toward the care and rearing of parents; the parents of this generation and the parents of future generations. This is the essence of preventive medicine and the medicine of the future.

15

THE INFLUENCE OF PSYCHOPATHOLOGICAL EMOTIONS ON PSYCHOLOGICAL TEST PERFORMANCE*

By LIVINGSTON WELCH, Ph.D. and THOMAS A. C. RENNIE, M.D.†

I. Introduction and Problem

THIS REPORT will review ten years' work at the Payne Whitney Psychiatric Clinic in studying the influence of pathological emotions on conditioning, association of ideas, concentration, and reasoning. Specifically, it will discuss the effect of anxiety on the formation of conditioned responses, the role of elation as it affects association of ideas, the effects of depression and elation on the capacity to concentrate, and the influence of anxiety in certain tests of reasoning.

The scheme of the report will be to take up each of these four aspects of learning, first defining the emotion studied and then presenting the procedure of the experiment devised and the general conclusions.

II. Conditioned Responses

1. *The Effect of Anxiety.* The effect of various emotional states on the rate of conditioning has interested a number of experimenters during the last fifteen years. In most instances, the inquiry involved specific psychiatric syndromes. In studies made by Welch and Kubis (18) and others (12) at the Payne Whitney Psychiatric Clinic, an examination was made into the effect of pathological anxiety, regardless of diagnosis, on the conditioning rate. The purpose of our studies was to investigate whether a correlation between the rate of conditioning and the intensity of anxiety occurred in the syndrome of any mental disorder. If positive correlation existed, then we would expect that people with pathological anxiety would require fewer

---

* From The New York Hospital and the Department of Psychiatry, Cornell University Medical College, New York, and the Institute for Research in Clinical and Child Psychology, Hunter College, New York.

† Cornell University.

trials to condition than those who had none. We would furthermore expect that those with marked pathological anxiety would condition quicker than those with mild pathological anxiety.

2. *Definition of Anxiety.* Clinically, intense anxiety was characterized by a strong feeling of apprehension and corresponding marked physical sensations (cardiovascular, gastrointestinal, and respiratory), marked disorders of concentration and attention, and elevated fasting blood sugar and leukocytosis. Moderate anxiety was noted when patients experienced a mild feeling of apprehension, some palpitation, a dry throat, moist hands, and revealed mild disorders in concentration and attention and a slightly elevated fasting blood sugar and white count. In mild anxiety, the patient felt merely uneasy and anxious and had occasional mild physical sensations. We are interested here only in the effect of anxiety regardless of the clinical diagnosis.

3. *Apparatus and Procedure.* The conditioned stimulus was a nonsense syllable of low association value among a list of fifty-four such syllables presented to the subject on a motion picture screen. On alternate occasions a buzzer was sounded when the conditioned stimulus, the syllable, KAX, appeared. In other words, the first time KAX appeared, the buzzer was sounded. The second time there was no buzzer, but the buzzer was sounded on the third appearance of KAX. The buzzer constituted the unconditioned stimulus which produced a psychogalvanic response detected by the Fordham two-stage D.C. amplifier connected in series with a graphic ammeter, which recorded in permanent form every response that was made. The criteria of conditioning required (a) three successive psychogalvanic reflex responses to the conditioned stimulus syllable without the buzzer, and (b) the magnitude of each response to be greater than that of any of the responses to the nonsense syllables presented between the corresponding two buzzes. An example of the fulfillment of the criteria can be seen in fig. 1, which is the record of an actual case.

The record is read from right to left, so that the first reaction occurs at the right of the chart. All eight reactions to the word, KAX, are indicated by appropriate designations at the top of the record, the first, third, fifth, and seventh presentations accompanied by the sound of the buzzer, the even presentations unaccompanied by any sound.

4. *Results.* In our normal group composed of eighty-two college

students, it was necessary to sound the buzzers from 9 to 58 times before the subjects fulfilled the criteria of three successive responses to the conditioned stimulus syllable. All but four had a score of from 14 to 58; the average score was 23.4. In the patient's group the scores ranged from 3 to 16. The average score of forty-three patients with anxiety was 8.6. Forty-two of the patients diagnosed by the psychiatric staff as having anxiety had scores of 14 or less, while all of the patients diagnosed by the psychiatric staff as having no anxiety had scores of 14 or more, or did not give a response to the buzzer. Taking

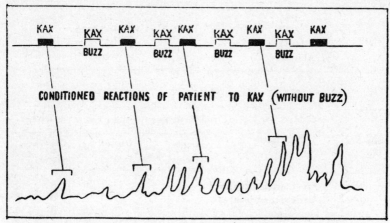

FIG. 1. Criterion of conditioning. (Actual record of patient.)

the score of 14 as a critical differentiating value, 98 per cent of the time the scores of the experiment were in agreement with the psychiatrist's observation as to whether or not the patient had anxiety. It is important to note that the experimenters were never informed of the condition of the patient tested. In most instances the patient was brought into the testing room by the nurse and the experimenter in the control room never saw the patient. The diagnosis of anxiety was made by members of the staff before they examined the scores.

In this study the degree of pathological anxiety was also considered. In Table I the relationship of the conditioning score to the psychiatric diagnoses can be seen.

In Table II we present the record of those patients who were tested three times. Here the scores on the original test are in agreement 59 per cent of the time with the psychiatrist's observation of degree of anxiety.

5. *Discussion.* If we are to think of learning in the broader sense as the establishment of new responses, then conditioning is indubitably a form of learning. But one might well ask, "Why should anxiety hasten this form of learning?" Pavlov was the first to observe that

TABLE I

Score	Diagnosis of Anxiety
3–6	Marked
7–10	Moderate
11–14	Mild
Above 14	None

TABLE II

Case No.	Diagnosis	1st Test		2nd Test		3rd Test	
		Degree of Anxiety	Test Score	Degree of Anxiety	Test Score	Degree of Anxiety	Test Score
7	Psychopathic pers.....	A	7	C	13	A	5
12	Anxiety neurosis......	A	7	B	5	B	8
11	Depression............	A	7	C	15	B	5
27	Psychopathic pers.....	A	10	D	18	?	8
32	Schizophrenic.........	A	8	?	X*	D	36
36	Psychopathic pers.....	A	3	C	11	C	11

Note: X* = The patient did not respond to the buzzer.
      ? = Diagnosis uncertain.

his excitative dogs conditioned quicker than did those who belonged to what he called the inhibitory group. From this experiment it might seem that Pavlov was referring in the first instance to a dog with anxiety neurosis, and yet his description did not fully suggest this diagnosis. Why should anxiety hasten this form of learning and not the higher forms? We also found no correlation between quick conditioning and high I.Q. Jules Masserman, in conversation, has suggested the possibility of anxiety strengthening a basic defense mechanism in this experimental situation which involves startle. We considered that subjects with anxiety might react with greater concentration to the conditioned and unconditioned stimulus than the normal individual who allowed his mind to wander in this uninteresting test situation. This hypothesis has been at least partially supported by an experiment which we have just completed (20). Twenty-four college students were given the above-described conditioning test with the following addition to the procedure. A wire recorder during the entire test kept reminding the subjects—"Do not let your mind wander; try to keep your mind blank, but concentrate fully on each syllable as it appears on the screen." Though 60 per cent admitted that the recording helped them to keep their minds from wandering, this group did not condition quicker than the original normal group unaided by the recorded suggestions. In fact, the group with the recorded suggestions took longer to condition. The mean for the first group was 23.9, whereas the mean for the last group was 34.6. Possibly the soft, rhythmic voice of the recorded speaker relaxed or diminished the anxiety of many of these subjects. On the other hand, the suggestions themselves, reduction of distraction, or the sound-screening effect of the recorder may explain this difference.

Can we conclude that a very low score on this test is a reliable clincial test for neurotic or other anxiety? Any such conclusion based on this test alone would be highly speculative. In a study by Schiff, Dougan, and Welch (12), this anxiety test was administered to three groups of children. The first group consisted of 47 juvenile delinquents at Bellevue Hospital. According to the test criteria, 47 per cent had pathological scores. The second group was made up of 32 children with I.Q.'s of 140 and over at the Hunter Elementary School; 28 per cent of these subjects had pathological scores. The third group consisted of 36 children from P.S. 166. Here only 8 per cent manifested pathological anxiety, approximately the same percentage found in our first normal adult group. We feel that it would be rash to conclude that the difference between the 8 per cent and 28 per cent was because of a high percentage of psychoneurosis in the accelerated group. What the true explanation is we do not as yet know.

III. ASSOCIATION OF IDEAS

1. *The Effect of Elation.* It is a well-known clinical observation that patients with pathological elation show symptoms of overtalka-

tiveness, quick repartee, and flight of ideas, which suggests an increased flow of associations. In order to determine whether during pathological elation the associative activity actually increases or whether distractibility is the essential factor Welch, Diethelm, and Long (17) studied patients and a control group of normal subjects. A test for hyper-associative activity which could be scored quantitatively was devised for this investigation.

2. *Apparatus and Procedure.* In the aperture of a memory drum, the 15 nonsense syllables of low association value were presented to the subject for three seconds each. Beforehand, the subject was instructed to mention immediately anything that a syllable might suggest to him. He was told not to force the association. This was a personality study, not a test. Many brilliant people responded to all the syllables and many did not respond to any. In the control group, 179 college students made an average score of 3.33 responses, ranging from 0 to 11. Only three of these subjects gave more than seven responses, and two of the subjects appeared to be hypomanic since they reported that they did not need more than an average of three hours' sleep a night and that they had very marked fluctuations from elated to depressed moods. On the other hand, patients in the hospital diagnosed as elated gave scores ranging from 8 to 14 responses. In this study, the test was in agreement with the psychiatric diagnosis 127 times out of 154. In all, 101 patients were tested, but some of these were retested, bringing the total number of tests up to 154. Some patients were diagnosed by the psychiatric staff as being elated and others were not. In 64 per cent of the cases, patients with scores above 7 were elated. It is to be noted that moderate or intense anxiety and resentment did not affect the scores on this test. In Table III the distribution of psychiatric patients according to diagnosis is given.

In the second phase of this study, the effect of an endogenous stimulant was studied. In this pursuit we gave 10 mgs. of dexedrine sulfate to twenty-three Cornell medical students. One-half of this group was given the dexedrine sulfate one hour before the first test and a placebo one hour before the repeat test a month later. The procedure was reversed in connection with the other half of the group. In the first group, those getting dexedrine, the scores increased, whereas in the second group the scores decreased with statistically reliable differences. (There were established repeated correlations which indicated that under normal conditions there was very little change on the repeat test.)

In another study by Dougan and Welch (1), there was discovered a second factor which may affect the flow of ideas; namely, the removal of inhibitions by special training. The same association test

TABLE III

DISTRIBUTION OF PSYCHIATRIC PATIENTS ACCORDING TO DIAGNOSIS

Diagnosis	Number of patients
Anxiety neurosis	12
Anxiety neurosis, depression	1
Compulsive neurosis	2
Confusional psychosis	1
Depression	8
Epilepsy	1
Epilepsy, depression	1
Epilepsy, manic	1
Hysterical reaction	2
Manic excitement	3
Manic-depressive psychosis	11
Manic-depressive, senile	1
Manic-depressive, psychopathic personality	9
Paranoid reaction	3
Pre-senile reaction	1
Psychopathic personality	18
Psychopathic personality, anxiety neurosis	4
Psychopathic personality, depression	3
Schizophrenia	19
Total	101

was given to forty-five unselected students and fifteen art majors and students whose interests were in the field of the creative arts. Both groups were also given the ten Rorschach cards for a minute and a half each, to determine the number of responses they would make. The correlation between the two tests was .70. The scores on the association test were comparable with those of the elated patients and normal subjects under the influence of dexedrine. The average scores for the artistic group were almost double those of the unselected group. The result may be due to the particular training art students receive in which originality and freedom from customary intellectual restraints may be the clue.

IV. CONCENTRATION

1. *The Effect of Depression (Problem and Procedure).* In pursuit of a test of concentration, Welch, Diethelm, and Long (17) devised a task lasting nine and one-half minutes which intrinsically had no interest and which required continuous attention. The subject was obliged to listen to a recording of nonsense syllables on a phonograph record. Twenty times during the test period a bell on the record would ring and the subject was obliged to repeat the last two syllables given. Only a span of two syllables was required to be remembered, so that there was no strain on the subject's memory. All he had to do was to prevent his mind from wandering. The test scale was 40 points, one point for remembering each of the two syllables on the twenty occasions after the ring of the bell.

2. *Results.* The scores of the normal group of 50 subjects were 30 and above in all but two instances, and the scores of the patients were similarly high except in cases of severe disturbance or marked deterioration. In a follow-up study by Welch (15) patients with depression showed characteristic results. Thirty-four cases in all were studied. Fourteen patients were diagnosed as having depression. Of these, 71 per cent (or 10 out of 14) did 50 per cent better on the second half of the test. In other words, they made twice as many errors on the first part as they did on the second part. The opposite was true of 60 per cent (or 12 out of 20) of the patients without depression. In this group, three manifested anxiety. If they are excluded, then 70.5 per cent (or 12 out of 17) did not do 50 per cent better on the second half of the test. These results are not too surprising. The depressed patient, or even the anxious patient, is likely to begin a task with a feeling of defeat which prevents him from trying his best, or special preoccupations may distract him. When, however, he realizes he is succeeding, his attitude changes and his interest increases. In many of these cases the patient tried too hard. He would repeat the syllables both forward and backward until he became confused and would want to stop. When persuaded not to try so hard, his performance improved.

3. *The Effect of Elation.* The effect of elation on this same test was

negative. There was no evidence that pathological elation interfered with performance on this specific test, since all of our elated patients obtained scores that were normal and above. Several of these patients presented excitements with delusion formation. They were continually talking in disconnected sentences about their delusions as they entered the testing room and while the first part of the instructions was given. Nevertheless, as soon as the test itself began, they remained absolutely attentive and obtained very high scores. Several manic patients gave vivid associations to each one of the syllables spoken on the record. They described everything that each syllable suggested to them and could not be prevented from so doing. This, however, did not prevent them from obtaining high scores.

V. Reasoning

1. *Effect of Anxiety (Problem and Procedure)*. A series of experiments for the investigation of inductive reasoning was applied to 187 patients suffering from various psychiatric illnesses in order to establish the influence of anxiety on reasoning (16). The experiments had been found by Welch and Long (19) to be reliable for children who had passed their fourteenth year. The correlation between general intelligence and reasoning ability in these tests was very low. The subjects were requested to isolate the stimulus which produced a given effect. In a three-dimensional problem the subject was required to find the causal factor by putting a block in the correct place to light a bulb. The blocks bore pictures of animals, food, and vehicles. The causal factor was indicated by the presence of the same class of pictures (e.g., boats) in the two rows with lights and by the absence of this class of pictures in the row which had no light. This can be plainly seen in fig. 2. The same type of problem was presented with pictures. The time was recorded for each experiment.

In fig. 3, the problem was essentially the same. The causal factor was not a three-dimensional object such as the block with a plug in it, but merely a picture. Looking from right to left on the top row, we see that on the first day a little girl ate a carrot and some pumpkin and was sick. In the second row, we see that on the second day she ate pumpkin and beans and was well. In the third row she ate a carrot and beans and was sick. The one vegetable common to illness was, of course, the carrot. Again, the same type of problem was presented in a written form. (See fig. 4.) The name of the food is printed instead of the picture, and the drawing of the child in bed is substituted by the word, "sick." In the linguistic problems, Mills' method of agreement was involved where the causal factor is presented in every instance where the effect is found. Mills' method of difference was included where the causal factor was found in situations where the effect was present but was absent where the effect was absent.

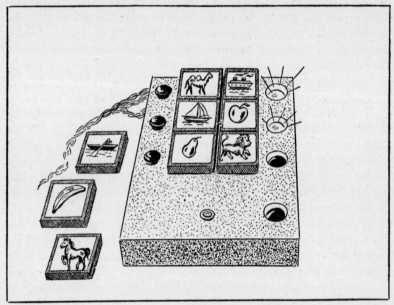

FIG. 2.

Mills' joint method of agreement and difference was the third method involved combining the two. In both the three-dimensional and the written problems, concrete material was substituted for abstract matter; that is, in the simpler problem, making use of the joint method, the subject had only to perceive that one particular kind of block, for instance, the camel block, was present in the row with lights and absent in the row without a light. In the abstract problem, it might be two species of the class of animal that made the light go on, or at still a higher level of abstraction, two species of the class of mammals; for instance, the camel and man.

These problems were further complicated by increasing the number of antecedents in the written test from two to four rows and by

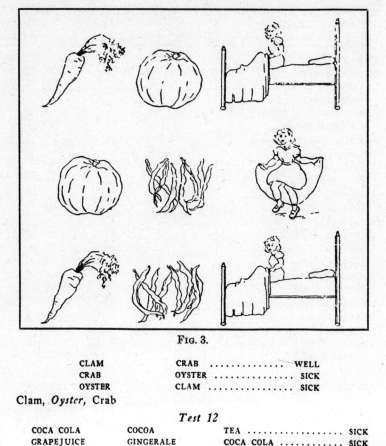

FIG. 3.

CLAM	CRAB	....	WELL
CRAB	OYSTER	....	SICK
OYSTER	CLAM	....	SICK

Clam, *Oyster*, Crab

Test 12

COCA COLA	COCOA	TEA	....	SICK
GRAPEJUICE	GINGERALE	COCA COLA	....	SICK
GRAPEJUICE	GINGERALE	MILK	....	WELL
MILK	TEA	COCOA	....	WELL

Gingerale, Cocoa, *Coca Cola*, Milk, Grapejuice, Tea

FIG. 4.

increasing both the abstractness and the number of antecedents at the same time. In all, there were eight three-dimensional tests, one pictorial test, and ten written tests. The criteria for the three-dimensional and pictorial problems were three consecutive successful trials accompanied by an adequate explanation. The score of failure was given if no adequate explanation was given in a span of ten trials. The linguistic tests involved 100 problems. An average of eight cor-

TABLE IV

Psychopathic personalities		40
Anxiety present	22	
Failures	14	
Normal results	8	
Patients without anxiety	18	
Normal results	All	
Psychoneurotic disorders		24
Anxiety present	18	
Failures	7	
Normal results	11	
Patients without anxiety	6	
Normal results	All	
Depressions		54
Anxiety present	47	
Failures	35	
Normal results	12	
Patients without anxiety	7	
Normal results	All	
Moderate manic excitements		12
Anxiety present	7	
Failures	All	
Patients without anxiety	5	
Normal results	All	
Paranoid reactions		8
Anxiety present	5	
Failures	3	
Normal results	2	
Patients without anxiety	3	
Normal results	All	
Schizophrenic disorders		45
Anxiety present	26	
Failures	All	
Patients without anxiety	19	
Normal results	All	
Alcoholism with depression		4
Anxiety present	4	
Failures	All	

rect answers out of a possible ten was taken as the criterion for each of these ten groups of problems.

2. *Results.* In all cases of failures anxiety was present. The failures were most numerous in the linguistic test (written problems, ninety-two patients). With twenty-two patients the experiments were repeated six weeks to four months later, after anxiety had subsided. In all repeated experiments the particular patients performed without failure. Twenty-one patients (including schizophrenic depressed conditions) had failures in the three-dimensional test, while five schizophrenic patients had failures with the pictorial material. Three patients were unable to classify the material correctly. For fifty-four patients the time was prolonged, apparently being influenced by the patient's attitude to the test and not directly by anxiety.

Anxiety affected inductive reasoning adversely in psychoneurotic, psychopathic personality make-up, depressive, elated, paranoid, and schizophrenic patients. It can be stated that anxiety can interfere with inductive reasoning in any of these psychopathological disorders but that, on the other hand, the presence of anxiety does not necessarily affect reasoning in all subjects. No explanation can be offered for this effect of anxiety in some patients. This effect has not been observed with normal anxiety.

Similar to the concentration test, there is a tendency for the patient to manifest the greatest amount of anxiety at the beginning of the test. The patient might weep and complain that he was a moron and that he could never pass any test. After a little success, this extreme manifestation of anxiety disappeared. Classification of the entire patient group can be seen in Table IV.

VI. DISCUSSION

Psychiatrists and psychologists, in collaboration, are making important studies of the intellectual processes and personality factors that are significant in the understanding of human personality disorders. Psychological tests bring precision into the clinical area whereas twenty-five years ago psychiatrists relied largely upon clinical impression and unrefined tests for substantiation. The studies herein reported represent ten years of such collaborative effort.

The psychiatrist can be little expected to know the whole range of the hundreds of psychological tests and experiments that have been devised to study one or another aspect of intellectual function in psychopathological states. The field of psychological testing is too vast and complex. The findings are often contradictory.

The greatest confusion came from the attempt to define specific psychological changes as occurring in specific disease entities. Psychiatry itself contributed to some of this confusion. Kraepelinian and post-Kraepelinian search for distinct nosological entities was too rigid to do justice to the enormous complexities and overlapping aspects of psychiatric syndromes. Furthermore, these attempts were too often predicated upon the unfounded conception of rigid disease entities of known etiology, course, and outcome. These older terminologies very largely leave out our modern conceptions of dynamic factors. They are increasingly recognized as having only limited usefulness. They are diagnostic entities not frequently enough substantiated by long-term studies of the changes and phases that take place in the progress of a disorder. It was such unsubstantiated categorical entities that led to great confusion in the interpretation of psychological as well as physiological and bio-chemical findings. Serious errors inevitably ensued. The Rorschach experiment, for example, was evolved largely from the study of psychopathological individuals. It remains to be re-evaluated from the study of so-called "normal" groups of individuals. The Minnesota Multiphasic Personality Inventory was developed and standardized largely around the no longer tenable Kraepelinian nosology. The time has come when we must discard the rigidities of "disease entities" in favor of the study of specific emotions regardless of the clinical state. We need to know more about the effect of anxiety, fear, depression, elation, resentment, anger, hostility, and other emotions on test performance regardless of clinical diagnosis and we must abandon the belief that specific diseases inevitably produce specific psychological changes. The studies herein reported are predicated upon this conception and substantiate, we believe, the importance of this kind of approach.

There is very little psychological literature which is aimed in this direction. One searches in vain for any good studies that reveal the effect of emotions on any psychological function. Far too often psychological tests have been carried out with total disregard of the emotional state of the individual at the time of his testing. Where such factors are mentioned, they are apt to be ill-defined with such terms as "emotional tone," "affective tone," "hedonic tone," "interest," "preference," "like-dislike," "success-failure." From a psychiatric standpoint these terms are inadequate to describe the nature of the emotion, its intensity, its psychological and physiological effects, its dynamics, and its relevance to test performance.

A few such basic assumptions are generally accepted. Anxious children are known to do less well on intelligence testing than non-anxious children, and their performances are known to improve appreciably when anxiety is relieved. Rapaport recognizes this in the subtests of the Wechsler-Bellevue Scale. In his manual on "Diagnostic Psychological Testing" (10), he states: "In normals, neurotics and depressives it is a general rule that impairment of Digit Span is greater than that of Arithmetic; or in other words, attention is more impaired than concentration. In the schizophrenic group, however, a considerable portion of the cases show attention to be less impaired than concentration. If concentration is considered to be related to the hold on and effort to maintain contact with reality, it is understandable that it should be better retained in depressives, neurotics, and normals than in schizophrenics."

Surprisingly little is known about the influence of emotions on the association of ideas. Most of the work done has to do with studying "feeling-tone" underlying the rate of association formation. Rapaport (11) sums up the results of all such psychological studies by saying: "Although indicating some influence of feeling-tone on reaction time and reproduction, (results) are inconclusive." Further, in his discussion of influence of emotions on remembering of learned material or memory, he states: "The existence of the influence of 'emotional factors' on memory has been established." In the studies reviewed by him, the intensity of the emotional factor proved to be of more importance than its quality in its influence on memory.

The effect that various mental disorders have had on the conditioned reflexes has been subject of considerable interest to many experimenters during the last fifteen years. Tatarenko (14) has investigated disorders of the conditioned reflex activity in patients with senile psychosis, Kantorovich and Lukina (5) and Rabinowich (9) have pursued the same inquiry in connection with cases of progressive paralysis, while Franklin (2) and Lukina and Matusova (6) have concerned themselves with the reflex activity of epileptics.

The most accurate and carefully controlled studies pertaining to the rate of conditioning in patients suffering from mental disorders were made by Mays (7) and Shipley (13) and Pfaffmann and Schlosberg (8). Mays endeavored to compare the "perseverational tendencies" in catatonic schizophrenics with those of normal subjects. He reported that the schizophrenics showed two or more times as much perseveration as normals in all comparisons. Shipley's study can be considered a continuation of Mays' investigation. His groups were ranked in descending order of perseveration as follows: schizophrenics, manic-depressive psychotics, psychoneurotics, and normals. Pfaffmann and Schlosberg found that schizophrenics were the least responsive and at the same time had more negative reactions than either the normal subjects or the manic-depressive group. These results are in agreement with those of Grecker (3).

Hilgard and Marquis (4), in commenting on the work of these men, state: "Inconsistencies in the findings make it difficult to give any general summary of their results." Even if there were no inconsistencies, Hilgard and Marquis believe that the results would merely indicate "a rather poor instance of the well-known clinical picture of excitement in manics and of the negativism that marks schizophrenia." Here again, these studies have been concerned largely with diagnostic entities.

At the Payne Whitney Psychiatric Clinic of the New York Hospital a series of tests were devised and employed to determine the effect of specific psychopathological emotions upon certain intellectual functions. These have been described. Regardless of clinical diagnosis, the presence of well-marked anxiety increases conditioning rate, affects the capacity to concentrate, and in some cases affects reasoning ability. This last point supports Rapaport's statement that "the stable balance of emotions, which is the prerequisite for the selection of the appropriate information making for good judgment, is easily disturbed by maladjustment." (10) In patients showing well-defined states of elation, there is demonstrable an increase in the flow of ideas, but no interruption in capacity of concentration as determined by the test of concentration. Depression, on the other hand, with or without concomitant anxiety, adversely affects concentration at the beginning of the test period. Depression alone without anxiety has no determinable effect on conditioning capacity.

These findings point to certain important psychiatric conclusions—anxiety, elation, and depression have specific effects on specific aspects of intellectual functioning regardless of clinical diagnosis. If we consider the vast range of disorders commonly grouped together under the designation of schizophrenia, we must immediately recognize that anxiety and other emotions produce changes which may be temporary or lasting, reversible or irreversible, and which must be heavily weighted before pronouncement of any specific schizophrenic thinking disorder. Disturbances in reasoning, judgment, and concept formation may, in many instances, be due to the interference of strong emotions. This must be borne in mind in all studies of so-called "deterioration" and will offer a new and fruitful avenue in the elucidation of the process designated as "deterioration."

Equally important for the psychiatrist as psychotherapist must be the recognition that strong emotions may adversely affect the freedom and amount of association, the ability to concentrate and comprehend, the degree of attention possible, and the quality of the reasoning that the patient brings to bear upon his problems. Anxiety may prevent psychotherapeutic progress because of its influence on these intellectual processes. Long-sustained anxiety may adversely affect the success of life achievement in neurotics and other severely disturbed individuals. Clinical signs which may indicate the adverse influence of anxiety upon intellectual performance are vagueness, circumstantiality and rambling, poor attention and concentration, inadequate definitions, impairment of Digit Span, rate of association formation, learning, and memory. Such clinical manifestations occur in patients readily when anxiety is stirred up, and may subside rapidly with the decrease of anxiety. These manifestations, if very severe, may give the impression of inadequate general intelligence.

VII. Conclusions

The studies herein reported reveal that:

1. Whenever strong anxiety prevails, regardless of diagnosis, it increases the rate of conditioned response formation in psychiatric patients.

2. Elation has a specific effect in increasing the amount of association.

3. The presence of depression, with or without anxiety, reduces

the first half of performance on tests of concentration, whereas elation has no distinctive effect on concentration capacity.

4. The function of reasoning in some patients can be shown to be reduced by the presence of moderate-to-strong anxiety.

REFERENCES

1. Dougan, C. and Welch, L.: A study of elation making use of the Rorschach test and an association test. J. Psychol., 26, 363–366, 1948.
2. Franklin, M. E.: Die bedingten reflexe bei epilepsie und der wiederungszwang. Imago, 14, 361, 1928.
3. Grecker, R. A.: As reported by G. H. S. Razran: Conditioned withdrawal responses with shock as the conditioned stimulus in adult human subjects. Psychol. Bull., 31, 111, 1934.
4. Hilgard, E. R. and Marquis, D. G.: Conditioning and Learning. New York, D. Appleton-Century Co., 1940.
5. Kantorovich, N. V. and Lukina, A. M.: The formation of associative reflexes in progressive paralysis. Nov. Refl. Fiziol. Nerv. Sist., 2, 369, 1926. (Psychol. Abstr., 2, 146, 1928.)
6. Lukina, A. M. and Matusova, S. A.: Characteristics of conditioning in epileptics. Nov. Refl. Fiziol. Nerv. Sist., 3, 419, 1929. (Psychol. Abstr., 4, 4344, 1930.)
7. Mays, L. L.: Studies of Catatonia. V: Investigation of perseverational tendency. Psychiat. Quart., 8, 728, 1934.
8. Pfaffmann, C. and Schlosberg, H.: The conditioned knee jerk in psychotic and normal individuals. J. Psychol., 1, 201, 1936.
9. Rabinowich, P. H.: Reflejos condicionados de Pavlov en paraliticos progresivos: estudio clinico experimental. Semana méd., 39, 1712, 1932.
10. Rapaport, D.: Manual of Diagnostic Psychological Testing. Josiah Macy, Jr., Foundation, 1944.
11. ——: Emotions and Memory. Baltimore, The Williams & Wilkins Company, 1942.
12. Schiff, E., Dougan, C., and Welch, L.: The conditioned PGR and the EEG as indicators of anxiety. J. of Abnormal and Soc. Psychol., 44, 549–552, 1949.
13. Shipley, W. C.: Studies of Catatonia. VI: Further investigation of the perseverational tendency. Psychiat. Quart., 8, 736, 1934.
14. Tatarenko, N. P.: Disorders of the conditioned reflex activity in patients with senile psychosis. Sovetsk. Psikhonevrol., No. I, 75, 1934. (Psychol. Abstr., 9, 757, 1935.)
15. Welch, L.: Unpublished study.
16. —— and Diethelm, O.: Effect of pathologic anxiety on inductive reasoning. Arch. Neurol. and Psych., 63, 87–100, 1950.
17. ——, Diethelm, O., and Long, L.: Measurement of hyper-associative activity during elation. J. Psychol., 21, 113–126, 1946.

18. —— and KUBIS, J.: Conditioned PGR (Psychogalvanic Response) in states of pathological anxiety. J. Nerv. and Ment. Dis., *105*, 372–381, 1947.
19. —— and LONG, L.: Psychopathological defects in inductive reasoning. J. Psychol., *21*, 201–226, 1946.
20. YANEKIAN, A., MARK, M., FRIEDMAN, A., TOBACH, E., FISICHELLI, V., and WELCH, L.: Effect of suggested relaxation on the conditioned PGR. Unpublished study.

Part Five: Discussion

By LOTHAR B. KALINOWSKY, M.D.*

I WISH TO CONGRATULATE the authors on their interesting and thought-provoking presentations. The difficulty of discussing such different papers in one discussion can be best overcome by limiting myself primarily to the value of psychological tests in psychiatry as the common feature in all of them. Only a few remarks should be made regarding the material on which this psychological work was done in the various studies.

I am particularly interested in Drs. Alexander and Ax' study because of the implications regarding questions of war neuroses. I hope Dr. Alexander will give us some conclusions which he might have drawn regarding our concepts of war and other traumatic neuroses. I wish he would elaborate on the statement that he found an improving personality integration under the stress of combat flying in some patients. In those who show some combat reaction he believed that he was dealing with a depression rather than with a neurotic reaction. However this may be, his results were certainly better than in some other material. His eclectic approach, using both psychotherapeutic and somatic treatments, is gratifying for those of us who believe that an integration of the various methods is the most promising way to obtain therapeutic results in psychiatry. It is of great interest that he made neuropsychiatric check-ups with testing after severe combat experiences as well as in those patients who did not present overt symptoms. I would like to know whether this made some of the subjects aware of the fact that they might be psychiatric problems. As a research project it was certainly of great value, but as a routine measure I feel that the psychological testing itself can easily lead to neurotic reactions. Would he rely on psychological, particularly Rorschach findings, and recommend the withdrawal of flying personnel on the basis of these tests, even if there were no evidence of clinical neurotic manifestations?

The interest of Drs. Glueck and Krasner's paper lies among other

* Columbia University.

things in the answer to the much-discussed question of lasting intellectual impairment due to electric shock therapy. The regressive ECT is certainly the most intense way of using this type of therapy As far as the treatment as such is concerned, I did not find it superior to ECT given in two-or-three-times a week intervals. However, those who use it exclusively, claim good results, especially in schizophrenia, and I have no doubt about this because they, at least, avoid the mistake of many other psychiatrists who discontinue treatment after the first clinical improvement which is usually seen after as few as three or four treatments. I think, however, that adequate treatment given in longer intervals yields the same results. I am quite sure that the amnesia is not a necessary feature in ECT since in our most spectacular cases, the simple depressions, such amnesia or any marked memory impairment can be avoided altogether. At any rate, the increasing I.Q. values, and the increasing improvement in the scoring with all the psychological tests used, should help to counteract the statement heard again and again that ECT should, if possible be avoided because of disintegration of the patient's personality.

The second conclusion from these findings is that psychotherapy at least can be done after ECT and is not made impossible by the side-effects of the treatment. However, the frequent statement that ECT is ineffective if not followed by psychotherapy must be denied.

As far as research is concerned, experimental organic reactions produced by ECT, should be studied further. Routine studies as done by the authors also have interesting research implications for studies of organic findings in tests, especially Rorschach tests. The differential diagnosis between neurotic and organic syndromes after head injury which would have great practical importance for medico-legal decisions, should find a new and better foundation if worked out in a broader way in such studies.

Dr. Dunbar's ideas as to the psychodynamics of illness and her concept of accident proneness are known to all of us and shall not be discussed here in detail. The beautiful clinical study she presented today certainly shows the interesting implications of the Rorschach test regarding research of such kind. In her introductory remarks she said that in this paper she would stress the usefulness of psychological tests to the psychiatrist in his clinical work a little bit more than necessary. I wonder whether Dr. Dunbar who has done so much work with psychological tests in her psychosomatic studies would tell us some more about how valuable she considers Rorschach as a diagnostically, prognostically or therapeutically useful device. This leads me to a brief outline of my own attitude regarding the possibilities and limitations of psychological tests.

This symposium has done a great deal to clarify the situation, particularly the critical attitude which some psychiatrists have taken and will certainly contribute to a more satisfactory cooperation between psychologists and psychiatrists. The symposium should be considered seriously by those psychiatrists who no longer have the courage to make a diagnosis without having it confirmed by a Rorschach test, or who even yield their own clinical judgment before the contrasting findings of a projective test. They are equally as wrong as are those psychologists who feel entitled to make a diagnosis of schizophrenia exclusively on the basis of their test findings. I recently came across a case where schizophrenia was diagnosed and treatment outlined by psychologists without any clinical psychiatric evidence for such a diagnosis and without consultation with a psychiatrist. It should be remembered that Rorschach himself never promised more than his test actually offers. It is true that his successors have contributed much to a more refined analysis as well as to a better statistical evaluation of the response, but we must admit that this has done little for the clinical achievements of the test. Attempts by some workers to elaborate complicated formulae express their belief in the scientific significance of the Rorschach test. Other Rorschach workers have a more intuitive approach in the evaluation of the patient's response. In my practical experience I must confess that this less scientific approach in the hands of gifted Rorschach workers is often more in accord with my clinical impression than the more statistical evaluation, but this deprives the Rorschach quite obviously of all characteristics of an objective test. There is little evidence that the results of any of the projective tests are superior to the clinical judgment of an experienced psychiatrist and the ordinary technic of psychiatric interviews. One of the few instances where the Rorschach test may help in the clinical evaluation of a case is the differential diagnosis between psychogenic and organic symptoms after head injury. In the diagnosis of schizophrenia and the important differential diagnosis between psychoneurosis and schizophrenia, however, the interpretation of projective tests is actually based on a knowledge of the psychopathology of schizophrenia which was well-developed before these tests were introduced. The conclusion, therefore, seems inevitable that none of the psychological tests are for psychiatry what laboratory tests are for general medicine.

Psychiatry has often been accused by research workers from other fields of being unscientific. Unfortunately, attempts to apply methods which have proven their value in other fields of medicine are not applicable to psychiatry. Diagnostic tests in general medicine supplement the findings of the physician's clinical observations. Laboratory tests are an objective confirmation of a condition which could be expected from clinical experience but which could not be demonstrated by direct examination of the patient. The psychological tests are nothing of the kind, and can only parallel clinical observations in more elaborate ways. A syphilis, which cannot be diagnosed by examination of the patient, can be diagnosed by a serological test. A schizophrenic psychosis cannot be and should not be diagnosed by any of the psychological tests available so far. This, of course, should not discourage study in this field, together with other attempts to work out more objective diagnostic criteria in psychiatry.

INDEX

Alcohol, conditional reflex and, 176

Anxiety
  and reasoning, 279
  deterioration test in, 82
  intelligence test in, 76
  pathological emotions and, 271
    definition of, 272
  Rorschach test in, 78
  Wechsler-Bellevue test in, 76

Apothecaries, historical role of, 121

Autonomic nervous system, test of. *See* Schizophrenia, abstract thinking, tests in

Aviation, military, Rorschach test in. *See* Flying personnel

Babcock test for dementia, 31

Bellevue Mental Clinic, development of, 15

Bender visual-motor gestalt test in electroshock treatment, 246
  case study of, 249

Binet test. *See* Stanford-Binet test

Chi-square tests
  in flying personnel, 239
  in schizophrenia, 142

Code of Percival, 122

Columbia-Greystone studies
  deterioration and, 100
  psychological tests and, 101
  schizophrenia and, 99

Combat flying personnel. *See* Flying personnel

Comprehension tests in diagnosis, 30

Conditional reflex
  adaptive function, levels of, 182
  comparison with other tests, 185
  discussion of, 180, 211, 213
  grading in, 168
  history of, 165
  pathological emotions and, 271
    apparatus and procedure in, 272
    discussion of, 274

psychiatry and, 165-189
  organic vs. psychogenic reactions, 184
  patient in, preparation of, 168
  procedure in, 168
  psychogenic vs. organic reactions, 184
  report sheet in, 169
  results in, 171
    alcohol and, 176
    fluctuations in same hand, 173
    hypnosis and, 173
    normal variations in, 171
    organic conditions and, 177
    pathological disturbances and, 175
    sensory disturbances and, 180
    toxic conditions and, 175
    types of, 171
  retention of, 183
  schizophrenia and, 184
  study of, 166
  summary of, 187
  vs. Binet test, 185
  vs. EEG, 185

Dementia, tests of, 31

Deterioration
  in Columbia-Greystone studies, 100
  test of, 81
    discussion of, 99
    Raven Progressive Matrices in, 83
    vs. schizophrenia, 82

Depression, psychological emotions and, 278

Dexedrine sulfate, psychological emotions and, 276

EEG vs. conditional reflex test, 185

Elation
  psychological emotions and, 278
  psychopathological emotions and, 275

Electroshock treatment
  Bender visual-motor gestalt test in,
    246
    case study in, 249
  case study in, 247
  conclusions from, 256
  definition of, 244
  description of, 244
  discussion of, 290
  figure drawings in, 247
    case study in, 248, 250, 252
  first test in, 245
  method of, 244
  Rorschach in, 246
  second test in, 245
  serial testing in, 244–257
  type of tests in, 246
  Wechsler-Bellevue in, 246
  word-association test in, 247
Emotional quotient, fantasy and, 263
Ethics, medical, history of, 122
Fantasy
  discussion of, 291
  illness and, 258–270
    conclusions from, 270
    case study in, 259, 264
    emotional quotient and, 263
    intelligence quotient and, 263
    Rorschach in, 263
  infant's
    classification of, 258
    tests and, 258–270
  of world destruction, 189
Figure drawings
  in electroshock treatment, 247
    case study in, 248, 250, 252
  in schizophrenia, diagnosis of, 196
    examples of, 197–201, 204
Finger painting, fantasy and, 259
Flying personnel, tests on
  case 1 (subject 117), 224
  case 2 (subject 216), 230
  case 3 (subject 338), 235
  case 4 (subject 53), 236
  case 5 (subject 232), 237

  case material in, 221
  chi-square findings in, 239
  combat fatigue, evaluation of, 242
  combat stress and, 223
    influence of, 224
  conclusions on, 237, 243
  discussion of, 290
  discriminative score, 238
    significant, 239
  interpretation of, 220
  method of, 221
  normal vs. operational-fatigue, 231
    classification of, 231
    scoring in, 234
  rationale of, 219
  response changes in changing stress,
    223
  Rorschach test in, 219–243
    analysis of, statistical, 237
  scoring in, 225
    analysis of, 237
    interpretation of, 242
    performance problems and, 233
    statistical, 237
Guilford-Zimmerman test of person-
    ality, 90
Heredity, illness and. See Fantasy
Human movement response
  in personality tests, 93
  in schizophrenia, 194
Hypnosis, conditional reflex and, 173
Illness, fantasy and. See Fantasy
Insulin in schizophrenia, Rorschach
    and, 69
Intelligence test
  and personality, tests of, 87–95
  development of, 26
  diagnosis and, 26, 74
  fantasy and, 263
  Guilford-Zimmerman test and, 90
  human movement responses and, 93
  in diagnosis, psychiatric, 74
  Mill Hill Vocabulary Scale, 87
  phrenology and, 8
  psychopathology and, 21

Raven's Progressive Matrices, 87
Rorschach and, 90
discussion of, 97, 102, 106
psychiatry and, 74
Korsakov, conditional reflex of, 177, 183
Kraepelin, theories of personality, 7
Learning set, definition of, 88
Medical ethics, history of, 122
Mental health clinics, development of, 15
Military aviation, Rorschach in. *See* Flying personnel
Mill Hill Vocabulary Scale in personality test, 87
Minnesota multiphasic personality inventory
in diagnosis, 80
discussion of, 98
in schizophrenia, 80
psychological emotions and, 284
Otis test, evaluation of, 16
Parent-child relationship, fantasy and. *See* Fantasy
Percival, Thomas, code of, 122
Personality
early theories of, 6
Guilford-Zimmerman test in, 90
human movement response in, 93
intelligence and
discussion of, 103
integration, 87–95
Mill Hill Vocabulary Scale in, 87
Raven's Progressive Matrices in test of, 87
Rorschach test in, 90
discussion of, 97, 102, 106
tests and, 12
trends in theories of, 7
Philosophy of scientific cooperation, 113–127
Phrenology, 4
history of, 5
intellect and, 8
Porteus Maze test of deficiency, 33

President's address, 113–127
Psychiatrist, role of, in psychology, 21
Psychiatry
conditional reflex in. *See* Conditional reflex
diagnostic use of psychological tests, 73
integration with psychology, 108
psychology and
application of, 125
cooperation between, steps toward, 114
ethical codes, 121
friction between, sources of, 117
aggressiveness, 119
causes of, 113
discussion of, 114
fear, 120
group pressure resistance, 121
hedonism, 120
inferiority sense, 119
possessiveness, 119
privilege maintenance, 120
scientific doubt, 118
scientific isolation, 121
history of, 113
interlocking committees in, 123
psychopathology and, 117
research in, 124
psychometric tests and, 31
Psychological tests
applications of, 3–14
discussion of, 47, 39
batteries of, vs. single tests, 11
Bender visual-motor gestalt test in
electroshock treatment, 246
case study in, 248
conception of, 10
criteria of, 10
deterioration test, 81
development of, in psychopathology, 15–25
discussion of, 40

Psychological tests (*cont.*)
  diagnostic use of, 49–110
    discussion of, 96–104, 105–109
    from psychiatrist's standpoint,
      73–86
    intelligence tests, 74
  evaluation of, 10
  exogenous factors, influence of, 129–
    218
    discussion of, 208, 212
  fantasy and. *See* Fantasy
  figure drawings in electroshock
    treatment, 247
    case study in, 248, 250, 252
  finger painting and, 259
  historical bases for, 1–49
    conclusions derived from, 10
    discussion of, 39–44, 45
  in electroshock treatment, 246
  in schizophrenia
    color response, 60, 62
    conclusions of, 65
    criteria for, 52, 53
    discussion of, 66
    environment and, 68
    form-color response and, 56
    grading in, 53
    high evidence, 3, 59, 62
    inductive perception, 53, 59, 62
    insulin and, 67, 69
    intellectual passivity, 55, 59, 62
    limitations of, 65
    methods of, 52
    prognosis by, after three years, 51
    purpose of test, 51
    relation of, to prognosis, 131
    results of, 62
    signs in, 53, 59, 60
    subjects for, 52
    summary of, 70
    time and, 67
    treatment and, 67
    validity of, 65
  integration of psychology and psy-
    chiatry, 108

Minnesota multiphasic personality.
    See Minnesota multiphasic per-
    sonality inventory
  of deterioration, 81
    discussion of, 99
  personalities and, 12
  personality and intelligence inte-
    gration, 87–95
  phrenology and, 4
  psychology and, 113
  psychometric tests. *See* Psycho-
    metric tests
  psychopathologic tests. *See* Psycho-
    pathology
  Raven's Progressive Matrices, 83
  Rorschach test
    discussion of, 97
    psychiatry and, 77
    Thematic apperception test and
      79
  what is tested by, 3–14
    discussion of, 39, 45
  word-association in electroshock
    treatment, 247
Psychologist
  certification of, 124
  in psychopathology, evaluation of,
    24
  internship of, 124
  licensing of, 124
  psychopathology and, limitations
    of, 22
  requirements for, 20
  role of, in psychopathology, 21
  training of, 124
Psychology
  clinical
    criteria in, 153
    definition of, 20
    discussion of, 208, 213
    evaluation of, 150–164
    growth of, 150
    prediction of success in, 150–164
    training program in, 151, 154
    candidate selection in, 151

conclusions of, 161
criteria in, 153–155
determination of, by sociometric
   measures, 155
discussion of, 161
predictive measures used, 157
results of, 159
tests used in, 157
variables in ratings, 158
integration with psychiatry, 108
research in, 124
Psychometric tests
comprehension tests, 30
development of, 27
digit symbol tests, 29
discussion of, 43
future directions of, 34
improvement of, 35
in diagnosis, 26
of abnormality, 32
of abstract thinking, 32
of dementia, 31
of geometric drawing, 34
of vocabulary, 33
Porteus maze test, 33
psychiatric concepts and, 31
quantitating quality, 34
   discussion of, 43
reliability of, discussion of, Wechsler, 42
Stanford-Binet test. See Stanford-
   Binet test
theoretical bases for, 26–36
   discussion of, 41
Wechsler-Bellevue test. See Wechsler-Bellevue test
Woodworth-Wells test, 29
Psychopathological
emotions, psychological test and,
   271–289
   anxiety and reasoning in, 279
   conclusions and, 287
   conditional responses, 271–274
   concentration and, 278
   depression and, 278

discussion of, 283
elation and, 275, 278
idea association and, 275, 285
reasoning in, 279
tests, development of
   early problems in, 18
   qualifications of examiners, 19, 20
Psychopathology
clinical psychology and, 20
clinical tests for, 15–25
deterioration test in, 81
discussion of, 39
evaluation of, development of, 17
intelligence test in, 21
Minnesota multiphasic personality
   inventory and, 80
psychologist's role in, 21
   evaluation of, 24
   limitations of, 22
Rorschach test in, 78
Raven's Progressive Matrices
in diagnosis, 83
in personality and intelligence, 87
Reflex, conditional. See Conditional
   reflex
Rorschach test
as prognostic criterion, 51
basis of, 10
from psychiatrist's standpoint, 77
high evidence in schizophrenia, 53
human movement in, in schizophrenia, 194
in anxiety, 78
in combat flying personnel, 219–243.
   See also Flying personnel
in diagnosis, 77
   discussion of, 97
in electroshock treatment, 246
in fantasy and illness, 260, 263
in intelligence, 90
   discussion of, 97, 102, 106
in personality, 90
   discussion of, 97, 102, 106
in schizophrenia, 194
   diagnosis

Rorschach test, in schizophrenia (*cont.*)
  inkblots in, 195
  movement responses in, 194
  rationale of, 191
  prognosis, 51
  inductive perception in schizophrenia test, 53
  intellectual passivity in schizophrenia test, 55
  psychological emotions and, 284
  requirement for psychiatrists, 47
  scoring in, 102
  signs used in, 53, 57
Schizophrenia
  abstract thinking and
    analysis of data, 133
    autonomic nervous system and, 131–149
      patterns in, 132, 135
      type A, 132, 134, 143, 147
      type B, 133–134, 143, 146, 148
      type C, 133–134, 144, 146, 148
    capacity for, 135–136
    chi-square test in, 142
    clinical observations on, 143
    conclusions from, 147
    Concrete Category score, logarithmic means of, 140
    concrete thinking and recovery, 140, 143
    criteria in, results of, 135
    discussion of, 144
    epinephrine in, 132, 134–135
    groups of patients, 132
      criteria for, 134
      intermediate measures of, 141
      logarithmic means of, 141
      mecholyl in, 132, 134–135
      method of, 132
      patients in, 132
    physiological tests, description of, 132
    prognosis of by chi-square tests, 142

  psychological tests of abstraction, 133
    results of, 135, 136
    summary of, 147
    tests in, 136–140, 142
  conditional reflex function in, 184
  diagnosis of, by psychological tests, 189–207
    advantages of, 193
    case study in, 197
    results of tests, 203
    color responses, 196
    conclusions of, 207
    discussion of, 210, 214
    figure drawing in, 196–201, 202, 204
    inkblots in, 195
    interpretation of, 192
    MAPS in, 197
    movement response in, 194
    personnel relations in, 193
    problems in, 206
    rationale in, 190
    Rorschach test in, 191, 194
    signs in, 193
    TAT in, 202
    tests in, 80, 190–192, 194
  prognosis of
    by Rorschach data, 51
    three-year study in, discussion of, 100, 106
  psychological tests and, relation to prognosis, 131
  symptoms of, 189
  vs. deterioration, 82
  Wechsler-Bellevue test in, 76
    responses to, 194
Scientific cooperation, philosophy of, 113–127
Serial testing in electroshock treatment. *See* Electroshock treatment
Stanford-Binet test
  basis of, 27
  vs. conditional reflex, 185

Tests
   intelligence. *See* Intelligence tests
   Otis, evaluation of, 16
   psychological. *See* Psychological
     tests
Thematic apperception test
   discussion of, 47
   from psychiatrist's standpoint, 79
   historical basis of, 10, 11, 13
   in diagnosis, 79
Vocabulary tests, 90
Wechsler-Bellevue test
   basis of, 27

evaluation of, in diagnosis, 27, 28
from psychiatrist's standpoint, 75
in anxiety, 76
in electroshock treatment, 246
in organic disease, 29
in schizophrenia, 76
   diagnosis of, 194
   rationale of, 192
responses to, 194
psychological emotions and, 285
reliability of, 28
Woodworth-Wells test in diagnosis,
   29